COLDSPRING

COLDSPRING

CHERI MANCUSO AND JOHN SCARANO

DANCING MOON PRESS
NEWPORT, OREGON

Coldspring

copyright © 2009-2010
by Cheri Mancuso and John Scarano
All rights reserved

This book is literary non-fiction, but is based on actual events, trial records, newspaper clippings, and family history.

No part of this book may be used or reproduced or transmitted in any form, or by any means, electronic or mechanical, including photocopy, recording, or any information storage and retrieval system, without written permission from the authors, except in the case of brief quotations embedded in critical articles or reviews. For information, address your inquiry to coldspring@ix.netcom.com.

ISBN-13: 978-1-892076-68-7 (paperback)
ISBN-13: 978-1-892076-69-4 (hardcover)
ISBN-13: 978-1-892076-70-0 (e-book)
Library of Congress Control Number: 2009939809
Mancuso, Cheri, and Scarano, John
Coldspring
1. Title; 2. Coldspring, New York; 3. Cattaraugus County, New York; 4. Seneca Indians; 5. Bernice Guernsey Kenyon; 6. Harold Farnsworth; 7. Alfred Lindsay; 8. Karma.

Manufactured in the United States of America
Front cover photo of Bernice Kenyon's farmhouse
by Walter Wilhelm (deceased)
Original glass plate of front cover photo courtesy of Tyler Searle
Cover production by Jana Westhusing, Studio Blue West
Book design by Carla Perry, Dancing Moon Press

DANCING MOON PRESS
P.O. Box 832, Newport, OR 97365
541-574-7708
www.dancingmoonpress.com
info@dancingmoonpress.com

SECOND EDITION

ACKNOWLEDGMENTS

The research for this book would never have been possible without the invaluable assistance of Jolynn Benn and her employees at Benn and Associates Private Investigation. We would also like to thank Marlynn (Olson) Ray, unofficial Randolph Town Historian, for uncovering the story of Bernice and Harold Farnsworth's murder. Equally important, we thank J. Michael Shane, Esq., son of Freddy Lindsay's defense attorney, G. Sydney Shane, for his dogged pursuit of the Grand Jury Testimony and the transcripts of Freddy Lindsay's trial. The last of our special thanks goes to Amy Morgan for her expert assistance in the development of the storyline for this book.

We also extend deep appreciation to the following individuals and organizations for their various contributions to this book:

Dean and Annette Waite
Lisa Matsukawa
Leone Pickup, Jr.
Jo Short
Ted Searle
Tyler Searle
Tim and Jane Arrance
Mrs. Paul Arrance
Jim Arrance
Harold Williams
George and Marlene Wendell
Doris Van Sickle, Coldspring Town Historian
Randolph Free Library
Salamanca Public Library
Gowanda Free Library
Gowanda Historical Society
Cattaraugus County Historical Museum and Research Center
Sandra Wogick, County of Cattaraugus
James K. Griffith, County of Cattaraugus
Olean Times Herald
April M. Vecchiarella, Town of Salamanca
Michael Hiller Photography

DEDICATION

THIS BOOK IS DEDICATED TO JOHN SCARANO, for being an amazing part of my journey to find my family, and for his help in bringing them back to life. Our path has opened doors for understanding a karmic journey we never suspected was there. We certainly did not see it coming when we began researching the life and death of Bernice Kenyon Farnsworth.

This book is also dedicated to my Aunt Olive Blessing who started my journey at age nineteen when she showed me a photo of Bernice in a family album.

Thank you to Jolynn Benn who moved our journey into action when she contacted Michael Shane through her detective agency. Michael Shane brought the story to life and was a crucial part of getting the legal documentation we would never have had access to otherwise. Thank you Dean and Annette Waite, Marlynn Olson, and everyone in the Randolph, New York, area who helped our journey come to fruition.

This first book is just the beginning, as John and I take you on our adventure through several of our lifetimes.

—Cheri Mancuso

FOREWORD

OUR RESEARCH INTO THE BRUTAL MURDER OF Bernice Guernsey Kenyon started innocuously in early spring 2000. We asked Jolynn Benn, of Benn and Associates Private Investigation, to look into the subject, just to satisfy Cheri's curiosity about the death of her great aunt. What we found caused us to return to Bernice's birthplace in upstate New York to continue the investigation in person. What we discovered there was an undeniable karmic connection between us and Bernice Kenyon, Harold Farnsworth, and Freddy Lindsay.

Through a chain of widely improbable but synchronous events, we were able to backtrack from Bernice Kenyon's life to what we believe were her past incarnations. *Coldspring* chronicles three documented lifetimes as well as two earlier ones we intuited in order to demonstrate the evolution of karma from lifetime to lifetime. This karmic evolution takes place over a period of twelve thousand years.

Because karma and reincarnation can be interpreted in many ways, we offer our interpretation here for clarification: When a soul is created, a blank slate called the Akashic Record is created alongside it. The sole purpose of this slate is to record a soul's past, present, and future lives. All of our positive and negative actions from each lifetime are recorded there. Each reaction caused by our actions is recorded there, too. Positive reactions result in good karma. Negative reactions result in karmic debt.

Every successive lifetime is governed by the accumulation of good karma and karmic debt, with the intent of creating a balance. For instance, if you viciously slap a child in one lifetime and save a child from physical abuse in another, these actions cancel each other on the Akashic Record. We believe our ultimate goal is to become perfect, so that we can transition to a plane of perfect existence. To accomplish this transformation, our Akashic Record has to be free of all karmic debt.

Sometimes karmic debt builds through successive lifetimes and reaches a point where we are compelled by extreme circumstances to extinguish it. In this book, we find one woman and two men locked inextricably in these extraordinary circumstances. Their roles mutate as they reincarnate together, lifetime after lifetime. Pressure builds until a karmic explosion occurs, which locks them into another karmic fugue of dire circumstances.

We invite you to begin this tale of millennia-old karma. Be advised that this book, and the other two to follow, may change your core beliefs regarding action and response. What you do and say in this life is inextricably bound to your actions centuries in the past, and your acts still to occur in your lifetimes ahead.

—John Scarano

CHAPTER ONE

THE SHORT, STOUT MAN STARED AT THE jagged red ice crystals on the tip of his spear. The ice crystals were frozen blood droplets. Absentmindedly, he held the spear tip over the glowing coals of the fire in the center of his crude hut. The dark red ice melted and hissed as the heat from the coals boiled the liquid away, leaving a residue of white ash in its place.

C'obine-no C'ugo, Swift Spear, was a hunter. As a hunter, he was highly revered and commanded the respect of all those he encountered. Thus, when he walked among the people of his Paleo-Siberian tribe, he appeared arrogant and prideful. His nomadic tribe was known as the Alazeya Yukaghir, The Far Off Tundra Tribe. His tribe had migrated from Mongolia to the borders of Northeastern Siberia over many hundreds of years. They had traversed what were once vast tundra plains in continual pursuit of the herds of giant animals now dwindling in numbers, the result of the final Ice Age push in the formerly temperate areas of their world.

Vast ice sheets, nearly two miles thick, now burdened much of the Siberian land making Swift Spear and his tribe struggle for survival. The glaciers had been slowly, but relentlessly coating the prairie grass plains that once fed huge, grazing herds of woolly mammoth, mastodon, and giant long-horned bison for centuries. Those wandering herds had provided his tribe with almost everything they needed for survival. It was the end of the sixth epoch of the Cenozoic era, the Pleistocene. It would be another 10,000 years before Jesus Christ would walk the earth.

Extreme changes in the tundra climate were making the old ways of hunting obsolete. Rarely were they able to dig the killing pits that were once easily created by Swift Spear's ancestral Yukaghir hunters. The frozen soil was now impenetrable using rudimentary tools. The Old Ones, in warmer days, would dig an enormous pit using tools fashioned from bone. They would line the bottom of the pit with pointed logs and then cover the pit with prairie grass. They would frighten the woolly mammoths or the giant long-horned bison into stampeding in the direction of the pit by beating sticks and making loud noises with their voices. When a hapless creature fell into the pit and was impaled or badly injured by the sharp logs, the hunters could safely jab the trapped animal from above with bone-tipped spears. It was the only safe way the behemoth animals could be killed.

The giant, long-horned bison were seven feet tall, with an overall length of ten feet from nose to rump. They towered two feet above the Yukaghirs. The distance between the points of a bison's horns could reach more than five feet. Bison could easily reach a weight of more than 4,500 pounds. Although one might assume their sheer size slowed them down, the bison's musculature made it possible for them to reach speeds in excess of 30 miles per hour.

Unlike the Old Ones, Swift Spear had to place himself in grave peril to provide the tribe with sorely needed sustenance, building materials, and clothing. The pit had to be replaced with a jumbled, stacked pile of double-pointed logs placed strategically on the ground. When a bison herd was forced to stampede through the logs, occasionally one animal would become entangled in the pile and, with some luck, severely injure itself. It was up to Swift Spear and the other hunters to risk their lives by jumping into and onto the log pile to take the animal down by piercing its thick hide with their bone-tipped spears. With the safety of pit gone, it was likely that one or more of the hunters would be injured by the animal or the logs. One deep gash usually invited an infection that could lead to a painful, agonizing death. Or, at the least, cause enough injury to relegate the hunter to the stature of the elders who made and repaired weapons for the hunt.

This new method required the hunters to work in deliberate and careful unison with one another. Only the bravest of men would dare stare death in the face time and time again for the good of the tribe. These men formed an almost cult-like organization of Yukaghirs who stood apart from their own people.

Swift Spear, along with the other hunters, resided in an area separate from the tribe. They lived in low huts whose frames were built from the bones of their kills. Elk antlers, large-horned deer antlers, and bison horns were driven into the ground then covered with stretched animal hide. The floors of their huts were cushioned with sacred white animal pelts. Their huts were littered with bone carvings of the animals and birds they hunted, gifts from grateful tribe members. When meals were prepared, the hunters ate first. Only those most skilled at sewing were permitted to fashion clothing for the hunters – using the highest quality bison and deer hides stitched together with fine deer hair. Tribal shaman personally decorated the hunters' garments with magical protection symbols drawn with precious and scarce vegetable dyes. The hunters' clothing was always the most ornate.

The hunters developed a secret language over many years that only they were allowed to speak. Any other member of the tribe who dared to speak a word of this secret language could be excommunicated from the tribe, for they were considered unworthy of its use. It was in this manner that the hunter completed his rise to an exalted position in the tribe. His rank stood barely beneath that of the Chieftain and the ever-important tribal Shaman. The hunters were the royalty of their time and they knew it.

Furthering the status of the Yukaghir tribe hunter was the tribe's belief in Animism. They believed in the existence of spirits and souls. They believed the hunters released the spirit of the great animals they killed and that they walked with those animal spirits for the remainder of their lives. This belief created an atmosphere of great power and danger around the hunters, causing the rest of the Yukaghir people to live in awe and fear of them. When the hunters walked through the nomadic village everyone else would scurry out of their way.

Swift Spear, true to his tribal stature, was used to getting whatever he wanted. Today he wanted a mate. He grew tired of the constant company of men and longed for the pleasure of a woman. The beauty of a particular woman had struck him. Her name was Ul'iana, Innocent One. Her skin was clear and smooth. Her raven-black hair cascaded to the middle of her back and delicately framed her eyes. She spoke softly in a singsong voice he found captivating. She was petite for a Yukaghir woman and walked as if her feet barely touched the earth. Swift Spear was in love with this beautiful creature and today he intended to announce it to her. Once that was done, she would belong to him and no other. The Yukaghir hunter need only ask once for what he wanted and, if it were unclaimed, it would be his unquestionably. Once spoken for, Innocent One would be his for the remainder of his life. She would be elevated in her tribal position and be given a hut of her own, for a hunter would never lower himself to reside with anyone but another hunter until he retired. Swift Spear would visit Innocent One whenever he wished, partake of her pleasure, and return to his hunter domain. If he resided with her, he could no longer be a Yukaghir hunter. And that is something he would never give up until death, injury, or old age was forced upon him.

In his single-minded fashion, Swift Spear marched through the small Yukaghir village. As he passed other tribal members, they cleared his path and averted their gaze as a sign of respect. Swift Spear barely noticed them. His attention was clearly fixed on the hut where Innocent One resided with her older sister, Kutika,

Weaver's Daughter. As Swift Spear continued his journey towards Innocent One's hut, he saw Weaver's Daughter engaged in conversation with another woman. That pleased him, as it would be easier to state his intentions to Innocent One if she were alone.

When he was within a few yards of the hut, Swift Spear heard a man's voice singing a familiar song. To his horror, the song was emanating from inside Innocent One's hut. It was the traditional Yukaghir love song a lover would sing to his intended, immediately after she had accepted his advances:

She is white as snow,
Her eyebrows are black as night,
Her hair is soft as rabbit fur,
She shines like the sun.
I am hurrying to her,
Never to part with her.

Swift Spear stopped dead in his tracks, confused. Then, like a seedling bursting forth with explosive force, he understood what was taking place behind the skins of the hut. His anger rose in waves of heat and propelled him forward. Screaming like a wounded animal, Swift Spear ripped open the flap that covered the hut's entrance and in doing so, exposed the occupants. His eyes bulged at the sight that lay before him. Innocent One was wrapped in the arms of Vasya, Good Friend, a common tribesman. The pair, frozen in place, stared back in shock at the hulking figure. The sunlight streaming past him lit the margins of his darkened silhouette but his identity was cloaked until Swift Spear stepped fully into the hut. Good Friend recognized the hunter immediately and trembled with fear. Innocent One jumped from Good Friend's arms and stuttered unintelligibly. Swift Spear advanced on Good Friend, screaming for his blood. Good Friend shrank backwards until the hut's curved wall trapped him from behind. It was at that moment that a hand was placed on Swift Spear's shoulder. He wheeled around to find Xolhut-Aibi, Mammoth Shadow, the Yukaghir tribal Shaman.

Mammoth Shadow stared deeply into Swift Spear's wild eyes, draining his anger. Whatever magic Mammoth Shadow may have been performing, it had a dramatic effect on Swift Spear. His body that had stiffened with rage, relaxed. The spell that the anger had cast over him was broken as he was drawn into the pools of the Shaman's dark eyes. Slowly, rational consciousness returned to Swift Spear and he again became aware of his surroundings. Looking past the Shaman, Swift Spear spied the villagers gathered around the hut's entrance. They were staring inquisitively at him. Swift Spear understood that he had brought shame upon himself and he reacted immediately.

Swift Spear asked Mammoth Shadow whether the Shaman had blessed the joining of Good Friend and Innocent One. When the Shaman replied that indeed he had, Swift Spear, addressing the villagers at the hut door, announced that since he had no need of spoiled fruit his business there was finished. He strode arrogantly past the Shaman and sent the villagers scattering like little children. Their fear reassured him that this incident had not reduced his standing in the tribe. He made his way back to his hut in the hunter's compound and did not emerge from it for the remainder of the afternoon.

Meanwhile, Mammoth Shadow calmed Innocent One and Good Friend as best he could. He then turned his attention to the lingering crowd at the front of the hut. Assuring them that there had been a misunderstanding between the three, he incanted a magical blessing that he promised would assuage the evil spirit that had descended upon Swift Spear, Innocent One, and Good Friend. Murmuring quietly, the crowd dispersed. Mammoth Shadow made his way to the tent of Kangitche, Hunting Leader, the tribal chieftain. He knew the old chief would want to know what evil had befallen them, as the Yukaghirs were a peaceful tribe who abhorred violence. Only an evil spirit could have been responsible for Swift Spear's violent outburst. It would surely foment fear among the tribe that Kaliany, Devilish Spirit, had taken up residence in the village. Mammoth Shadow sighed as he thought about the long, arduous ritual that would have to be performed in the chieftain's hut. As he had done from the beginning of his term as Tribal Shaman, Mammoth Shadow would act as an intermediary between the tribe and the spirit world.

Mammoth Shadow was not born to be a Shaman, as was the case with most Shamans who had come before him. He had been born to a common tribal family. Mammoth Shadow was known at birth as Vasili'I, Decision Maker, a family name. Life for him had been normal until the evening of his ninth birthday. Without warning, he had fallen into a deep trance that lasted two days. He sweated profusely and writhed in his bedding as if he lay on a bed of hot coals. He babbled sounds that no one in his family could comprehend. His mother was sure he was near death's door.

At that time, the tribal Shaman was an older woman named Matika, Kind Spirit. She instantly recognized Decision Maker's condition. Sensing her old age, she had been waiting patiently for the one the spirits would send as her replacement. She had borne no children and therefore she had no heir to replace her. She gazed down upon Decision Maker as he lay in bed and smiled as one who knows a special secret. Her wait had come to end.

Kind Spirit sat with the boy and listened until she heard him speak the name of the spirit that had taken up residence within his body. That was how Decision Maker became known as Mammoth Shadow, the most powerful spirit of all. The boy's fever slowly waned and when he awoke from the trance, Kind Spirit held his hand and called him by his new name. She arranged for the boy to be transferred to her hut where she began his shamanistic training. True to his name, Mammoth Shadow showed tremendous power from the start of his apprenticeship.

Many gods and spirits occupied the world of the Yukaghir people. It was their belief that ancient spirits lived everywhere – in the sky and air, in the stone and the tree, in the water and the ground. They believed that the natural elements, the animals, the vegetative world and, certainly, the Humans were compelled to submit to these spirits. The spirits could be kind or malicious, powerful or weak. They helped and harmed, protected and attacked. Like their human counterparts, the spirits rejoiced, were afflicted, loved, hated, gave, took away, thanked, and extorted. In daily life, it was the Shaman who communicated directly with the spirits, made the obligatory offerings to them, and asked for their help. Without a Shaman, the Yukaghirs believed their lives would descend into chaos. It was with great relief that Kind Spirit had found her successor.

Kind Spirit wasted no time. She began by teaching Mammoth Shadow about the Sacrificial Ceremonies performed for the good of the tribe. The regular sacrifices were the Autumn Slaughtering, the Winter Slaughtering, the Ceremony of Antlers, the Sacrifice to the New Moon, the Sacrifice to the Fire, and the Sacrifice for Luck in Hunting. In each of these ceremonies, a large-horned deer or Saiga antelope was sacrificed by ritual stabbing. After the sacrificial animal was stabbed, the Shaman watched carefully to see on which side the animal fell. It was a good omen if the sacrificial animal fell on its unwounded side and a bad omen if it fell on its wounded side. Great misfortune was forecast if the animal fell backwards. In such a case, the Shaman was compelled to make the journey to the spirit world and intercede on the behalf of the tribe. This was the most dangerous task the tribe could ever ask of a Shaman, for the spirit world was treacherous for a Human.

After several years, Kind Spirit announced that Mammoth Shadow was ready to accept the mantle of Shaman and she taught him how to construct his own Shaman's tambourine. Tambourines were an essential magical tool for the Shaman. He would call the spirits to him when he shook and beat it vigorously. When he traveled to the spirit world, the tambourine could be transformed into anything he desired.

The wood for Mammoth Shadow's first tambourine was from a tree he selected while wandering blindfolded in the forest. He shaped a two-inch wide oval hoop and attached horizontal rods using leather lacing from a bison. He fastened special magical metal pendants to the untethered ends of the rods, then beat a wet piece of wooly mammoth hide with a wooden mallet until it was translucent. Next, he inscribed a picture of the spirit world on what would become the inside of the tambourine. The final step was stretching the hide over the wood hoop until it was taut, covering both top and bottom.

Mammoth Shadow used his tambourine to perform his first healing ceremony for a tribal member stricken with fever. He talked with the spirit in a way no one else had ever tried. He threw numerous spirit voices around the hut to the astonishment of all those present. Kind Spirit was very proud of her student.

Kind Spirit called the tribe to meet at the ceremonial circle in the center of their encampment at the conclusion of Mammoth Shadow's healing ceremony. When everyone was present, Kind Spirit held up her tambourine and pierced it with a sharpened stick, symbolizing the end of her reign as the Yukaghir Shaman. More importantly, it signaled the end of her life. The Yukaghirs knew this and cast their eyes upon the ground, some weeping with sorrow and others with gratitude. Without a word, Kind Spirit, her head held high, strode away from the gathering and calmly left the encampment without casting a backward glance. She was never seen again. With this simple, self-effacing act, the Shaman's mantle was passed to Mammoth Shadow. The fate of their tribe rested in his hands and the weight of this huge responsibility pressed down heavily upon him for the remainder of his life. He was barely thirteen years of age.

Now, at 26, Mammoth Shadow made his way to hut of the tribe's chieftain, Hunting Leader. He paused to review the ritual ceremonies that the chieftain might ask him to perform on behalf of the Yukaghir tribe, then called out Hunting Leader's name. The chieftain bade him to enter.

As he expected, the chieftain already knew what had taken place at the hut of Innocent One and her sister, Weaver's Daughter. News traveled like wind among the tribe. He was also correct about the tribe's reaction to Swift Spear's violent outburst. It was unanimously agreed – Devilish Spirit was in their midst. The chieftain was waiting for Mammoth Shadow's confirmation of this fact and his solution for ridding them of the evil spirit.

At the request of the old chieftain, Mammoth Shadow prepared himself to enter the spirit world. Hunting Leader positioned a guard at the hut door and then shut out all light by tightly closing the hut flap. He knocked the hut fire down so that the only light came from the red glow of the remaining coals. Mammoth Shadow closed his eyes as he slowed his breathing and his heartbeat. With his tambourine clasped in his left hand, he shook it at a slow tempo at first and then, methodically, increased the tempo until it was rapid. He chanted magical words over and over until he fell silent and still. His head slumped to his chest. Hunting Leader knew from experience that Mammoth Shadow now walked in the spirit world. He listened intently as the words formed on the Shaman's lips. Some he understood, but others were unintelligible. The chieftain sat silently and patiently for a long time, waiting for Mammoth Shadow to return to the Human world. Slowly, the Shaman's head rose, and when his eyes opened they stared as if sightless. The chieftain knew the Shaman would return soon, now that his eyes were open. Hunting Leader was rewarded for his patience when Mammoth Shadow's eyes blinked and he shook his head as if waking from a deep sleep.

Mammoth Shadow reported to Hunting Leader that the tribe was right; Devilish Spirit could not be found in the spirit world. He said Devilish Spirit walked beside Swift Spear. He informed Hunting Leader that the only way to drive the spirit away from Swift Spear and the tribe was to perform a ritual sacrifice on a Saiga antelope, one of Devilish Spirit's favorite disguises. Word was sent immediately to Swift Spear that he alone must trap a Saiga antelope as soon as possible and have it brought to the ceremonial circle.

That done, Mammoth Shadow whispered something into Hunting Leader's ear he wanted no others to overhear. He said that while in the spirit world, he was given a message for the chieftain by his spirit guide, Xolhut, the woolly mammoth. The spirit said the chieftain needed to know that the long-horned bison herd grazing nearby would begin to move very soon. Hunting Leader gazed upward and gave thanks to the spirit. He gave the command to begin the preliminary preparations necessary to strike camp.

Word of departure spread quickly through the Yukaghir camp and the tribe sprang into action. As nomads, they were used to being uprooted at a moment's notice. Many of them found it exciting, as they grew bored and restless remaining in the same area for too long. The tribe moved in machine-like precision as they implemented the first steps of uprooting themselves, just as they had done for time immemorial.

In the meantime, Swift Spear wasted no time trapping a Saiga antelope. He, aided by his fellow hunters, tied the animal upside down by all four legs onto a stout pole, and carried it into the encampment early the next morning. The entire tribe gathered around the antelope that lay in the ceremonial circle as they waited for the arrival of Hunting Leader and Mammoth Shadow. The tribe members could hear the familiar sound of the Shaman's tambourine long before he and the chieftain arrived to stand in the center of the circle. The chieftain and the Shaman were dressed in their finest ceremonial garments. The pair represented the finest aspects of the tribe. All that was good in the Yukaghir tribe resided in their two most important members – their ruler and their holy man.

Hunting Leader faced Swift Spear and asked, Who has secured this animal for sacrifice so that the tribe might be rid of the evil spirit, Devilish Spirit? Swift Spear announced in a loud, confident voice that it was he who had secured the animal. The chieftain then commanded that the sacrifice begin. He stepped back out of the circle.

Mammoth Shadow stepped into the circle and called upon the hunters to leash the animal but release its feet. When this was done, the frightened animal rose on wobbly legs. Its breath shot from its nostrils in white clouds as it struggled to break free of its tether. The Shaman reached into his hip-pouch and drew out his ceremonial bone knife. He held it in the air with his palms outstretched and began an incantation directed skyward. The tribe stood transfixed by his every move. As the Shaman finished his incantation, he gripped the knife by its handle and approached the antelope on its right side. The animal, wild-eyed with fear, affixed its gaze with one eye on the Shaman as it struggled fiercely against the leash. The hunters held their ground and maintained expert control. Mammoth Shadow took aim halfway down from the top of the animal's back, just behind its foreleg. With one swift and powerful movement, he plunged the knife through the animal's thick hide and into its heart. He withdrew the knife immediately. The wound spurted hot, red, steaming blood as the antelope's heart attempted to continue beating. The antelope swayed from side to side and then fell dead on the side opposite to the wound. The tribe shouted in thanksgiving for the good omen. The spirit of Devilish Spirit had been expunged. Mammoth Shadow had restored the tribe's spiritual equilibrium.

The Shaman called Swift Spear to step forward into the

circle. He complied. Facing the eastern sun, the Shaman recited a cleansing incantation and then repeated it facing the other cardinal points, moving accordingly around the hunter's body. In this manner, the Shaman completed the expulsion of the spirit that had been attached to Swift Spear. In doing so, he removed any stain that the evil spirit may have left on the hunter. With this act, the ceremony was complete. The tribe would now regard Swift Spear as if the incident in the hut of Innocent One and Weaver's Daughter had never taken place.

Good Friend and Innocent One, who were standing together near the back of the crowd, felt relief. The confrontation in the hut had left them uneasy that the hunter might yet harbor anger towards them. However, Swift Spear seemed to treat them with indifference now, and of this, they were glad.

Mammoth Shadow had barely finished the cleansing ritual for the hunter when a shout was heard. Everyone turned towards the direction of the sound as the figure of a man came into view. It was Tompula, Strong River, a herd scout, running towards the crowd. He shouted again and again that the bison were moving to the northeast. The crowd turned back to Mammoth Shadow in amazement. Then, Hunting Leader, facing the Shaman, dropped to his knees. The crowd followed suit and they all bowed their heads in a sign of great respect and admiration. Mammoth Shadow, standing in the center of the genuflecting crowd, bowed his head as a sign of humility, for the position of Shaman was not one of power. Rather, it was one of servitude and this simple act reaffirmed that fact.

Shortly, Hunting Leader rose to his feet, raised his fist-clenched arms into the cold morning air, and gave the command to break camp. The crowd rose to their feet and shouted with excitement. Before they hurried off, each one briefly touched the cheek of the Shaman in one last gesture of their gratitude. Tears of joy streaked Mammoth Shadow's face as he silently thanked the spirit of Kind Spirit, his mentor. The honor that the tribe bestowed upon him would not have been possible without her instruction. Within minutes, the encampment reached a state of controlled pandemonium.

To the untrained eye, the encampment was in turmoil, but nothing was further from the truth. Each adult tribal member had a specific task. The older female children kept the younger children out of harm's way while the adults dismantled the camp. Within a few hours, the entire encampment had been struck and packed onto sleds and into shoulder packs. Each family, with their meager possessions, assembled at the ceremonial circle. When everyone was present, Mammoth Shadow gave the tribe a ritual blessing to assure the journey would be a safe one. Hunting Leader gave the signal to move out when the Shaman was done.

The tribe, headed by the chieftain and his hunters, assembled into a thin line of sleds and bodies that threaded its way over frozen ground in the direction of the bison herd. Good Friend and Innocent One walked midway in the line, holding hands. Something made Innocent One look up towards the head of the procession. In doing so, she saw Swift Spear turn his head backward to her and his glowering eyes met hers. An icy shock shot down her spine as she realized that his indifference had been an act. An old fear overtook her as the hunter broke eye contact. She sighed as she realized there would be no peace for her and her lover. She gave Good Friend's hand a squeeze and smiled wanly at him when he gave her an inquisitive look. Bravely she remained silent, and walked on.

The tribe met up with the bison herd in less than an hour and joined the small troop of herd scouts waiting for their arrival. When the sun began its descent to the western horizon, the herd stopped to graze on meager patches of grass that poked though the ice. The tribe prepared a temporary camp, ate their evening meal, and then bedded down for the night. In the morning, as on many mornings to come, they broke their temporary encampment and moved relentlessly forward, allowing the bison herd to guide them to their final destination.

As the days wore on, the scouts noticed a sharp difference in the terrain and in the odor of the air they breathed. They were puzzled by the smell of the ocean without having any visual indication of its presence. The scouts grew uneasy because they knew they should have reached the Siberian coast by now, so they fell back to inform Hunting Leader of this fact. He reminded them that the spirit of Xolhut, the wooly mammoth, directed their journey and therefore they had nothing to fear. The scouts accepted his decree, but remained on sharp lookout for signs of danger. The scouts could not have been aware that the herd of bison led them onto the landmass that would someday be known as the Bering Strait Land Bridge.

Because the amount of water in the Earth's hydrosphere is constant, the great ice sheet's hoarding of global waters caused sea levels to fall significantly. As a result, landmasses grew dramatically in areas of gradual slope along the continental shelves, as was the case along the Bering Strait. The term "bridge" was a misnomer, for at this point, the exposed landmass between the Eurasian and North American continents was fully a thousand miles wide and fifty-five miles long.

The Alazeya Yukaghir tribe continued to snake across the Bering Strait Land Bridge in pursuit of the bison herd, unaware that they were walking on land that had never been previously impressed with the print of a human foot. And, of course, they were unaware that within a few days, when they reached the opposite side of the land bridge, they would make history that no journal would ever record. They would be the first Humans to set foot on the vast lands of the North American continent. Their descendants, the American Indian, would not welcome the first European explorers for another 11,500 years.

CHAPTER TWO

THE HOT MID-SUMMER SUN BEAT DOWN UPON the pair that walked swiftly and silently along the banks of the O'Hi'Yo, the Beautiful River. Rivulets of sweat streamed from beneath bison-leather headbands that kept their heavy, wooden, hide-covered backpacks from tilting backwards, preventing excruciating strain on their shoulders. The backpacks extended nearly a foot above their heads. Eventually the leather headbands irritated the skin on their foreheads causing a burn that would give them no peace. To make matters worse, they sweat profusely beneath their deerskin shirts and pants that protected them from the harsh rays of the sun. Neither man wanted to be the first to ask to stop under the shade of a hardwood tree for fear the other might think him weak, so they trudged on in quiet discomfort. Finally, it was Niyaka Hanu'wa, Little Turtle, who announced he was hungry and wanted to stop to eat. His companion, Tuwistuwi'kúwá, Killbuck, shrugged his shoulders as a sign that he did not care whether they stopped or not, but was inwardly relieved that his companion had offered the perfect excuse to stop and cool off. They were within a half-day of reaching their clan's encampment and a brief stop would not prevent them from arriving home before sunset. They removed their leather headbands and then unshouldered their backpacks. It would be a great relief when their journey home ended and they could hand over their backpacks that were laden with a precious, weighty cargo.

Little Turtle and Killbuck had set off in early May for the place known simply as "The Place of the Flints." They made a half-day's journey by foot from their encampment on the Genesee, the Pleasant River, to the banks of the O'Hi'Yo. Then they traveled over water for two days to the point where it joined the Monongahela River, and the O'Hi'Yo grew and became the Great Beautiful River. The water at that conjunction became too swift to canoe and they had to disembark and carry the canoe by land downriver to where the water was calmer. Then it was another two days journey down the O'Hi'Yo to the point where they had to disembark again to make the rest of the trek over land to the Place of the Flints.

The Place of the Flints was a flint ridge that Paleo-American Indians discovered several thousand years before Little Turtle and Killbuck's time. It consisted of an exposed ridge of Vanport flint, a variety of hard, durable quartz. The Flint Ridge was a large vein that had been slowly exposed to the surface through natural erosion, making it easy for early man to locate the flint and mine it. The exposed flint jutted out of the ground in outcrops that ranged from one to twelve feet wide. The flint, usually a light to dark gray color, was also found in hues of red, white, orange, purple, green, yellow, and blue. Red and purple flints were highly regarded because those colors were rare.

The flint ridge area was not suitable for settlement because there was no source of water nearby. Therefore, the flint was available to anyone resourceful enough to make the journey and mine the flint as he pleased.

The most important use of flint by Little Turtle and Killbuck's clan was for spear arrowheads. Other tools constructed of flint were scrapers for shaving spear shafts and hides, drill bits, cutting tools, and knife blades. Flint was a precious commodity and it became the Paleo-American Indian's first form of currency for trade with other clans.

By mid-May, the two men had completed the part of their journey that crossed water and they headed for an encampment of friendly Indians who would accept their canoe in trade for much needed supplies. After a respectful amount of haggling over the terms of the trade, the two men left on foot for the Flint Ridge with ample supplies of food and leather bladders they would fill later with water.

They reached the Flint Ridge in another eight days and began the simple, but arduous process of flint mining, known as "knapping." Little Turtle and Killbuck used a variety of flint-chipping tools. These included hammer stones and wedges made of rocks; club-like tools of wood, bone, or antler; punches made from deer antlers; gritty stones to help make striking platforms; and thick hide pads to protect their hands. They could not use the exposed flint because it was weather-checked from exposure, so they had to dig out the usable portion of the flint outcropping by hand. This proved to be more work than the actual knapping of the flint because the outcrops were buried in dry, hardened clay soil. Once the buried flint was exposed, they took advantage of natural cracks to split and pry small slabs of flint from the outcropping.

The work was slow and methodical. Little Turtle and Killbuck were chosen specifically for this task because each was known for quiet patience, self-discipline, and determination. They rarely spoke to one another as they became engrossed in the work of flint knapping. The sun broiled them as they toiled over the flint outcrops and, as a result, they consumed large amounts of water each day. They needed to leave the Flint Ridge every day at sunset to procure water from a stream located some distance away. They camped near the small stream at night and then returned to the Flint Ridge at dawn. They repeated this pattern for five days in a row. By the end of the fifth day, they had reached their quota of flint, so they packed their cache into their backpacks and left on foot for home.

Their return journey took significantly longer because it was necessary to make it over land. The current of the O'Hi'Yo was still too strong, as the river was being fed by runoff from the melting snow packs above it. The two men could not paddle the three hundred miles upstream. It had taken forty-one days to hike to the spot where they now stopped to eat their midday meal under a large, spreading white oak.

Their food consisted of bison jerky and a paste made from ground maize and water. As they ate, Little Turtle reached into a pouch on the side of his pack and fished out a small, rounded piece of red flint he had chipped out of a spent red flint outcrop just before they left the Flint Ridge. He rubbed it absentmindedly between his thumb and forefinger as he daydreamed about the beautiful pendant he would create from it. Killbuck broke Little Turtle's reverie by announcing that they should leave now so that they could avoid the dangers of traveling at night. Little Turtle carefully returned the red flint to his backpack and shouldered it for the last time. He smiled to himself as he placed the leather headband on his forehead. It would be wonderful to sleep in the confines of his family's bark-covered teepee tonight with the people he loved so much.

Within minutes, they found the well-worn trail that led them away from the river's banks and into a deciduous forest. They headed east towards the head of the beautiful and broad Genesee Valley that had been carved by the ever-flowing waters of the Genesee River. Soon, the mixture of oak, hickory, ash, and black locust trees gave way to an immense red oak forest. Their pace quickened because they knew it would be no more than an hour before they broke out of the oak forest and caught their first glimpse of valley. The two men moved with increased intensity.

Soon, they reached the edge of the forest, stepped out from under its green, leafy canopy and stood in the warm, golden rays of the late afternoon sun. They stared in awe and joy as they glimpsed the valley for the first time since giving it one last backward glance two months earlier. The valley stood out like a rare jewel. Heat waves shimmered from the ground, making the view seem surreal. The broad, green, fertile valley floor was divided into two verdant, tree-dotted meadows along a glistening river that gently flowed to the north. Eagles rode the spiraling thermal vents that lifted them high above the shale cliffs that zigged and zagged their way to the horizon. Here and there, large and small waterfalls poured from fissures in the rock walls and created clouds of lazy, dangling mist where their waters met the river below. Little Turtle, Killbuck, and their clan loved this valley dearly. For them, it was a testament to the power and majesty of the Great Spirit who had created it.

The spell the valley placed on them was broken when they noticed the sight of wispy trails of smoke that rose to the sky. The smoke issued forth from the fires of home. The two men broke into wide grins and rushed down into the valley. Their backpacks bobbed up and down like corks in water with the rhythm of each step, eventually forcing a slower pace.

Within twenty minutes, Little Turtle and Killbuck heard the familiar, everyday noises of their clan's encampment. They strained their ears to identify faint voices rising from below. Soon they heard the chattering of children punctuated occasionally by the sound of an adult female voice. They spied a group of small children seated in a semi-circle around a woman seated on a tree stump. The woman was Kaga, the Chronicler. As the two men approached, they heard Kaga recite a story she had learned from her grandfather:

My Grandfather was always telling funny stories. 'Now, this is a fact,' he would say. 'It happened by the O'Hi'Yo.'

He was walking along the O'Hi'Yo River. Suddenly, he saw something in the sky. It looked like two birds. He watched them flying in the sky for a long time. What big birds they were! They kept flying around in circles up there in the sky. They might have been eagles.

Suddenly, the two birds dropped down towards the

earth and picked up a fawn and carried it off to the lower bank of the O'Hi'Yo. My grandfather was surprised! They were not birds at all, but mosquitoes!

One mosquito says to the other, 'Let's go over to the other side of the river first and eat it there, I am so hungry I could split.' 'No,' says the other, 'The big ones might take it away from us.'

The children exploded with laughter as the Chronicler delivered the punch line to her grandfather's story. Little Turtle smiled to himself as he remembered the times from his youth when he was among the little listening circle that the Chronicler conducted for children. It was there he heard the most frightening story of his life, the story of Kakuwanë Unö'ëë', the Big Heads.

The Big Heads were enormous heads without bodies that swirled around in the sky during big storms. They found little children to be particularly tasty. The Chronicler had warned the children that they must never be caught outside in a storm or the Big Heads would find them. After that, Little Turtle slept very little for many nights due to visions of Big Heads gnashing their teeth and chasing him throughout the valley during the course of a thunderstorm. Now, of course, he realized that the story was only meant to keep him safely indoors whenever there was a storm.

Although the Chronicler, a teller of the clan's stories, served as the clan's unofficial historian, she maintained a much more important role. She was also the Keeper of the Names. Each clan had a pool of names. When someone in the clan passed away, the Chronicler returned his or her name to the pool. Children were initially named for an event that occurred at the time of their birth and they kept that name until they reached adolescence. Once they reached adolescence, the Chronicler would give them a name from the pool of names stored in her memory. When the child received his or her new name, the tribe considered that child the reincarnation of the person who had passed away. It was very important that this rite of passage be performed. In this way, the clan was assured that they retained the spirits of their ancestors. Little Turtle was named after a grandfather he never met.

One of the boys spotted the returning travelers. He shouted their names and all the boys sprang from their sitting positions and surrounded the pair. The younger boys were eager to hear about their trip and treated Little Turtle and Killbuck as if they were great heroes. The two men were patient and responded kindly to the boys, but they continued to make their way into the encampment. That was how the rest of clan first saw the returning adventurers – awash in a sea of children.

As the adult clan members approached Little Turtle and Killbuck, they gently shooed away the children. The pair removed the packs from their shoulders and set them on the ground while answering many questions. Little Turtle was in the midst of one of these responses when he heard a familiar voice. It was the voice of his nemesis, Motega, New Arrow.

Little Turtle and New Arrow had been close friends as boys until the day Little Turtle tattled on New Arrow. New Arrow had stolen a wooden figurine from another boy. When confronted, New Arrow lied. The boy's mother took Little Turtle aside and shamed him into telling what he knew about the theft. New Arrow never forgave Little Turtle and they became bitter adversaries. Little Turtle grew immune to most of New Arrow's tricks and taunts over time. He understood that New Arrow felt betrayed, and he felt guilty for betraying his friend. Little Turtle wished many times that he could undo what he had done to New Arrow.

However, something was different about the tone of New Arrow's voice this time. It was arrogant and more hateful. Little Turtle shifted his gaze towards New Arrow and was surprised to see Aiyana, Everlasting Flower, standing next to him. She avoided his eyes and that alarmed him. Everlasting Flower was the object of Little Turtle's affections and although he had not made it known to her, he had meant to make her aware of it soon. The piece of red flint that he had carefully pulled from the ground in The Place of the Flints was meant for her, after it was properly shaped and polished.

New Arrow spoke out in a loud voice and the other clan members went silent in embarrassment. His words were sarcastic digs about how long Little Turtle and Killbuck had been gone and how so many things had changed since they left. This puzzled Little Turtle, as he could not imagine where this talk was leading. Then, a mean smirk spread across New Arrow's face as he reached for Everlasting Flower's hand. She fumbled a weak attempt to avoid clasping his hand, but failed. After securing her hand in his, New Arrow threw his head back and laughed victoriously. He knew Little Turtle was in love with Everlasting Flower. Many times he had seen Little Turtle secretly watching her. The clan was shocked by New Arrow's behavior. No one had ever been deliberately nasty in their presence.

It took a few seconds for the scene to make sense to Little Turtle. When he finally realized that New Arrow had purposely taken Everlasting Flower from him, it detonated a rage that lay deep within him. Without thinking, he lunged at New Arrow, knocking him and the girl to the ground. Everlasting Flower, terrified, scurried away on her hands and knees as Little Turtle grasped New Arrow by throat in an attempt to choke him. New Arrow ripped the hands from his throat and the two men rolled on the ground, striking at each other. Finally, several men intervened and tore Little Turtle off New Arrow. New Arrow stood and screamed epitaphs of hate as Little Turtle struggled to get free from the many strong hands that held him at bay. The veins in New Arrow's face bulged with fury as he ramped up his verbal attack. He said Little Turtle was unworthy of Everlasting Flower because he came from an unworthy family line that had no honor. Again, the clan members were shocked. No one had ever spoken about other clan members with such disrespect. They wondered if New Arrow knew something about Little Turtle and his family that they did not.

The men dragged the kicking and screaming Little Turtle from the scene. They did not release him until they deposited him into his mother's teepee. His mother entered the teepee followed by his brother who had carried Little Turtle's backpack. The men waited until they were sure that Little Turtle had calmed down before they exited the teepee. One of the men remained at the entrance for a few minutes, just in case Little Turtle might erupt in anger again.

Little Turtle's mother, Wenoah, First Born Daughter, was outraged at the words New Arrow had spoken. When she was certain that her son was unharmed, she marched out of the teepee, leaving Little Turtle in his brother's care. She went back to the crowd still standing at the scene of the ruckus. She approached every elder woman of the clan and asked what they intended to do about the insults that New Arrow had publicly uttered regarding her family. One by one, each woman shrugged her shoulders as if to say she did not know or did not care. There was no law in their clan and there was no leader to guide them through a crisis of this sort.

At that time, the Paleo-American Indian clans consisted of small groups of people who looked upon one another as extended family members. There were no leaders and no shamans. Everyone filled the positions needed in their clan based on their natural talents. For example, if someone showed an aptitude for the art of healing, he or she could practice that skill if they wished. The member who was the clan's existing healer would take the youth in as an apprentice. If someone showed an aptitude for leadership in certain matters, they might be allowed to make decisions concerning those issues with the general consent of the clan. Most often, decisions were left to the elder women of the family or families most affected by the outcome of the decision.

Each family was lead by the eldest woman and she made the important decisions for her family. Men took care of the physical needs of their families and deferred all other decisions to eldest female. The clan made few decisions as a whole beyond when and where they should move each summer and each winter. It never occurred to the elder women that they should hold a council to decide on important clan matters.

When First Born Daughter reached the last of the elder women, she clucked her tongue and shook her head at them as a sign of her disappointment. She turned and walked away without uttering another word.

When she returned to her teepee, she called her family together to explain what had just taken place. She said she needed to leave the teepee again, but assured them that when she returned she would have a decision. First Born Daughter then went to visit her brother and her sister's teepees and after conferring with the elder women there, she returned to her own teepee.

Again, First Born Daughter gathered her family around her and made an announcement that left them speechless. It had been decided among herself, her sister, and her sister-in-law that all three families would leave the clan. This decision had to be final because not one clan member raised a hand or a voice in defense of their family's honor. When Little Turtle tried to protest her decision, First Born Daughter silenced him. She told him that the decision was made. They would begin packing their belongings that night, dismantle their teepees in the morning, and leave. She would let them know the location of their destination tomorrow, after they left. She did not want any other clan member to know where they were heading. They were through with this clan.

Little Turtle sat in misery on the floor of the teepee. The expulsion of his rage left him feeling worn out and empty. He could hardly believe the turn of events that had taken place in such a short time. An hour ago, he had been the returning hero. Now, he and his family were outcasts and the woman he loved was gone from him forever. He buried his head in his hands and remained that way until his mother prodded him to get up and pack. The process took an hour. The clan always traveled light.

After a long, sleepless night, the three families woke early and began to dismantle their teepees in preparation for their journey. Many clan members watched in silence. They had hoped that over night the three families would realize the mistake they had made in their decision to abandon the clan. Many of the women wept and wailed as they saw that the families were following through on their promise to leave. They wondered what would become of them once the spirit of their ancestors was diminished. Some of the women tried to dissuade First Born Daughter from leaving, but she would not look at them or acknowledge their presence. It was as if she could no longer see or hear them. This filled them with a great sadness that would leave a scar on the psyche of the clan for a long, long time.

When all three family units were ready, First Born Daughter gave the command to move out. She led the brave and proud families, laden with all of their belongings, out of the encampment and headed west. Little Turtle carried the backpack with half the precious flint meant for the clan still inside it. The clan stood in a small knot and dejectedly watched until the figures of their former clan members disappeared from view. Many cried. Some remained stoic. In years to come, the Chronicler would tell the story of their departure and how Little Turtle and New Arrow were the cause. She renamed Little Turtle and called him Matchitehew, He Who Has A Bad Heart. She renamed New Arrow, and called him, Matchitisiw, He Who Has Bad Character.

When the little band of outcasts were far enough away so that their voices could not be overheard, First Born Daughter told the group where their new summer home would be. It was a place near the O'Hi'Yo, about three days journey. Her father, and his father before him, had visited that place many times and spoke of the rich land teeming with game and useful vegetation. There, they would start their life anew and resurrect their family's honor.

In three days, they arrived at the spot that First Born Daughter had described. It was not far from the O'Hi'Yo and true to her promise, the area was rich in resources. Best of all, numerous artesian springs bubbled from the ground and ran downhill to a small stream that terminated at the O'Hi'Yo. They selected a clear, flat spot and erected their new camp. Knowing that their new home needed a name, First Born Daughter knelt down and cupped some of the water from a large spring. She rose to her feet and named their home Utôshút'nú, Coldspring.

CHAPTER THREE

THE HORSE'S NOSTRILS FLARED AND HIS EYES opened wide a split second before he reared up on his hind legs nearly unseating the white man in his saddle. Charles Bent clung tenaciously to the horse by clamping his legs around the horse's broad sides and pulling tight on the reins in a desperate attempt to avoid being thrown. His companion, a Seneca Indian Guide named Lame Wolf, was doing much the same to control his own spooked horse. Eventually, both men, still mounted, calmed their animals, and continued down the trail.

Lame Wolf answered Charles' question before it was asked – the horses had seen a ribbon snake slither across the trail in front of them. For the rest of the day Charles worried about encountering more snakes but thankfully the rest of their journey was uneventful. The two men were heading to an Iroquois village.

Evening had begun to settle as they emerged from the forest and faced an unbelievably tall elm post-and-bark palisade. Charles had never imagined such a towering fence could be built. He could see that the palisade curved around the entire village they were about to enter. The two men guided their horses through a single-gate entrance. On the other side, he was so astounded by the sight of the assemblage of longhouses that he stopped his horse and stared in wonder. The longhouses reminded him of large, lidded, rattan baskets. The buildings were incredibly tall, topping out at fifteen or twenty feet, and equally wide. Smoke curled from holes in the woven roofs and the charred smell lingered even at ground level.

Lame Wolf signaled to Charles to dismount and they tied their horses to a pole outside a nearby longhouse. Looking up above the entrance to the longhouse Charles knew immediately that this was the longhouse belonging to Lame Wolf's Seneca Indian clan. The same turtle symbol that adorned the back of Lame Wolf's shirt was emblazoned above the entrance to the longhouse.

Charles Bent was employed by the Holland Company as a surveyor. The Holland Company completed the purchase of a large tract of land in Pennsylvania and New York in 1797. Joseph Ellicott, who was their chief surveyor, had hired Charles the following year. Lame Wolf, also an employee of the Holland Company, had been assigned to act as a guide for Charles as he surveyed land in the Southern Tier of western New York. Now, in 1799, they were surveying land in an area the Seneca Indians called Coldspring. The land was located near Lame Wolf's Iroquois village. Over time, Charles had gained the trust of his Indian guide and they had become friends. One day, Lame Wolf honored Charles by inviting him to attend an Iroquois listening circle normally closed to non-Indians. Charles accepted the offer with enthusiasm and felt honored to have received the rare invitation. His heart beat with excitement as they passed through the entrance of the longhouse.

The interior of the longhouse was dark and it took a moment for Charles' eyes to adjust. The log-pole walls were interwoven with large sheets of birch bark. The circumference of the longhouse was lined with raised sleeping platforms covered with cornhusk woven mats and furs. A second platform, located above the sleeping platforms, was used for the storage of personal belongings. The roof of the longhouse had five holes that glowed eerily through the smoke issuing from four separate fires burning in the center of the room. The rafters of the longhouse were strung with suspended bark baskets filled with dried corn and beans, braided corn stalks, dried medicine plants, blowguns, bows and arrows, and ceremonial items.

The room was abuzz with the sounds of its occupants hastily preparing for that night's listening circle, which was about to begin. Lame Wolf quickly introduced Charles to several men, and then they took their places sitting cross-legged in front of Lame Wolf's family platform. Charles scanned the scene around him. The women and children all sat on the sleeping platforms, while the men sat in front of them on the ground. After a brief introduction by Lame Wolf on what to expect that evening, the Story Teller took up his position at the far end of the longhouse. The longhouse went silent as each member turned and focused his attention.

The Story Teller began the listening circle by filling a long pipe with ceremonial tobacco, lighting it, and passing it to the first man on his left. Slowly the pipe made its way around the circle of men, stopping briefly now and then to be refilled and relit on its journey back to the Story Teller. Charles watched intently as each man drew from the pipe, held the smoke in his mouth, and then slowly exhaled. When it was his turn at the pipe, Charles mimicked them exactly, which elicited a murmur of approval. When the pipe made its way completely around the circle and returned to the Story Teller, he placed it on the ground and began his first story. It was a children's story, The Story of the No-Face Doll.

> *"The Iroquois people have three sustainers of life. They are called the three sisters. They are the Spirits of the corn, the beans, and the squash. The Spirit of the Corn was so pleased at being one of the sustainers of life that she asked the Creator if there was more that she could do for her people. The Creator told her that he could form a beautiful doll from her cornhusks. So, the Creator set to work forming the doll. When he was finished, he gave the doll a beautiful face. Then he sent it down to the children of the Iroquois people to play with to make them happy. The doll went from village to village playing with the children and doing whatever*

> *she could to make them happy. Wherever she went all the people would tell her how beautiful she was. The doll became very vain after a while. The Creator spoke to her and explained that this was not the right kind of behavior and she agreed not to be vain anymore. The Creator warned her that if she continued with this behavior he would have to punish her. He did not tell her what her punishment would be. The doll went back to making the Iroquois children happy.*
>
> *One afternoon, as she was passing by a creek, she glanced into the water. When she admired her reflection, she could not help but think how beautiful she was, because it was true, she was beautiful. Seeing this, the Creator sent a giant screech owl out of the sky and it erased her reflection from the water. When the doll looked again into the water of the creek, she saw that she had no reflection. That was the punishment the Creator had warned her about. And that is why the Iroquois women give their children dolls with no face. It is to remind them that it is wrong for people to think they are better than anyone else. The Creator gives a special gift to everyone."*

The children oohed and aahed as if this were the first time they had heard the story. When they quieted down, the Story Teller went on to tell several more stories. Two women approached the Story Teller just when Charles thought the evening was coming to an end. One woman carried a large, heavy gourd and the other carried two smaller, empty gourds. The Story Teller took the larger gourd and used its contents to fill the two smaller gourds held by each of the women. The substance was a milky, brackish liquid. When the gourds were both full, the women gave one gourd to the man on their left, and one gourd to the man on their right. The men took a swig of the liquid and passed it to the man next to him. Lame Wolf was apparently surprised by this turn of events. He quietly instructed Charles that he must drink the liquid, which had been prepared from crushed, soaked morning glory seeds, when it reached him. And, he added emphatically, no matter how foul it tastes, Charles had to swallow a mouthful of the liquid. If he did not, the clan would be gravely insulted.

Lame Wolf passed the gourd to Charles after taking his drink. Charles quickly filled his mouth with the bitter, seed husk liquid and swallowed it immediately. He shivered as the bitterness of the liquid assaulted his taste buds. Lame Wolf cast a worried glance at Charles, but relaxed when he saw that the liquid had gone down and stayed in his stomach.

When the last man drank from the gourds, the Story Teller announced that in honor of Lame Wolf's guest, Mister Charles, he would recount a legend that took place in Coldspring many, many moons ago. Charles felt lightheaded. Then he heard a distant eagle let out plaintive cries. His vision started to blur as the hallucinogenic properties of the morning glory concoction took effect. When the Story Teller began the legend of the Woman and the Two Braves, Charles was transported back in time....

....As a chilling fog filled the eastern dawn, the hulking figure of a man stormed among a group of bark-covered Indian huts that kept their sleeping occupants insulated from the cold, moist morning air. The silence hanging over the encampment was pierced only by the shrill cry of an eagle that slowly circled overhead. Reaching his hut, the man tore aside the flap of animal hide that covered the hut's entrance, nearly ripping it from the poles. His violence shook the frame of the hut, setting off a dry clattering sound. The grotesque, shriveled scalps that hung randomly from the hut ceiling on thick strands of black hair swung to and fro and jumped up and down in an eerie dance as they collided with one another. Charging Bear, a fierce Seneca and Iroquois warrior, was angry, a sharp contrast to his demeanor just a few minutes earlier.

His amorous advances had just been soundly rejected by the Shaman's daughter, She Who Wears Many Moccasins.

Charging Bear's anger stemmed from the callousness with which her rejection had been delivered. He had approached Many Moccasins as she finished her morning Sun Dance ritual, conveying the tribe's gratitude to the Great Spirit for the creation of another day. Reaching for her hand, Charging Bear clumsily expressed the love that he felt for her and the hope that she could return it by marrying him. Many Moccasins' jaw dropped in surprise at this declaration of love. For a few moments, she was truly speechless. Her silence was broken as she said, "How dare you approach me in this manner, Charging Bear. I am the daughter of a great and powerful Shaman. You cannot honestly believe that I could ever consider a betrothal to you, a common warrior. My marriage must be to a man who befits my status in our tribe. I cannot accept your advances towards me. It is out of the question!"

She spun around and walked away, cutting off any response Charging Bear may have offered. He was bitterly stung by her words and the anger that was usually reserved for his enemies in battle welled up in him and spilled out like boiling hot liquid. His brows knitted into a deep furrow and his lips tightened into a menacing scowl as he wheeled around and headed for his hut.

He screamed incoherently as he vented his rage on the contents of his hut, disturbing some of the sleeping members of his clan in the process. When his rage was spent, Charging Bear sat sullenly on the mat-covered floor of his hut brooding over the morning's events. Foolishly, he convinced himself that he could change Many Moccasins' mind if he explained that as a great and mighty warrior his station in the tribe was sufficient for a woman of her status. He jumped up, left the hut, and set off in the direction that Many Moccasins had taken after abruptly ending their conversation.

Charging Bear stopped at the Wolf Clan Longhouse and peered quietly into its interior in the hope of seeing her within. She was not among the sleeping occupants of the longhouse. He continued walking to the end of the village, where he picked up signs of her egress towards the Coldspring creek. He had tracked her progress for quite some distance when he heard voices up ahead. With warrior-like stealth, he crept through a thicket of berry bushes, carefully avoiding the hooked barbs that covered their slender arching branches. A clearing appeared at the edge of the berry thicket. He froze as he recognized the two figures lying in an embrace on the ground. It was Many Moccasins and Speaking Eagle, the son of the Hawk clan and Seneca Tribe chieftain, Hunting Horse. They were locked in the act of making love.

Charging Bear's brain exploded with anger. The Indian maiden's thoughtless statement, made earlier that morning, instantly replayed itself in his mind. Operating on instinct rather than rational thought, he charged out of the thicket screaming furious and threatening epithets at the two lovers. Speaking Eagle disengaged from Many Moccasins and scrambled to his feet. He unsheathed a knife from his belt and took up a fighting stance. This enraged Charging Bear even further. He and Speaking Eagle had been good friends since childhood. Now, he felt betrayed that his friend had taken the object of affection, even though Speaking Eagle had known nothing of his feelings towards Many Moccasins. And here was his friend, taking up arms against him!

Charging Bear halted his progress, reached for the small tomahawk hanging from his belt, and launched it at Speaking Eagle with blinding speed. Speaking Eagle was unable to react quickly enough to avoid the hurtling tomahawk. It landed with a dull thud as it pierced his chest cavity, unleashing a torrent of blood. The sheer force of the thrown tomahawk knocked Speaking Eagle backwards onto the ground. He died quickly.

Many Moccasins, who had been motionless with horror and confusion, rushed over to Speaking Eagle and cradled his lifeless head in her arms. Charging Bear walked up to her, grabbed her by her long black hair, and yanked her to a standing position. She spun around and broke free as her hair slipped from his grasp. She ran for her life, bounding over the lazy creek and into the brush on the other side.

Charging Bear sprinted off in the direction of the fleeing maiden and caught up with her on a rocky outcrop not far from the creek's edge. He threw her to the ground and attempted to mount her. He wanted nothing more than to defile the haughty woman who had cruelly rejected him only an hour ago. For a split second their eyes locked, their bodies motionless. Then Charging Bear slowly brought his mouth to within inches of her succulent lips. But the cry of an eagle broke the spell that had overcome Many Moccasins. Her indignation at Charging Bear's attempt at rape was evident in her brown eyes as she furiously clawed him with her fingernails. He roared as the pain manifested in his anger-dulled brain. He reached again for a weapon in his belt and produced his razor-sharp hunting knife. With one deft motion, he slid the keen edge of knife across Many Moccasins' throat, reducing her screams to dull gurgling sounds. He threw her blood-gushing body down and stood above it as if he were victorious in battle.

Throwing his head back, Charging Bear let out a war whoop and stepped away from her body. In a few seconds, rational thought began to creep its way back into his brain.

It took a few moments before the vision of Many Moccasins' bloody body lying at his feet registered. He barely remembered having killed the maiden and her lover. He had blacked out, which had rendered him incapable of controlling his primal rage. He raised his hand and stared at the bloody knife blade protruding from his knife's handle. He stumbled back as the full realization of what he had done spread over him. He turned and ran from the scene, leaping over the creek and back into the berry thicket. He wandered about aimlessly for hours in the forest, trying to decide what his best course of action should be. When darkness finally fell over the land, Charging Bear crept back into the village unseen and went directly to his hut.

Fear and guilt prevented him from leaving the confines of his hut the next day. Somewhere in the middle of the day, two braves appeared at the entrance to his hut. Hunting Horse had sent his messengers to demand his appearance before the Seneca Nation Council in the longhouse of the Hawk clan. They grabbed Charging Bear by his arms and forced him outside, through the hut flap. They dragged him the entire distance to the longhouse where Hunting Horse, Black Robe, the Seneca Council, and members from all eight Seneca clans awaited his arrival.

The two braves deposited Charging Bear in front of Hunting Horse and Black Robe, father of Many Moccasins, who stood at the head of the Council circle. Hunting Horse demanded that Charging Bear produce his tomahawk. Charging Bear averted his gaze and stared at the ground in shame. In the shock and horror that had followed his murderous acts, he had forgotten to remove his tomahawk from Speaking Eagle's body. He sighed, realizing he could not defend himself.

Black Robe, with blazing eyes, approached Charging Bear and ripped his knife from his belt. Charging Bear looked up just as Black Robe swung his arm and backhanded him in the face. When Black Robe began another attempt to land a blow on Charging Bear's cheek, the two braves grabbed the Shaman's arms and forced him back towards Hunting Horse. As Black Robe wept inconsolably, the crowd in the longhouse jeered and shouted until Hunting Horse demanded they be silent.

"Your silence and your inability to produce your weapon is proof of your guilt," he said, venting his anger. Then he produced

Charging Bear's blood-encrusted tomahawk from behind his back.

The crowd became agitated again upon seeing concrete proof of Charging Bear's violent acts against members of the Seneca Nation. Once again, Hunting Horse quelled their response. He wasted no time in declaring his judgment against Charging Bear.

In a loud but quivering voice, Hunting Horse said, "You have broken the trust that your Seneca brothers and sisters have placed in you. You have taken the lives of the son I loved more than myself, and the flower of Black Robe's family, as if the two were nothing more than animals of prey. You are cast out of the brotherhood that you have dishonored, never to return. The Seneca Nation has no Charging Bear, nor will there ever be a member again that bears that name. Go from us, you who has no name, and do not return."

The crowd murmured their approval of his decree and they spit on Charging Bear as the two braves dragged him from the longhouse. The braves cast him on the ground at the edge of the Seneca village as if they were discarding a load of garbage. They stood watch as Charging Bear slinked into the forest and disappeared from view.

Charging Bear wandered through the forest as he summed up his predicament. He knew he could never return to a tribe of the Iroquois Confederation. He also knew that no warring tribe would ever welcome an Iroquois, especially one that had been a warrior. Without any tools, he was almost sure to die from hunger and exposure in the forest. After a couple of days, he made his way back to the spot where he had killed Many Moccasins and Speaking Eagle. He knew they would be buried just beyond that spot on Sacred Indian Burial Ground.

He found their freshly dug graves and collapsed to his knees, which was the beginning of the unraveling of his mind. Charging Bear was racked with guilt and remorse and could find no way of redeeming himself of his savage acts. He paced the graves for hours as his sanity gave out. He did not leave for food or water.

Charging Bear's body began to cannibalize itself and he grew emaciated from hunger and thirst. He slept only when he dropped, exhausted, and allowed himself to be exposed to the elements. He raved and paced until the day he could no longer muster the strength it took to stand. He lay prostrate on the graves until death mercifully released him from his anguished existence. The first snow of winter blanketed his decomposing body and hid the final process of decomposition from view for the remainder of the harsh winter.

When spring came, Black Robe and his wife, Singing Voice, Many Moccasins' mother, paid a visit to their daughters' grave. When they saw the scattered pile of bones that lay on the graves, they knew immediately whose they were. Singing Voice screamed with rage and disgust that Charging Bear had defiled her daughter's grave with his remains. At that very moment, a chilly wind tore through the burial ground. The voice of Charging Bear was borne upon it. He demanded that they leave the burial site. He told them Many Moccasins belonged to him and no one else. Singing Voice was terrified. She dropped the sacrificial tobacco and sage she had brought and ran from the burial grounds, terrified. She fled back through the forest alone, running in fear of the raging warrior's spirit.

Without hesitation, Black Robe started to chant the ancient prayers of his forefathers. He gathered sticks to prepare a small fire, while he sang and called forth the heavens to heal the sickness of Coldspring Creek. The medicine man struck his hatchet against a dry stone sparking a small flame. As the smoke from burning wood and sage filled the air, the Shaman continued to pray. The spirit of Charging Bear resisted all efforts by Black Robe to remove him from the land.

But Black Robe continued to pray, blessing the earth with the elements and the power of his ancestors. When the fire had burned itself cold, the Shaman covered the ashes with tobacco and dirt. He placed eagle feathers in a circle of peace and blessed the earth. Tears of sadness filled his eyes because even with all his wisdom, he could not understand Charging Bear's violence. Alone he wept, his cries heard by no one except the majestic eagle that served as witness to all that occurred at Coldspring Creek. He turned to the wind that now blew harshly in his face once again and declared, "I assure you that my people will never visit this land again, evil spirit. This is the only way to destroy you. It is from the living that you derive the energy that prolongs your presence in this world. You will fade from existence because there will be no one left to empower you with the hate they feel for you."

As the sun met the horizon, the land became quiet and Black Robe began his journey back to the village. Accompanied by the cries of the eagle flying above his head, he made his way through the thick forest. When he arrived at the village, he was greeted by several members who asked him to confirm what Singing Voice had told them. Black Robe simply nodded and said, "It is true. The land is filled with an evil spirit. I have prayed to our ancestors for help and they have given me the benefit of their wisdom. We shall not walk the land of our buried ancestors again. It is best now to honor them with silent prayer and leave them be in the earth. The evil spirit will wither and fade with time. Let no one set foot in that part of Coldspring Creek again."

The tribe listened to his words and took them to heart. Never again did the Seneca cross over to the other side of Coldspring Creek. They left the burial land for the eagle to watch over. And, true to the wisdom garnered from the spirit of the Seneca ancestors by Black Robe, the spirit of Charging Bear slowly faded from the land. The only reminder of the karmic explosion that took place there was the disintegrating, sun-bleached, moldy bones lying scattered on top of the graves of She Who Wears Many Moccasins and Speaking Eagle.

CHAPTER FOUR

THE MEMORY OF THE COLDSPRING INDIAN MURDERS faded and the hand of the white man was now taming the land. Forests were cleared and land was sectioned off into counties, towns, and villages. Coldspring became a town within Cattaraugus County in the state known as New York. Farming was the chief means of sustaining life in the new community.

Foster Omens claimed a plot of land in Coldspring that encompassed the territory once inhabited by the Seneca tribe. He had traveled across the vast Atlantic Ocean to find a better life for his new family. His wife, Annamae, and his young son, Caleb, were among the first settlers to endure the harsh winters in the fertile lands. They built their family farmhouse using their own brute strength. Every log came from the surrounding forest and all of their meals came from the crops they could grow and their livestock. Together, the Omens family worked the land to sustain their lineage and bring forth a generation of new Americans.

When Foster died from heart failure in 1845 and his wife of pneumonia the following year, the family land was passed down to Caleb, as he was their firstborn son. Continuing on with the family tradition, Caleb worked hard raising wheat and corn, selling what he could in town, and establishing himself as a good Christian in the community. He married shortly after the death of his mother. Addie Bourne was a kind and loving widow who brought with her a young son named William.

William Bourne and his stepfather were very different creatures. While Caleb was deeply connected with the land and the traditions that had been set forth by his ancestry, William questioned all manner of authority. Throughout his childhood, William argued with his stepfather as to why things were to be done in accordance with previously established rules and regulations. Although Caleb cared for his new stepson, the fatherly tolerance he lacked was apparent in his disregard for William's words. When his stepson repeatedly asked 'Why' and 'How come,' Caleb simply ignored the curious child. This created tremendous distance between them.

The dedication and hard work his stepfather put into the land did not find its way into William's idle hands. Rather than attending to livestock, the young boy was likely to be found lying under a large tree singing songs about an imaginary world far different than the one in which he lived. While his mother tolerated his poor work ethic, Caleb had a far different opinion. Caleb resorted to violent lashings of the boy with his broad, black belt, and when that did not convince William, he beat him with his bare hands. After several of these stormy confrontations, the boy sourly succumbed to a life of servitude to his stepfather.

Without his fantasy world as an outlet, the young boy grew into a sullen man, turning to liquor to dull his emotional pain. When William was not working on the farm, he could be found in the woods drinking himself into a stupor. The only peace he found was in the smell of his mother's kitchen and the quiet tunes she would hum as she scrubbed the floor. His mother unknowingly soothed his rage with kind words and gentle hymns, yet her tenderness fell short of healing his wounds.

One day, William drove his stepfather's buggy into town and encountered love. It was the first moment of light in his dark world. Her name was Sophronia Brand. She was a shy, fragile flower hiding behind her mother's large dress skirts. Following them into the supply store, he saw them selling jars of honey and blueberry jelly to the owner. William's rugged face softened when Sophronia's cheeks blushed as she became aware of his stare. He watched her breathlessly and when she and her mother left the store with their meager earnings, he raced to the counter to ask whom they were.

William was told they were a struggling family living on the edge of town in a small rundown farmhouse. Mrs. Mary Brand was a hardworking widow who kept a bee farm, a small garden to provide food for herself and her daughter, and anything else she could think of to keep food on the table and wood in the stove. Tuberculosis had taken the life of her beloved husband, Elisha. The few unmarried men in town did not find her attractive enough to court. Sophronia Brand spent every day with her mother, helping to keep up the house and maintain the gardens and hives. Isolated and sheltered from society, Sophronia's social skills were minimal and her education limited. She was shocked and somewhat terrified when she discovered the man who had been staring at her in the store now stood at the steps to their porch.

Arriving without announcement or invitation, William frightened both of the Brand women at first. He hurriedly rushed up to Mrs. Brand with a small bunch of wild flowers.

"Hello, Mrs. Brand, my name is William Bourne. These flowers are for Sophronia."

She graciously took them as her daughter monitored the conversation from inside the house.

"My family and I live at the farmhouse near the Coldspring Creek. I'm sorry to have arrived without proper introduction ma'am, but I have never courted a lady before."

Relieved by his intentions and his sincerity, she politely smiled.

"Would you like a glass of honey water?"

"Yes, ma'am," William gently replied.

Together they sat on the porch while Sophronia hid nervously in the hallway, hoping to hear as much of the conversation as possible. Mrs. Brand chatted happily while

William squirmed uncomfortably in his seat. Finally, his impatience forced him to graciously interrupted her, "Mrs. Brand, I don't know how this is done really, my family has a large farm and I am a very hard worker. I realize Sophronia is all you have left, so I do not want to take anything away from you, but I would like to start a courtship with her. I would like to arrange for you both to be taken care of. I am saying, well, I am trying to say...."

Mrs. Brand stepped in graciously. "Mr. Bourne, I know who your family is and the farm that your father owns. It would be my pleasure to allow you to court my daughter and proceed with an engagement. Sophronia is my only family, but I would be foolish to stand in the way of a good match. I can see you are sincere and it would be lovely if you would join us tomorrow afternoon so we can set forth an arrangement."

Elated, William jumped to his feet to thank her, knocking over the rest of the honey water in his glass. "Oh, I'm sorry ma'am, I'm sorry."

Dipping her head to hide her smile, she excused his blunder, "Do not worry yourself, dear. It's fine, just fine."

Embarrassed, he nodded with a slight bow and excused himself. "Well good evening then ma'am, I will see you tomorrow around four in the afternoon."

"Yes, Mr. Bourne. That will be fine." Mrs. Brand smiled and glowed slightly

William turned around on his way down the porch steps and asked, "You will give the flowers to Sophronia, ma'am?"

Again, she smiled and softly replied, "Yes, Mr. Bourne, I will."

William left quickly as the early autumn sun was setting behind the thick forest on the edge of town. His horse's hooves pounded the earth as his heart burst with a joy new to him.

As the buggy arrived at his stepfather's stable, William tensed with worry about the reaction Caleb would have to his announcement. He slowly unhitched his loyal workhorse and rested the arms of his buggy in the sweet straw. While he rubbed down the bay gelding with a soft towel, William practiced his speech. He imagined explaining to his family why he was late and that he would make up the chores he neglected early the next morning. The words needed to convince his stepfather of the soundness of his impetuous decision seemed to evade his grasp, and his anxiety grew until he heard his name called from across the field.

Running fast, William burst into his family's home with rare exuberance. His mother looked at him and said, "Well, look who found his smile! Wherever have you been, my son?"

Caleb said nothing as he finished the meal served a short while before his stepson's arrival.

"I'm sorry for my timing mother, I have some news." William addressed Caleb with the utmost respect. "Are you very angry with me sir?" he asked sheepishly, wishing to end this magical day without a fight.

"No, William, I'm sure you will tie up the bundles early before breakfast, won't you?" Caleb gave him a stern glance.

"Yes sir, absolutely, sir."

His mother prepared a plate of beef and corn for him as he sat politely in his assigned position at the table.

"So what is your news, son?" asked Mrs. Omens.

"I found myself a wife today," William said with a mature tone to impress his stepfather. A blanket of silence covered the dinner table as his parents absorbed his statement.

"Well now, that certainly is some news," his mother said nervously, unsure of her husband's reaction.

Caleb pushed his plate away and took a deep breath. For the first time in the ten years they had shared as a family, a tremendous smile spread across the man's face as he reached out a hand to his stepson. "I knew it!" he proclaimed. "I knew I would make a man out of you. Is she beautiful? Is she from good stock? How old is she? How did you meet her?"

Elated at his stepfather's reaction, William clenched his teeth and swallowed the tears of relief he refused to reveal. "Her name is Sophronia Brand. She is sixteen and she has a very kind mother."

Ecstatic that her son and her husband were finally in accord, Mrs. Omens hugged her boy and smiled at Caleb. "Brand, Brand, I know that name."

"What does her father do?" Caleb continued his questioning.

"Well, Mr. Brand passed three years ago. It is just Sophronia and her mother, Mary, now. They have a bee farm and a small garden. They don't have much, but they get by," William said quietly, hoping to defer judgment of their finances.

"Well, then they should consider themselves blessed to have a hard worker like my son to lead their family into the next generation."

William looked at Caleb in amazement. This was the first time Caleb referred to him as his son. Together they sat laughing as William finished his dinner. The celebratory joy the family shared that night had never happened before. As the evening stars glistened across the sky, peace filled the distinguished farmhouse and old wounds began to heal.

The eager young suitor woke early the next morning to finish his chores and prepare for his introduction to the lovely blonde-haired girl. The horses and cattle were fed and their bedding was changed. He joyously tied the bundles of wheat, knowing that soon, his wife would be baking breads from the crops he would nourish.

In early afternoon, when William finished his work, he rewarded himself with a hearty lunch and long bath to make the best impression possible for his new love interest.

Sophronia rushed downstairs to her mother's side when she

heard the muted clip-clopping of the hooves of the dark bay horse as it came up the dirt road outside her small bedroom window. William's small bouquet of flowers sat immersed in water within a tiny blue glass in the middle of the old, wooden dining table. The Brand ladies had spent all day cleaning the house for their afternoon guest and the modest home sparkled as much as it ever could.

They waited quietly until they heard William knock gently on their door. Mrs. Brand motioned for her daughter to remain seated at the table as she rose to greet their guest.

"Good afternoon, Mrs. Brand. Thank you for having me again," the young man said, smiling enthusiastically.

"It's good to see you again, Mr. Bourne. Please come in." Mrs. Brand opened the door as William stomped the dirt from his boots before crossing the threshold. His eyes rapidly scanned the room, not to assess the interior of the home, but rather to finally connect with Sophronia without any impropriety. When he saw her sitting nervously at the table behind the flowers he had handpicked, his heart lifted as he raced across the room to meet her. She was taken aback by his awkward manner and sweaty brow. He pulled up immediately and looked down at the floor, embarrassed by his lack of experience with women.

Sensing the naiveté of both her daughter and her son-in-law to be, Mrs. Brand took it upon herself to open the conversation for them. "Sophronia, this is Mr. William Bourne. He is here to begin courtship with you and enter into an engagement for your marriage."

Sophronia stood slowly and reached out her hand. Gently, William took her fingertips and kissed them gently, as his eyes looked deeply into hers. A powerful wave of emotion overcame him as he forced himself to let go of her soft, tiny hand.

"It's nice to meet you, sir," Sophronia replied without revealing the odd fear she felt. They sat together in silence, sipping cool water. Mrs. Brand refrained from her normal chatter and watched as the young couple began to relax in each other's presence.

No longer able to endure the silence, William's voice cracked as he said, "I am so very happy to be here, I have told my family about you and they are most pleased with the news. We would like to invite you both over to the house for supper as soon as you are able. I want you to see where we will live Sophronia. The farmhouse is very large and has room for us to start a family."

Taken aback at his forwardness, Sophronia politely smiled and looked to her mother for reassurance. Mrs. Brand smiled back at her daughter and nodded, encouraging her to accept his offer. Sophronia reluctantly sighed and responded, "That is very exciting Mr. Bourne. I look forward to meeting your family and seeing your home."

Thrilled with her consent to his offer, William smiled and proclaimed, "You have made me so happy. So very happy! When will you come? Will you come Sunday? After church?"

Mrs. Brand, realizing that her daughter was overwhelmed by the whole situation, accepted the offer for her. "That would be lovely, Mr. Bourne, we look forward to it. We will be there directly after morning services, if that suits you."

"Oh, yes, ma'am, that would be fine. Very fine indeed, ma'am."

William left with a feeling of victory that far exceeded his expectations of love. Somehow, he had conquered a foe that had dogged him his entire lifetime, even though he had been unaware of its presence. The taste of power filled his hungry spirit as he proudly maneuvered his horse and buggy across the road covered with autumn's leaves. William decided that he would never need another flask of liquor. The intoxication he now felt was far more potent than any scotch could ever deliver.

Sophronia was not quite as convinced she was so blessed.

Not wishing to dishonor her mother's, guidance she said very little in resistance to the engagement in which she found herself encumbered. Yet some force deep in her heart pressed her to question her mother's choice of suitor. That evening, as they sat together in front of the small fire, Sophronia summoned the courage to speak. "Mother?"

Mrs. Brand smiled lovingly and replied, "Yes, dear?"

Sophronia chose her words carefully. "Do you believe Mr. Bourne is the man God has chosen for me?"

Proud of her Christian upbringing, Mrs. Brand tilted her head as she spoke. "Why of course, my dear, how else would we have been at the right place at the right time? That is why Mr. Bourne is so excited. It is because the Lord has inspired him to find you and that is why he is not concerned with your dowry or your widowed mother. The Lord has chosen this union. In that you must trust, no matter how frightened you may feel."

Disappointed with the answer to her question, Sophronia sighed and reluctantly agreed. "Yes mother, that all seems true." Powerless to alter the situation that she found herself in, Sophronia accepted her fate with a deep faith in the God she believed guided her footsteps.

The next few days were filled with chores that helped keep Sophronia and William's minds off Sunday's meal. When William found himself at the Grace Episcopal Church in nearby Randolph, New York, it dawned on him that he and Sophronia were no longer strangers to one another. He allowed himself to visualize their upcoming betrothal as he sang the church hymns. When he peered across the sea of faces in the congregation searching for her, Sophronia remained focused on her prayers. As the priest closed the service with his final prayer and guidance for the week, William's smile could no longer be contained. His mother felt his exuberance and shared his happiness for nothing meant more to her than the joy of her only child.

As the congregation exited the quaint church hall, the Omens family waited together for the Brand ladies to emerge from the large wooden church doors. William immediately recognized the yellow flowers from Sophronia's delicate hat and pointed her out to his stepfather. Proud and infused with authority, Caleb stood tall as Mrs. Brand walked towards them.

"Good afternoon, Mrs. Brand, it is good to meet you. I am Caleb Omens and this is my wife Addie."

Mrs. Brand beamed and nodded. "Good afternoon. It is lovely to meet you both. You have a very fine son."

Caleb motioned to the buggy. "If you would like to come with us, William I'm sure can manage your carriage."

Embarrassed, Mrs. Brand replied, "Oh, we walked to the church this morning, sir."

Caleb quickly diffused the awkwardness by saying, "Well, even better then! We can all travel together."

The two women courteously smiled and followed William's enthusiastic jaunt to the large black carriage sitting under a shade tree across the road from the church.

As they sat atop the driver's perch, Caleb and his stepson bonded a little deeper as they escorted their women back to the beautiful farmhouse Caleb had worked so hard to maintain. "She's a lovely girl, William," Caleb said quietly. "I'm sure she will bear you a fine family and be an excellent addition to our home."

Glowing at his stepfather's praise, William said nothing but felt happy in his new relationship with the man he had loathed for so many years. They had finally found common ground and began to accept one another. As they rounded the bend on the approach to the house, William closed his eyes and thanked God for bringing Sophronia into his life.

They all rejoiced at their first meal together. Mrs. Omens and Mrs. Brand chatted endlessly about the upcoming wedding plans, while Caleb and William discussed building an addition to the back of the house to shelter the newlyweds and the children yet to come. Although Sophronia desperately wished to feel the same sense of excitement the rest of the others experienced, her fear refused to subside. She listened and forced a smile to her lips even though her stomach was clenched with anxiety. Unable to justify her feelings, and with no escape from her destiny, she pushed her inner knowing to the back of her mind and swallowed her doubts.

The wedding was set for the first day of December. They determined it would be best for all to sell the Brand home at the beginning of the next year, and have Mrs. Brand live in the large Omens farmhouse to ease her loneliness. Caleb and William worked ceaselessly on construction plans to expand the house to accommodate the married couple. Laughter and high hopes filled the crisp air as the excitement of the wedding permeated the Omens' farmhouse.

Mrs. Omens spent the month of November sewing a wedding gown for her future daughter in-law. Sewing was an art she had practiced throughout her life as a necessity, but this was to be her masterpiece. The delicate lace she purchased was stitched across the white satin in perfect scallops to provide a fairy tale effect. When she battled the snowy roads and arrived at the Brand home for the final fitting at the end of the month, the dress was perfect. Sophronia cried at the sight of herself in the antique mirror. It was every girl's fantasy to be decorated in such luxury, and this gift transformed her from a child into a woman.

"Thank you, Mrs. Omens! Thank you so much! It's so beautiful!"

Delighted by the girl's response, and pleased with her work, Addie Omens said, "Please, Sophronia, call me Mother." A surge of emotion overwhelmed all of the ladies as they gently dabbed their tears with handkerchiefs.

With the wedding only a week away, final preparations for the celebration were taking place at the Omens' farmhouse. With romance surrounding the event, a resurgence of passion between Caleb and his wife created a harmony and flow within their marriage and the household. William watched his mother glow for the first time in ten years, and the love he had begun to feel for his stepfather gave him a new optimism.

The Saturday evening before the wedding, the Omens family sat together in front of the fire after dinner and warmed themselves with memories and laughter. William watched as his mother fell into a deep sleep in Caleb's arms and he imagined Sophronia snuggled in his arms the same way. Suddenly, Addie screamed in agony and slapped her hand over the right side of her neck, startling both her husband and her son. They ran to her aid but they could not stop her sobbing.

"What's wrong my love, what happened to you? What can I do for you?" Caleb pleaded.

She finally gasped, "Something bit me, my neck. Something bit my neck!" When she removed her hand, the men could see tremendous swelling and redness.

"What should we do?" William asked his stepfather.

"Let's get her to bed. We will put a poultice on it and I'm sure it will be fine by morning," Caleb said and gently carried his whimpering wife into the next room.

William was worried as he prepared a ground wheat and mustard poultice to soothe his mother's pain. Nothing had brought him more joy than seeing her so happy over the past few weeks, and now her suffering brought his celebration to a crashing halt. He ran to her room where he found his stepfather sitting next to her on the bed, stroking her hair as she fell into a state of unconsciousness. William covered her swollen neck with the poultice and stepped quietly out of the room, trusting Caleb's wisdom. He wandered into the new bedroom that had been made ready for his new bride and he crawled into bed. Before he allowed himself to drift off to sleep, he spoke aloud, "Lord please look after my mother tonight. Let nothing spoil this wonderful life you have suddenly given me. Please, Lord, I beg you ease her pain."

William slept soundly, believing the morning would bring relief to his anxieties. He dreamt of his new bride and her radiance.

In the middle of the night, Caleb's shouts woke William and he felt dread, unwilling to face what he was about to see. He ran into his parent's room and found his stepfather clutching his mother's dead body. "She's gone William!" Caleb screamed at his stepson. "I woke up to check on her and she won't wake. She's gone cold and I can't understand what happened."

Horrified, William ran to his mother's body and grabbed it away from Caleb's arms. "What have you done? What have you done? You let her die! How could you let my mother die?"

Enraged, Caleb slammed his fist against Williams left cheek with all the strength his body could find. "I've done no such thing, you idiot! It must have been the bite on her neck. It must have poisoned her to death!"

William fell hard against the wall. Regaining his footing, he launched himself across the room and repeatedly punched Caleb's face. "I hate you! I hate you! I will kill you! I'll kill you!" he screamed. Tears filled his eyes as strength left his young body. Unable to move, William collapsed in shock. His mother was gone forever. The two men, bloodied and bruised, looked at one another and both started to sob. No words of apology or understanding were spoken. Their pain was overpowering and nothing could undo what had just happened.

They waited silently until dawn and wrapped her body in bed linens. Caleb wrapped himself tightly in coats and scarves to ward off the cold, and rode his horse into town to bring the doctor back to the farm. He was sure the insect bite had killed her and he wanted expert testimony to prove his theory. When the doctor,

Oliver Guernsey, finally arrived at the farmhouse, he found William sitting in silence next to the cocoon holding his mother's corpse. The physician carefully pulled the linens away from her face and addressed William without looking at him. "Are you sure you want to be here for this, son?"

Glaring at his suggestion, the young man replied, "I am not leaving. Proceed with your examination, Doctor Guernsey."

Diligently, the doctor proceeded to investigate the body. He wiped the poultice from her neck and closely examined the swollen mark. Caleb watched from the doorway without entering the room.

"She was sound asleep in my arms, then woke up screaming. She said something bit her and then it began to swell. What happened to my wife, Doctor Guernsey?"

"I believe she was poisoned," the doctor replied without hesitation.

"Poisoned from the insect bite?"

"Yes, Caleb, the poison looks to be from a spider, most likely a black widow." Silence filled the room as the three men sat powerless against the fragility of life. "There is nothing either of you could have done, the bite was deadly. I have nothing that could have saved her. In the time it would have taken you to get to my home, she would have been too far-gone. I'm so sorry." Doctor Guernsey rose and collected his things.

"Thank you for coming out in the snow, I know it's bad out there," Caleb said coldly. "I'll walk you out."

The two men left William alone again with his mother's body. Tears filled his eyes as he covered her again with the bed sheet.

Together, Caleb and William buried her that day, under the snow, below her favorite tree behind the farmhouse. It took what seemed an eternity to dig through the frozen ground. Neither man could bring himself to speak to the other. They uttered a few brief prayers at her passing and filled in the grave. William's heart broke anew as each shovelful of dirt cascaded down onto his mother's linen-wrapped form. Caleb remained stoic and if he was emotionally upset, he hid it from William.

The accusations and altercation that had ensued earlier in the master bedroom had wedged a fresh gap of hatred and distrust between the two men, imprisoning them in an isolated reality of their own. They told no one of her death and refused to speak to one another until late that evening when Caleb poured himself a large whiskey. "Would you like one?" Caleb tentatively asked William.

"Yes, thank you," replied William in a flat tone.

"What are you planning to do about the wedding?" Caleb asked.

"I haven't thought about it. Postpone it, I suppose," William muttered, finishing his drink quickly.

"Well, out of respect, you should ride over there tomorrow and tell Sophronia what happened," stated Caleb with fatherly authority.

"Yes, that would be the right thing to do." William filled his glass with more whiskey, emptied it in one swig, placed his glass on the table, and left the room without uttering another word.

The next morning came quickly, the liquor having made it easier to sleep through the night. William plowed through the icy snow and fed the animals, knowing his mother would be saddened if he were to neglect her cherished livestock. He then returned to his bed, unable to bring himself to continue working.

Caleb woke and began his daily routine until he realized no coffee was brewing and no breakfast had been prepared. The tears streamed down his face as he stared at the mirror, attempting to shave as if nothing in his life had changed. In a rage, he threw his razor into the sink and collapsed onto the bathroom floor. William heard the commotion but chose to ignore it, returning to his depression-fueled slumber. Moments later, Caleb burst into his room, thrusting the door open so abruptly that William sprung from his bed ready for a brawl.

"What the hell are you doing?" the young man demanded.

"What the hell am I doing? What the hell are *you* doing? There is a beautiful young girl waiting to marry you in three days and you haven't even told her there isn't going to be a wedding! And you ask me what the hell *I'm* doing? You're just laying here like a useless old mule. Look at yourself!"

Caleb moved towards the bed to shake his stepson into motion, but the aggression that had always intimidated William in the past did not work. William shot out of bed and said, "I'm not afraid of you anymore, old man. You can't hurt me anymore. There is nothing left for you to do to me!" William sat back down on his bed and sobbed. Tears flowed without hesitation or concern.

Disgusted by the weakness he saw in the boy, Caleb left the room and returned to the bathroom to shave. He finished scraping the salt-and-pepper stubble from his powerful jaw and rinsed his face with cold water. The wife he had loved for over a decade was suddenly gone, but he would not allow himself to become anything like the hysterical mess of the man who lay idle in the other room. Without regard for his personal feelings or needs, Caleb dressed himself warmly and prepared a strong cup of coffee.

The truth was that his life had to go on regardless of his wife's sudden death. For Caleb, solace lay in taking up the reins of his daily routine and moving forward. The joy that had filled his farmhouse during the past thirty days was gone. It left with Addie's death. Caleb wondered glumly if joy would ever return. The world was cast with a gray pall that seemed quite permanent now.

Caleb rode into town across the snowy banks in his rig loaded with goods for his numerous customers. He said nothing to any of them when they routinely inquired about his family's wellbeing. He merely nodded to them all and continued about his work out of sheer survival. Every bundle of jarred goods was delivered to its expectant buyer and no one in town was aware of the Omens' tragedy.

On his way home, Caleb passed the fork leading to the Brand family home and rather than trusting his stepson to be responsible, he took it upon himself to handle the crisis. Arriving unannounced caught the ladies off guard, but they were more than happy to accommodate their new relative's schedule.

"Well, good evening to you, Mr. Omens," Mrs. Brand called from the front porch. "What brings you out here so unexpectedly in this cold weather?"

"I'm sorry to barge in on you like this Mrs. Brand, but I have some terrible news."

Her heart sank, as she was sure William was going to call off the wedding and abandon her young daughter to a fate of poverty. Sophronia, hidden from view as usual, quietly prayed for the tidings that her mother so desperately feared. Caleb fastened the brake on the carriage and walked slowly up the porch steps to speak with the women face-to-face. He took a deep breath and shoved his sadness deep inside his heart, then looked in her concerned eyes and spoke softly. "Mrs. Omens suffered a black widow's bite and the poison was strong enough to take her life. We had to bury her early this morning. All of it happened so fast we had no time to tell anyone."

Mrs. Brand trembled as tears filled her eyes and guilt filled her mind for having thought of such selfish motives. "Mr. Omens! Oh dear, oh dear, I am so sorry. This is so terrible. Oh, no. It can't be true! I am so sorry!"

Caleb's pain eased with every tear that streamed down Mrs. Brand's face. "Thank you. It is such a shock. I just don't know what to do with myself."

Looking up through her tears, she asked, "Where is William? Why isn't he with you?"

"I'm afraid he has fallen into a deep sadness from which he may not return for quite some time. I expected him to come here immediately to explain the situation to you and to tell Sophronia that he plans to postpone the wedding, but I am concerned that he is too young to handle this kind of tragedy." The disappointment was audible in Caleb's voice.

"Yes, of course. I am so sorry, Mr. Omens. Please come inside. Sophronia and I will fix you some supper."

She took his arm as if he were her child and led him gently into the modest kitchen. Sophronia had heard everything said on the porch and was sitting at the old wooden table sobbing. When Caleb walked into the room, her young heart burst open for his suffering and she ran to his aid. She unabashedly threw her arms around him and stood in his embrace without reproach. Unable to find propriety in the midst of the trauma, Caleb held her small frame close and found it impossible to let her go. Their sadness bound them together in a way Mrs. Brand could not understand, yet she allowed them to stay united as long as need be. When Caleb finally stepped away from Sophronia, a bit embarrassed and highly uncomfortable, it was the elegance of Mrs. Brand that came to his rescue.

"Would you care for some bread and soup, Mr. Omens?"

"That would be fine, Mrs. Brand. Thank you." Caleb's voice strengthened as he spoke.

Sophronia wiped the tears from her face and immediately started to help her mother prepare a place for their suffering guest at the head of the table. As he sat quietly eating the entire dinner that the ladies had prepared for themselves, his heart realized that it could not go on living without the love of a good woman. He looked at the young woman he had held so close to his chest and thought that she was the only person who could possibly understand how to endure this hardship with him. Caleb cleared his throat and placed his spoon down onto the table before speaking.

"Ladies, I know we have had plans to allow for a union between William and Sophronia, yet after the loss we have endured, I just don't think that my stepson is ready for that kind of responsibility."

Mrs. Brand stiffened as he continued speaking. Here it comes, she thought. I knew it was too good to be true. We are truly doomed to be poor now for the rest of our lives.

"However," Caleb continued, "I am very much in need of comfort and support. I am deeply committed to the continuing success of my family's farm, and I cannot run a household alone. I would like Sophronia to be my new wife and have you both come to live with me at my farmhouse."

Stunned at the dramatic change in their fortune, the Brand women were speechless. They sat motionless, hardly breathing, for what seemed an eternity to Caleb. As he rethought his impetuous words, Sophronia blurted out her reply without consulting her mother's council.

"Of course I will be your wife. It would be my honor to comfort you in your time of need. This is the Lord's doing. Mrs. Omens is in heaven now, God bless her beautiful soul, and I know she would want me to take care of you and your family."

Mrs. Brand was terribly concerned with this abrupt change in plans and incredibly uncomfortable with the sudden response from her daughter. Yet, her personal needs for security and safety for herself and her daughter overwhelmed her instincts that this change was too hasty, the ramifications not properly thought through. "I agree, Mr. Omens, this is a time for togetherness and we all must endure this sadness with one another's best interest at heart. What will Mr. Bourne do, Mr. Omens?"

Caleb had not considered William's involvement when he

made his offer, and Mrs. Brand's question took him by surprise. He paused, then replied in a restrained manner. "William will stay on at the farm, out of respect for his mother. I will allow him to work the land with me until he has secured a future for himself elsewhere. We have spent many years together and he will need my support if he is to overcome the loss of his mother."

Searching for the words to convey her message without implying an insult, Mrs. Brand continued. "That is very kind of you Mr. Omens. You are a very generous man. So you feel he will not be at all upset to rescind his engagement to Sophronia and step aside so that your house may be put in order first?"

Caleb understood her gracious tact and looked down towards the weathered floorboards to ponder his answer. Finally he said, "I believe William is a very young man for his age, and I feel that he will be relieved of the burden of responsibility in being a husband, as well as feel proud to have aided me during this time of emptiness."

Sophronia finally felt able to breathe normally for the first time in a month. She had never felt that William was an appropriate choice for her, and she noticed that the anxiety she had been experiencing vanished immediately upon hearing the words of her new husband-to-be. "Shall we say a prayer to honor Mrs. Omens?" Sophronia suggested.

"That would be lovely, my dear" Caleb replied looking deep into her soft eyes.

Together they sat bowing their heads at the kitchen table while Caleb recited the Lord's Prayer in honor of his wife's passing. When he was finished speaking the three of them remained together in silence, taking a quiet moment to remember Addie's life, her kindness, and the joy she brought with her everywhere she went.

Caleb then proposed that the wedding continue as planned, as well as the sale of the Brand home after the first of the year.

The ladies agreed to the suggestion, for it was becoming a financial necessity for their survival. As the sun began to set, the exhausted farmer excused himself from their home and made his way through the dimness of dusk to his farmhouse.

By the time he arrived at the stable a full moon shined brightly across the tree shrouding his wife's fresh grave. Looking closer, he noticed that William had created a small rock formation at the headstone to commemorate her life. Touched by the love the young man felt for his mother, Caleb regretted his horrible accusations and started to punish himself for the irrational words he spoke to his stepson. Unhitching the buggy and toweling down the large gray gelding, he decided to apologize to William and make peace within the house.

Caleb walked in and found that William had prepared a small plate for his stepfather and left it sitting on the kitchen table. Touched at the symbolic apology, he made his way back to William's room and knocked on the door. William opened the door slowly, his eyes swollen.

"I am so sorry, son," Caleb said as he reached out and drew William into his arms.

Shocked and relieved, William accepted the affection and returned it the best he could, still unable to ignore the hateful feelings he had encountered early that morning. They stood locked together until William could no longer stand to be held in his stepfather's embrace.

"I am sorry as well," William replied without emotion. "I left some supper in the front room. It's not my mother's fare, but I did my best."

"That's fine, thank you." Caleb said. "Come to the table, we'll have a drink. I want to talk with you about some things."

"Well, if it's alright with you, can we just talk in the morning? I really need to sleep."

"All right then, we'll work together tomorrow, and we'll

discuss the future," Caleb replied. He returned to the front room and poured himself a large whiskey while investigating the small meal laid out for his nourishment. Caleb smiled as he tasted the salted beef and lukewarm corn his stepson had so kindly prepared. The strong intoxicating smell of the liquor was far more enticing, so he opted to save the meal for breakfast. Sitting near the small wood-burning stove, he looked out the window and watched as fragile snowflakes danced around the trees and speckled the ground. Finishing his drink, Caleb felt the weight of exhaustion pressing down on him. He stumbled to his bedroom and collapsed across the quilted feather bed.

As could have been predicted, neither man woke early the next morning. They had both suffered such severe emotional trauma that their bodies ignored the call of dawn and the needs of the livestock eagerly awaiting the sound of footsteps rumbling in the feed room.

William was the first to rise, jumping out of his bed in a startle, quickly pulling on his overalls, and racing out to the front room to avoid any more trouble with his stepfather. He discovered a quiet house except for the loud snoring emanating from the master bedroom. Releasing a deep sigh, he wrapped himself in scarf and jacket and crossed the snowy path to the stable.

Shuddering from the cold, William rushed into the feed room and began to fill the wheelbarrow with hay and oats. The horses, cows, and sheep seemed to dance with delight. As he walked down the dirt aisle, William smirked at how pleased an animal could be simply from receiving a small meal. He found himself wishing that his own happiness could be attained so easily. No longer joyous at his future prospects or about building new farmhouse rooms, he shoveled the manure with disdain and disgust. When he finished, he dumped the loads into the marshy mulch and quickly rushed back to the main house to prepare a meal.

Caleb had risen while William was out handling the morning chores. He had prepared a large pot of coffee and warmed the plate of food William left for him the night before. When the hungry young man entered the house and knocked the snow off his boots, he inhaled the smell of freshly brewed coffee and looked forward to filling his empty stomach. Realizing that the animals must have shared exactly the same experience, he began to understand how often simplicity is profound.

"There is some coffee here, if you want, William," Caleb announced as he heard the front door close.

"Thanks, Caleb, I'll be right in," William called out.

"This beef isn't half bad," said Caleb as William entered the kitchen.

"Oh, you didn't eat it last night?"

"No, I stopped by the Brand house on my way back and they fed me," said Caleb.

"What?"

"You heard me. I stopped in to see the Brand women on my way home last night," Caleb said without emotion.

"Why did you stop by there?" asked William, irritation straining his voice.

"Because I knew you wouldn't, and someone had to be responsible in the middle of this mess."

"What did they say? How did they take the news?"

"They were very upset, as to be expected. As we all were."

"Were?" William said.

"Were and are, William. But I doubt your mother would want to see the farm fall apart because we were so consumed with grief," Caleb said. "Life must go forward, William. When you are older and have lived through more loss, you will begin to understand this."

"I understand it now, thank you very much. I just have to mourn in my own way, for God's sake. I am the one who took care of the animals this morning and made a plate for you. How is that proof of not being responsible?" William barked.

"Calm down, William. I don't want to fight with you anymore. I was just explaining," Caleb said, attempting to soothe the young man. "Sit down, William, there is something I need to tell you."

William sat, warming his hands with a cup of hot coffee.

"When I saw the Brands yesterday, we decided that I would be in need of a wife far more than you at this point, so I am going to take Sophronia as my bride on Saturday," Caleb stated, as if he were talking about buying a new mare.

William slammed his cup down onto the table. "What?"

"You're a very young man, William, and I have this farmhouse as well as the land, and I suddenly find myself in need of a good woman. Sophronia is good stock and will bear me some fine children to carry on the family name. The Brands have barely enough money to make it through the winter, and when Mrs. Brand's house is sold she will come live here."

"And you think this is just fine for me as well?" William asked, incredulous.

"I can see where you might be disappointed," Caleb said, "but there is plenty of time to find a woman for you. You are young and have a long way to go before you acquire such a tremendous burden that comes with having a family."

"But she was mine! I found her! I arranged the marriage! She was to be my wife!"

"Well, now she is to be mine," Caleb stated. "You can accept this and stay here with us, work the farm and earn your way, or you can get the hell out of my house and see how long you survive alone out there this winter!" Caleb's final words came out strong and loud.

"What choice do I have?" William muttered with fresh contempt for Caleb.

William and Caleb sat together, divided once again in silent hostility. William drank his coffee and gnawed at bread his mother baked several days prior. The hope that had flared since the end of summer transformed itself into bitterness. The sullen boy was transmuted into a poisonous man and venom filled his veins.

Soon enough Saturday arrived and the priest from the Grace Episcopalian Church brought the Brand women to the Omens' farm. William was forced to serve as witness to the union between his stepfather and his own betrothed. That simple act served as the final blow to his civility. As Sophronia stood before the minister in the beautiful wedding dress constructed by his mother, and Caleb spoke out declaring his wedding vows to the young woman, violent thoughts blossomed in William's mind. His brow sweat and his eyes twitched as he restrained the rage in his body. The ceremony concluded with a tender kiss between the new couple. William's insides were twisted into a knotted mess.

When he could no longer take the smiles and embraces shared by the intimate group gathered in honor of the future of the Omens clan, William slipped silently out into the freezing snow and collapsed into a heap of defeat behind the barn. The icy white frost soothed his burning body and calmed his nerves enough to allow him to regain composure. Without knowing how he would survive this circle of hell, he picked himself up and returned to the house to continue appeasing the man who just had just stolen the love of his life.

Inside, the happy couple and their guests were celebrating with various liquors and rich foods. Caleb rose from the table with a proud grin and walked out of the room, heading towards the hall closet. The wedding party glanced at each other with confusion, and eagerly awaited his return.

"I have a special wedding gift for you my bride," Caleb bellowed from the hallway.

Enthralled, Sophronia leapt to her feet and danced in a tiny circle awaiting the arrival of her present. The sound of Caleb's heavy boots rumbled across the wood floor. As he re-entered the room, Caleb held his hands behind his back to keep secret his surprise. He walked towards Sophronia and presented her with a small wooden box.

"Thank you," she said softly.

"Do you know what this is, my darling?" Caleb asked, knowing she had no idea about the magic of the gift he had purchased.

"I'm sorry. I don't know what it is," she replied, embarrassed by her lack of experience with luxury.

"That's because you haven't opened it. Open the top of the box," Caleb instructed.

Sophronia gingerly lifted the lid of the box and inside she found a statue of a miniature Virgin Mary lying on a bed of soft, red velvet. She began to cry, for her deepest spiritual connection was to the Holy Mother.

"Here, darling, watch this," Caleb said, as he gently turned a small gold lever on the underside of the oak box. Magnificent sounds of Christian music burst forth. Overwhelmed by the luxury of such a fantastic gift, Sophronia and her mother sat mute, awed by their new life.

"What do you think, my dear?" Caleb's words came out sounding like a boast.

"It's wonderful! What do you call it?" asked Sophronia.

"This is a music box and it will play music whenever you twist this tiny bar underneath."

"Thank you, Caleb. It is just beautiful. I love it!" Sophronia exclaimed.

Everyone in the room sat silently, listening to the harmonies, and swaying to the music. Everyone in the room seemed suffused with joy by the miracle of the music box. Except for William. William stood alone in the corner.

Mrs. Brand turned around and could see the young man's suffering. Her steady gaze on William was drawing the guest's focus away from the happy couple. William forced a smile to his lips, hoping Mrs. Brand would turn her attention elsewhere. He moved away from the wall to pour himself a large drink, then sat down at one corner of the dining table. He tried to soothe himself by concentrating on the delicate music emanating from the music box. Tapping his foot lightly to the gentle notes, William let his thoughts drift away, deliberating avoiding the feelings of hate filling his heart.

Caleb sat at the head of the table, with Sophronia on his left. He fed her small bits of sweets from his plate, encouraging her to sample the liquor from his glass. Immersed in his arousal for her, he remained blind to the agony his stepson suffered. Liberated from the sadness that had recently consumed the house, Caleb rose to his feet demanding a wedding dance with his new wife.

"Come my darling, we shall dance to the music from your new music box," he said, reaching out his hand to Sophronia.

The girl stood up proudly, enamored by the romantic gesture and the man's powerful stance. She stretched out her hand and Caleb pulled her in, spun her in circles, then held her against his chest. He kissed her cheek as her blonde hair caressed his chin. Her proximity elicited a lust in Caleb he had never felt before. The older man and young girl swayed back and forth together, the motion joining their souls in an ecstasy of passion neither expected. When the music ended, the couple embraced as if there was no one else in the room.

William was about to lose control. He forced himself to rise from the table and excuse himself. His words came out in a weak whisper. "Good night, everyone, I must retire."

The insightful Mrs. Brand spoke up. "Yes, it is very late. We should all be on our way home. Good night, Mr. Bourne, and thank you for helping with the preparations," She said to William with a tender bow of her head.

"Good night, ma'am," William whispered and left the room.

"Well then, I suppose we should ready ourselves for the journey home," the priest said, quickly grasping Mrs. Brand's tact.

"Thank you for everything, Reverend. This was truly a blessing," Caleb said, Sophronia still snug under his arm.

"It was my pleasure, Mr. and Mrs. Omens. May your house be filled with a healthy family and your farm with rich soil," the minister said.

"Thank you," Caleb said again.

As the guests wrapped themselves in their warm coats and scarves, Sophronia gently removed herself from her new husband's hold and reached for the arms of her fragile mother. Mrs. Brand cried softly as she kissed her daughter goodbye, knowing that the innocent youth she had so forcefully protected was now no longer her responsibility.

"I love you, my darling. Take good care of your new husband and your new home." Mrs. Brand spoke quietly in her daughter's ear. "I will see you again on Christmas."

"Good-bye, Mother. I love you," Sophronia whispered back, tears streaming down her face.

Sophronia gathered small bits of meat, cheese, and cakes into a soft cloth and delicately slipped the package into her mother's coat as the guests prepared themselves for their journey home. Reaching into his coat pocket, Caleb pulled out his wallet and filled the priest's hands with appreciation for his services. He gave what remained to his new mother-in-law, endearing him to her heart. Caleb walked the priest and Mrs. Brand out to the yard to help the priest unhitch the buggy and to assist the elderly woman into the carriage.

Caleb returned inside where he and Sophronia watched from the window as the large horse's hooves pounded through the snowdrifts and the carriage disappeared from view.

Sophronia and Caleb turned to each other, alone for the first time, and kissed passionately. Caleb lifted his bride's small body into his arms and carried her effortlessly to his bed. Innocent and unsure, Sophronia lay still while Caleb unbuttoned her silk skirts and removed the gown his former wife had sewn as a gift. With tenderness, he placed the dress on the rocking chair and removed the undergarments that covered her flesh.

Sophronia's virginal body tightened as Caleb touched her skin with his weathered hands. He kissed her neck, then slipped out of his clothes – the finest pants and shirt he owned. No longer hidden behind costumes or protected by the eyes of others, the newlyweds explored their intimate natures. Caleb smiled as the rush of youth surged through his blood and aroused his body. He was so preoccupied by his passion for Sophronia that he failed to hear the footsteps approaching his bedroom door. Sophronia abandoned all restraint and without hesitation unleashed a power inside her that had longed for expression.

The sounds of their lovemaking permeated the hallway where William sat drinking whiskey and eavesdropping. Tears trailed down his face as he listened to the couple's pleasure. Devastated by the cruelty of God's hand and disgusted by the creation of man, William's soul writhed in agony. When the light in his stepfather's bedroom finally dimmed, William walked back to the bedroom he now considered his prison cell.

Sunday's morning light wakened them all, summoning the motley threesome into the kitchen for their first morning meal together. Sophronia hurriedly searched through the cabinets, getting acquainted with the implements left by her predecessor. Gathering her strength, she lifted the large kettle to the top of the wood-burning stove and filled it with fresh water for boiling. She rushed to prepare coffee and creamed oats to satisfy the hungry men sitting in silence. While the coffee steeped and the oats simmered on the stove, Sophronia fluttered through the room clearing the mess from the celebration of the night before.

William and Caleb sat without words, neither of them able to stomach the truth of the circumstances. As Sophronia served their food, they both smiled at her in thanks, but continued to ignore each other. Feeling the tension between the two men, as well as the return of the irrational anxiety that had surfaced when she became engaged to William, Sophronia decided to avoid her new stepson's presence as much as possible. Her instincts warned her of his hatred of her new husband, so she was quick to mimic her mother's diplomacy.

A household routine began as if Sophronia, Caleb, and William had been together for years. Sophronia cleaned the house and washed the linens while William fed the stabled livestock and Caleb tallied the financial accounts. Whenever the tension between the two men sucked the air from the room, Sophronia wound her beautiful music box, filling the vacancy with Christian hymns and melodies. Upon hearing the soothing sounds, Caleb would fill the fireplace with wood and settle into his soft chair with Sophronia tucked gently under his arm.

They were barely aware of William's presence in the house even though he paced through it often, giving the appearance of attention to duty when, in fact, he found himself without any work to accomplish.

The winter was harsh that year, freezing the farm and limiting the time spent outside. Trapped together under one roof, they were forced to endure the strangeness of their lives. Sophronia said nothing about her discomfort to her husband so as not to disrupt his harmony or to cause an even greater stress. As the slow days passed, she grew closer to her husband and expressed her love for him during the dark cold of night. Every evening, William sat hiding in the shadows listening intently to their marital bliss, torturing himself endlessly with thoughts of things that might have been.

Storms of snowflakes covered the ground, keeping all of Cattaraugus County tucked firmly inside warmed farmhouses. Unable to travel the icy terrain, Mrs. Brand could not spend Christmas with her daughter, leaving William as the only guest at the Omens' first holiday meal. Sophronia worked continuously, perfecting her first feast for her proud husband's belly. Her creation was a tremendous success, proving Caleb's excellent choice in a woman. The couple celebrated one another constantly, driving William to a state of frustration and compulsion that the cold of winter could no longer subdue.

As the dusk of New Year's Eve settled onto the farmhouse, William found himself desperate for an outlet for his rage. He fled to the stable and found a large axe he could use to unleash his fury on the hardwood tree trunks in the nearby forest. Alone, he traveled deeper into the woods, guided by the light of a dim, rusty lantern held at arm's length in front of him. Locating a large fallen tree, he grasped the wood axe handle and commenced to hurl the metal blade against the frozen bark. Defeated by the frozen, rigid wood that refused to submit to his need for destruction, he carried the axe and the lantern deeper into the forest, hoping to freeze his anger into submission. His footsteps eventually led him through the snow-capped trees along the silvery, frosted edge of Coldspring Creek.

A strange yearning drew him to a cloistered spot. His eyes squinted to focus as the darkness revealed a shimmering light up ahead. Staggering across the frozen, white ground, William ventured far enough to discover the source of the light. His legs buckled and he fell. He heard a voice chanting unfamiliar sounds that somehow he could understand. An apparition dancing in front of him took the form of a man. Confused and bewildered by his intoxicating delusion, William laughed as an Indian warrior paced in a circle in front of him.

Suddenly the Indian warrior stopped his song and locked

eyes with William. The ghostly figure's hypnotic stare penetrated deep into William's eyes, transforming time and space into a murky consciousness. William sat transfixed as the warrior acted out the story that began when he spoke to Many Moccasins in the Indian village, through the moment he drew his final breath on the grave she shared with Speaking Eagle.

As the past drifted back into the present and the Indian warrior's wretchedness united with the kindred emotion of his newfound agent, the cry of an eagle shrieked from high above in the night sky. The haunted earth in the old Indian Burial Ground was re-energized by the conjunction of memory across many lifetimes. Freshly aware of the history of the repeated transgressions wrought time and time again against his soul, William was filled with a profound knowing.

Sobered by the ghostly encounter, William picked up the axe that had fallen from his gloved hand into the powdery snow. He absentmindedly tossed the lantern deep into the woods and began a march across the snow with predatory precision. As he neared the farmhouse and caught a glimpse of Caleb and Sophronia through a window, his blood heated and his eyes narrowed to slits. Taking a deep breath of the icy air, he quickly made his way to the unlocked kitchen door. Without pause, he threw the door open and powered his way across the kitchen floor into the front room. He found Sophronia sitting in Caleb's lap, lit by the fireplace's flickering wood. Rage, hot and red, exploded as William screamed an ancient war cry and flew across the room with the axe raised over his head.

He brought the axe blade down with deadly force as Sophronia let out a terrified screech. The ice-cold metal sliced through her throat, instantly silencing her in mid-scream. Her blood splashed clear across the room. The blow decapitated the woman, sending her body into grotesque convulsions as it hit the wood floor. Snarling with hate, William looked directly into the eyes of the man that had wounded him for lifetimes, and without hesitation, he raised the bloody axe once again.

Paralyzed by shock, Caleb could only watch as the bloodied metal blade whistled through the air towards him. William swung over and over, severing muscle and bone into bloody fragments. He released the poison coursing through his veins with every stroke of the axe.

When the Caleb's body was minced so badly that it was no longer recognizable, the axe fell from William's hands. Having spent his wild rage, he stepped back to survey his act. His heart thumped loudly as he looked down upon the bloody panorama. Shocked at what he saw, and unable to understand what had happened, he stood motionless until his breath slowed and his body stopped trembling. As he looked down at his red-stained hands and bloodied clothing, the realization of what he had done washed over him. His body convulsed as he gagged in response to what he saw.

William turned and headed for the kitchen, peeling off his bloody clothing as he ran. He used his shirt to wipe the sticky, coagulating blood from his hands. He discovered a bucket of wash water Sophronia had used to clean the house earlier that day and shoved his blood-reddened hands into it. Unable to scrub himself clean, he panicked. His thought about the ghost he had encountered in the woods and realized he had been in this situation before. Fresh paranoia sent him running into the washroom. He jumped into the cold, dirty bathwater Sophronia had not emptied from the large galvanized tub that sat in the middle of the room. Reaching for the Fels Naptha bar on the floor, he soaped himself, rinsed, and leaped out of the tub. Rummaging through his belongings, he found an extra set of overalls and a warm sweater. He found wool socks and covered his wet head with a knitted shell his mother had made for him. He looked for his boots and realized he had left them in the kitchen, bloodied with evidence. He entered Caleb's room to search for suitable winter coverings for his feet.

As William rushed into the bedroom, he smelled the sweet scent of Sophronia's intoxicating perfume and rage once again permeated his brain. He ransacked his stepfather's wardrobe and found a pair of old work boots still good enough to wear. Sized a bit larger than his own feet, William put on a second pair of socks to fill the boots of the dead man lying in the other room. He tied up the boots, put on Caleb's heavy coat and scarf, then left through the bedroom window to avoid viewing the brutal murder scene.

He made his way to the stable and saddled the large bay gelding at a furious pace. Alarmed by the unusual activity so late in the evening, the horse danced from side to side. Freezing cold air instantly filled the stable as William led the horse through the barn doors. Without thinking, he left the doors wide open, allowing the livestock to wander aimlessly through the barnyard. He mounted the horse and galloped off into the night. Not sure as to where exactly he was going, William rode across the frozen snow in a desperate search for sanctuary.

Dawn was breaking by the time William felt the cold creeping into his extremities, warning him that he and his animal had to find shelter. Without friends or family, he found himself confronted with only one solution. He headed for Mrs. Brand's farmhouse. Having no idea what he would say to her, but trusting that her kindness would allow him shelter for the night, William made his way up her road.

Still in bed, the sound of someone pounding at her door terrified the defenseless woman. Without weapons to protect her, she was too afraid to open the door. Mrs. Brand peered outside her tiny window and saw the bay gelding in the yard. Relieved, she knew it belonged to the Omens family. Worried that her daughter might be in some sort of trouble, she ran to the door in a panic. As the door flew open and she looked into William's bloodshot eyes, she gasped.

"What's happened, William? Where is Sophronia?"

"She is at the house ma'am," said William sullenly.

"Is everything all right? What are you doing here?" she demanded.

"I just can't live under that roof anymore ma'am. I would not have come here except I don't have anywhere else to go. I've been riding around most of the night and I'm freezing cold," he said, looking down at the icy porch boards.

"Oh, I see." Mrs. Brand said, rubbing the sleep from her eyes.

She opened the door and encouraged him to come inside the warm house. She immediately filled the small, wood-burning stove that heated her barren house. She went to the kitchen and filled the teakettle from a bucket of water she had sitting on the floor. As she heated the water for him, she looked with concern at his disheveled appearance.

"William, you don't seem well," she said tenderly.

"I'm having a hard time with...," he stammered, and then bursting into tears, he started to tremble. No longer able to quell the agony trapped within, he alternated sobs and moans. Mrs. Brand wrapped her arms around him, and held him close to her breast.

"It's going to be all right, William. God has you in his arms. This, too, shall pass, you poor soul," she said softly.

William's loud sobs increased in intensity at the mention of God, and his tears streamed down his face with the realization that no God could ever forgive his horrible deeds. Mrs. Brand stayed at his side until his tears subsided, and then tended to the teakettle whistling shrilly. She poured a cup of hot water and added a pinch of last summer's dried peppermint, and offered it to William.

"Here dear, drink this. It will warm you up. I'm sorry there is no coffee or regular tea, but I haven't been to the store in quite some time."

"Thank you, Mrs. Brand. You are so kind."

William sipped the hot water and it began to warm his body. Mrs. Brand watched with tremendous concern. She sensed a profound instability in him. She guessed it was due to losing his mother and his bride in one fell swoop. Unable to rescue him from the loss, her heart went out to him for she too had suffered deeply in this life and understood the horrible aching that resulted.

"I know this has been a difficult time for you, William. I really do know how crushing these life experiences can be." Mrs. Brand spoke with sincere compassion.

William looked up from his hot water and searched her eyes for a connection. When he saw her vulnerability and witnessed her earnest concern for his welfare, his heart softened. Then he remembered what he had just done to her daughter. He looked at her with sorrow and regret knowing he was unable to apologize or make right the wrong. Placing the cup on the floor, he stood up and reached out his hand to help her rise with him.

"Thank you so much for your understanding, Mrs. Brand. I am so sorry to have put you through this; I am ashamed of my weakness. I should be a much stronger man than I am right now. My mother would be beside herself at my behavior," William said quickly.

"That's all right, William. I am glad you chose to come to me. Everyone is weakened by grief at least once in their life."

"Would it be all right if I stayed here for a day or so until I figure out where to go next?" he asked gently.

"Of course. You should tend to your horse now. I'm sure he is freezing out there, I don't have any feed in the stall out back, but you can take him some water and put him inside."

"Thank you," William said, nodding at her reminder of his horse's welfare.

William went outside and found his horse covered in snow and shaking with cold. He quickly brushed the powder from the horse's body, untied him from the porch rail, and led him around the back to a small covered stall. Mrs. Brand made her way out to the old barn with a bucket of warmed water and some oats she had saved for herself. Startled by her strength to endure the cold, William looked at her in amazement. "Here, let me take that from you ma'am. Thank you so much, I could have come back for this."

"No animal should suffer, William, especially horses. After all, where would we be without them? I haven't had a horse in years. It is best to appreciate what you have when you have it. Otherwise, we miss the pleasure that these gifts bring," Mrs. Brand said. She smiled as she stroked the magnificent bay gelding.

The horse eagerly drank the water and munched the oats from her cold, work-worn hands as she nuzzled his large head and felt the warmth of his sweet breath. William watched her and was reminded of his mother's love for animals. He realized his mother's spirit must have watched his horrible acts and would be so ashamed of her son now. The hatred he felt for his stepfather was suddenly transformed into self-loathing and a desire for his own death. He removed the tack from his horse's weary body and placed the equipment onto the ground. Exhausted, he looked at Mrs. Brand hoping she would understand his need for sleep. Without hesitation, she placed the bucket on the floor, wiped her slobbered hands against her skirt, and motioned for him to follow her back to the house.

"I'm sorry, William. I have only one bed that Sophronia and I shared, but we can take turns using it if you like."

"That will be fine, ma'am, I will be here for only a short while. I am sorry for the imposition."

"It is fine, William. I'm sure the Lord will provide you with a solution to your dilemma. His guidance is always available if we are able to hear it." Mrs. Brand spoke knowingly.

She led him to her bed and offered it to him freely while she began her chores for the day. He removed his stepfather's boots and his overalls, then climbed under the warm blankets and dropped immediately into a heavy slumber. William did not wake until Mrs. Brand shook his body into consciousness.

"William, dear, I'm sorry to wake you, but day has passed into night and I need to sleep now. I'm very tired," Mrs. Brand whispered.

"Oh, I'm sorry," William mumbled as he struggled to raise himself from the warm feather bed.

Mrs. Brand handed him his overalls and a small candle to light his way to the front room where she had left a tiny plate of food and a warm fire. He made his way through the darkness, finding his meal next to a wooden rocking chair by the woodstove. Hungry and somewhat disoriented he gobbled the bread and corn while he watched the flames of the fire dance and sparkle. That entire night he sat alone, consumed by thoughts of his fate. He wondered where he could go to escape his past, and whether he could find the will to survive the deeds he had done.

Morning came slowly and when Mrs. Brand finally made her way to the front room, she found William staring into the fire, mesmerized by the flames.

"Good morning, William," she said quietly, interrupting his meditation.

"Oh! Good morning, ma'am," he replied, still vacant and distracted by the burning wood.

"Would you care for something to eat?"

"No ma'am, I'm fine," he mumbled.

"How are you feeling?"

"I'm fine, ma'am," he answered without looking up.

Mrs. Brand was worried about his mental state and wondered how to handle this difficult situation. She prepared hot water and the remaining oats, never taking her eyes off William. He sat immersed in thought without realizing her surveillance of him. She finished her meal and proceeded outside to care for the horse she knew he had neglected. Finally understanding what Caleb Omens had meant when he spoke of William's inability to manage responsibility, she thanked God that Sophronia was in the hands of a capable provider.

Mrs. Brand returned to the house and found William exactly where she had left him. An unexplainable sense of anxiety and fear rose in her. Mrs. Brand tended to her daily chores without speaking to William, who did not move from the rocking chair. Occasionally, when the fire died down, he placed more kindling and wood inside the stove and watched as the wood caught fire. The blaze cast a bright orange light over him. Concerned that her questions or a suggestion to return to the Omens' farm might upset him, Mrs. Brand pondered how to approach this damaged man. Finally, as dusk settled into dark, she summoned the courage to speak.

"So, what have you been thinking, William?" She spoke softly, as if to calm a wild animal.

"I'm sorry... what did you say, ma'am?" he said, startled at the sound of her voice.

"I asked what you have been thinking about all day," she said with a wan smile.

"Oh, well, just what I should do I suppose. I do not have family you see, so I'm a bit lost. I don't really know where to go, but I'll work it out." He spoke, but did not look at her.

"Well, son, how long do you plan on staying here?" she asked, frightened by his vague response.

"Not long ma'am. I need to get moving. Maybe tomorrow or perhaps the next day if you can allow it," he said, turning at last to look at her, but showing no expression on his face.

"That's fine. Just make sure you attend to your horse. I

brought him some oats and water. He was very grateful," she hinted gently.

"Oh, thank you," William answered without understanding her subtle hint.

"Well, I'm going to bed now. I will see you in the morning. Good night, William," Mrs. Brand said softly.

"Good night, ma'am," he replied.

Hungry and tired, William's eyes closed as he curled back into the hard wooden chair. He hoped to drift far away from harsh reality into a sweet dream. The dark of night passed but his body ached with stiffness from being locked into a seated position for so long. He woke as the light of dawn shined through the small window and reached his face.

Stretching his body out from the knotted form the chair had created, he walked across the front room out the door onto the chilly porch. There he sat, watching the snow's stillness and attempting to vanquish the memories of his entire life. As the frost sent shivers through his body, the sounds of hoof beats filled his ears. His eyes focused on the winter woods, hoping to discover the source of the echoes disturbing his thoughts. The noise grew louder and into view emerged three horses galloping across the frozen ground directly towards William. He sat waiting for their arrival without concern for their unexpected presence.

Their shiny silver badges glistened as the light of day shimmered across the metal stars. William looked at the men on their horses, knowing why they had come. He watched as they removed guns from their holsters and pointed the barrels directly at his face.

"Don't make a move, William, or we'll shoot you down where you stand. Understand?" the town constable demanded. "William Bourne, you are under arrest for the murders of Caleb and Sophronia Omens. You are coming with us. Is anyone in the house?"

"Yes, Mrs. Brand is in the house. She's sleeping," William answered, sheepishly.

"Does she know what you've done?" the constable asked.

"No," William responded without emotion.

"Well, she will now won't she, you bastard!" he said as he deftly bashed William in the head with the pistol.

William fell to the ground, unconscious, and one of the deputies tied his hands behind his back with a short piece of rope. The constable entered the front door tentatively and called for Mrs. Brand, silently praying she had not become another of William's hapless victims.

"Mrs. Brand! Mrs. Brand, are you here?" the constable shouted, walking through the house.

Hearing a strange voice calling her name, Mrs. Brand stumbled out of bed, shocked to find the constable in her home.

"What is this? What is happening here?" Fright made her voice tremble.

"I'm sorry, ma'am, but I have some very bad news for you." replied the constable.

"What is it? What's wrong?" she asked, tears of panic filling her eyes.

"Your daughter and her husband were murdered and we believe William Bourne is the man responsible for their deaths."

"No, no! You can't be right. What? No, not my baby! Not my Sophronia!" wailed Mrs. Brand.

The woman's knees buckled and she fell to the floor crying out in anguish. The constable went to her aid as his deputies secured William's ropes and ushered him towards the horses. Lifting her to her feet, the constable walked Mrs. Brand to the rocking chair near the warm woodstove.

"When was the last time you saw your daughter, ma'am?" asked the constable.

"At her wedding. Over a month ago. She was so happy. I

can't believe it. I just can't believe it. Where is she? I have to see her," pleaded Mrs. Brand.

"No, ma'am, you don't want to see her in her present condition. I will not allow it. It would be best if you remember her as she was when you last saw her. I can't be graphic, but William killed them both with an axe." Grief laced every word that left his lips.

Mrs. Brand collapsed into the chair and began sobbing uncontrollably. She clutched at her heart. The constable handed her his handkerchief and excused himself.

"Ma'am, I'm afraid we have to leave now. I am sorry for your loss. We will be back tomorrow to ask you some questions. Again, I am sorry to be the bearer of this bad news," he said with true compassion. He was furious with the man who had caused the poor Brand woman such horrible grief.

The constable left the room to search for a coat and boots for William. He found them placed neatly near the rear door leading to the horse stall out back. When he reached the stall, he saddled the horse and led the bay gelding around to the front of the house where deputies had tied William to a long rope. They raised him onto the animal, tied him to the saddle, and then covered his body with the coat. The constable stuffed William's feet into the boots taken from Mrs. Brand's house. Bound, and unable to flee, William said nothing to the constable or deputies. They led him back through the snow to the county jail to be questioned and held while awaiting trial for the brutal murders of Caleb and Sophronia Omens.

CHAPTER FIVE

WILLIAM BOURNE WAS DELIVERED TO THE Cattaraugus County Jail without incident and placed in a small, vacant cell until the County Sheriff was ready to question him. He sat in silence, staring at the dirty floor in complete acceptance of the fate he had chosen for himself. When the sheriff's footsteps approached, William knew his interrogation was about to begin. The scowling sheriff swung open the cage door and growled, "Are you ready to talk, boy?"

"Yes, sir," replied William without fear.

A deputy sheriff entered the cell, grabbed William by one arm, and pulled him down a narrow corridor. They came to a small room with a lone chair inside. He shoved William down onto the seat.

"Did you kill Caleb and Sophronia Omens?" the sheriff demanded.

"I don't know," William replied.

Taken aback by the unexpected answer, the sheriff paused to collect his thoughts. "Don't give me that load of nonsense, boy. Let me ask you once again and listen to me real carefully this time. Did you kill Caleb and Sophronia Omens?"

"I told you already. I don't know," William answered.

"Okay, boy. Have it your way. It's going to be a long night."

"Yes, I guess it will be," William said, nodding his head.

The Sheriff and his deputies took turns over the next four hours trying to wear William down and glean a confession from him. They had no success. William remained steadfast and insisted that he did not remember a single detail of the events of the fateful night at the Coldspring farmhouse. The sheriff finally gave up and his deputies dragged the bruised, beaten, and mentally exhausted prisoner back to his cell and dropped him on the cold, hard, brick floor.

Meanwhile, word spread of the horrible deed committed in the nearby town of Coldspring and for several days, crowds of angry citizens gathered outside the jailhouse and shouted a torrent of threats beneath the window of William's cell. When it was time to move William to the Cattaraugus County Courthouse for his trial, he was transported quickly and quietly over the short distance in order to avoid contact with the crowd waiting to fill the courtroom.

The Cattaraugus County Courtroom in Little Valley was filled to capacity with angry town members who wanted William hanged in public for the horrific crimes he had committed. Jurors were selected from a pool of citizens from nearby towns such as Randolph, Franklinville, Salamanca, New Albion, Ellicottville, and Napoli. Winfield Scott Kenyon, a prominent Randolph citizen and Civil War veteran, was selected as jury foreman.

When Mr. Kenyon stood to deliver the verdict of Guilty at the end of the trial, the sober tone of his voice silenced the courtroom. "We the jury of the County of Cattaraugus, this fifth day of February in the year of our Lord eighteen seventy-four, find William Bourne guilty of the crime of murder of both Caleb Omens and Sophronia Brand Omens."

"Is this finding unanimous?" the judge asked.

"Yes, your honor, it is," answered Mr. Kenyon.

"Thank you Mr. Foreman, you may be seated." The judge then addressed the prisoner. "William Bourne, you have been tried and found guilty by your peers of the crime of murder on two counts. It is my duty to sentence you for your crimes. Do you understand this?"

"Yes," William replied.

"Do you have a statement you would like to make to the

court?" the judge asked.

"No," William answered.

"I have considered your sentencing with great care, and in hearing the evidence and weighing the testimony of those who have witnessed your behavior, I have decided to spare your life," the judge proclaimed.

The angry crowd of spectators shouted with disapproval. The judge pounded his gavel. "Silence! Silence in my courtroom or I will order it cleared!" the judge commanded. "It is my finding that the prisoner did not resist arrest, nor did he attempt to flee from Cattaraugus County to avoid his arrest. I truly believe this man when he says that he has no recollection of these crimes, as they were committed in the heat of passion. As a result, I will not hang this man. As it has been entrusted to me to uphold the law to the best of my ability, this is my final decision. William Bourne, you will serve the rest of your natural life in Auburn Penitentiary." The judge slammed his gavel down with a sharp crash. "This trial is complete, and the jury is excused. Sheriff, this man will remain in your custody until such time as you see fit to transport him to the Auburn Penitentiary." The judge stood and removed himself from the bench.

Photos were taken of William as he was escorted from the courtroom by the sheriff and placed into a caged buggy. The crowd that had packed the courtroom threw stones and mouthed anew their empty threats as the buggy passed by. When the buggy was out of the sight, the crowd finally dispersed. They returned home, angry that the murders had not been vindicated by the execution of the perpetrator. William Bourne was guilty of the most brutal murders ever committed in the town of Coldspring, New York.

The last person to leave the courtroom was the jury foreman. Winfield Scott Kenyon stood quietly, taking in the emptiness of the room. He, too, had hoped the judge would hang the vile creature who had butchered a woman in such a violent manner. The photos he had been required to view disturbed him at a level he could not comprehend. He had seen a lot during his service in the Civil War, but had never seen a body so mutilated and disfigured as Caleb Omens. In all his worst nightmares, Mr. Kenyon could not have imagined the evil he glimpsed in those photos.

Mr. Kenyon found his way to the front door of the building and, stepping out, encountered the court photographer standing on the porch enjoying a cigar.

"Good day, sir," the photographer said as he watched the foreman exit.

"And to you, sir," Mr. Kenyon responded. Just as he was about to walk down front stairs, the specter of the victim's photos filled his mind, and he turned back to fix his attention on the camera sitting on a tripod next to the cigar-smoking man.

"Excuse me, sir," Mr. Kenyon said to the photographer.

"Yes?"

"Did you take those photos of the victims?"

"Yes, I did," answered the photographer.

"I just can't seem to get them out of my mind."

"I'm not surprised at all, sir. That was a quite a blood bath."

"How were you able to stomach it?"

"It's my job to take pictures. I just did my job, that's all," the photographer replied without concern.

Pausing for a moment to regain his composure, Mr. Kenyon said, "Yes, of course, I'm sure. Forgive me, I have not introduced myself. Winfield Scott Kenyon. Please call me Scott." He stretched out his hand.

"I'm J.H. Blessing, photographer extraordinaire," the photographer replied with a slick grin. He clenched the cigar in the corner his mouth to free his right hand.

"Good to meet you," Scott said, as the two men shook hands and looked one another straight on.

"I need a drink. Care to join me?" asked J.H. Blessing.

"That sounds like a hell of an idea. Where's the tavern?"

"It's down this way." J.H. said as he picked up his box camera and walked down the front stairs.

The two men strode quickly towards the tavern, not saying much, still overwhelmed by the violent tragedy they had witnessed. The frost of winter remained to chill the air, but the ice on the road had turned to slush. As they approached the tavern, they could hear the sounds of celebratory music. Some in the drunken crowd recognized J.H. and warmly greeted the arrival of the two men. The barkeep shouted, "What ya havin', J.H.?"

"Gimme a bottle of scotch and two glasses Jimmy!" J.H. yelled back.

"You got it!" the barkeep replied.

"This one's on me, pal," J.H. said to Scott, slapping him good-naturedly on the back.

They made their way to the bar to procure their liquor and then wound their way to a small table in the corner of the room. Away from the loud cries of drunken arguments and the stench of unwashed flesh, the two educated men began a more professional conversation. As J.H. poured the golden liquor and filled their hand-blown glasses to the top, he engaged his new acquaintance with his own questions.

"So, what is your field, Scott?" J.H. asked matter-of-factly.

"I'm a businessman," replied Scott, not eager to divulge anything about his life to a stranger.

"What sort of business?" J.H. smiled.

"I own land outside of Randolph and I sell musical instruments in town," Scott said, downing the last of the liquid in his glass.

"So, you're a farmer and a shopkeeper," stated J.H.

"Well, isn't everyone around here either a farmer or a shopkeeper?" Scott smiled, his face reddened by the warmth of the scotch in his veins.

"Yeah, I suppose so. I take pictures, though," J.H. said as he searched the eyes of the stranger sitting across from him.

"That must keep you busy. Do you have a family that runs your land?" Scott asked, trying to direct the questions away from his personal life.

"Just got married earlier this year. Gonna start a family soon as we get the farmhouse squared away. Got some work to do on it first. How about yourself? You got a family?"

"I have two daughters so far. Morna is one year old, and Dora was born two months ago. Just got to get this wife of mine to start producing some boys," Scott laughed as he slammed his glass on the table, demanding another drink.

"Yeah? Well at least the breeding work has its benefits!" J.H. teased as he filled Scott's glass again.

Laughing together and celebrating the liberties of manhood, they drank and talked far into the night. Although their characters were quite different and they had not known one another for more than a few hours, a kinship formed between the two men. When the tavern closed and the patrons were forced out into the night, J.H. Blessing and Winfield Scott Kenyon staggered their way onto the front porch to enjoy one last cigar. The night sky was crystal clear, leaving a blanket of heavenly stars to light the darkness and aid their vision.

"How's your smoke, Scott?" J.H. asked his new comrade.

"It's fine, very fine, thank you," replied Scott with intoxicated satisfaction.

"It sure was a nasty thing, those murders," J.H. commented.

"Awful, just awful," Scott agreed.

"I have more photos, you know. Some I didn't give the sheriff," said J.H.

"Really?"

"Yeah. Sometimes I take what I call 'occupational liberties.'

As long as I get the job done, anything else I photograph is none of their damn business as far as I'm concerned," J.H. explained.

"Well, what's in the pictures?" asked Scott, intrigued by his new friend's revelation.

"I tell you what, come by my studio in Salamanca one day and I'll show ya," J.H. said as enticement.

"All right, I will." Scott replied.

"And I'll give ya a good deal on some family portraits. Seeing as you don't have any boys, you're gonna need all the savings you can get," J.H. laughed loudly.

"Ha, ha, ha! Laugh now, J.H. Just you wait. I bet your house is full of girls one day," Scott joked back, a smirk on his face.

"Ha, ha, ha to you, you son of a bitch," J.H. yelled, laughing even harder. "How much you wanna bet?"

The two men smiled at one another and smoked their cigars until they grew weary from the long day and the consumption of strong spirits. They made their way through the slushy streets back to the hotel. As they retired to their respective rooms, they nodded to one another with mutual admiration.

The next morning Winfield Scott Kenyon hired a buggy and made his way to Salamanca to catch the morning train back to Randolph. J.H. Blessing, meanwhile, had risen early, claimed his horse and buggy at the livery stable, and returned to his shop in Salamanca to keep an early appointment with a customer.

As the whistle blew on the westbound morning train out of Salamanca, J.H. watched as a crowd gathered to wave goodbye to their loved ones about to be taken away by the iron horse. His eyes searched the platform and recognized his drinking partner boarding a passenger car that would transport him to the Randolph Station. J.H. bellowed to Scott with a raised hand of farewell.

"Scott! Scott! Over here! I was hoping to catch you this morning. So long, my friend! Come back soon to Salamanca! I'll snap your photo and make you look more distinguished than you'll ever hope to be!" he shouted with a smile.

"Be careful, J.H. You are beginning to sound like a snake oil salesman! Hope you get those daughters you want so badly!" Scott yelled back.

They both threw back their heads in laughter. Although they lived in different towns and engaged in different occupations, J.H. Blessing and Winfield Scott Kenyon shared an instinct for upcoming business trends. Times were changing drastically as the Gilded Age was bursting into full swing, and these two men were growing in power and position as respected leaders in their communities. Their blossoming friendship formed a bond that would link their fates in a peculiar fashion.

When Scott returned home to his wife, Olive, and their baby girls, Olive sensed a changed man. From the moment he walked into their large farmhouse, Olive noticed subtle differences in his manner and appearance. As she threw her arms around him and embraced his body, she felt his detachment towards her affection. Unsure of what had taken place, and concerned for his welfare, Olive welcomed him with a barrage of questions.

"It's so nice to have you back, Scott. Was the trip very taxing?" asked Olive between kisses.

"No, not too bad. The locomotive is actually quite a thrilling experience. I am sure it was the first of many adventures in my future," he replied gallantly.

"How was the jury duty? Was it an interesting trial?"

"It was," Scott said, revealing nothing.

"What was Little Valley like? Is it a nice town?" she persisted.

"Yes, dear, it was a nice town. Where are the girls?" he asked, attempting to distract her from the interrogation.

"They're upstairs taking a nap. Such good girls, so delicate. So feminine," Olive gushed.

"Well let's get started on another one. Maybe this time we'll get a tough, young boy," he said kissing her back.

"Oh my goodness, Scott! Not so loud! The help may hear you!" Olive blushed at her husband's late afternoon advances.

Olive ran upstairs followed closely by her husband's rapid footsteps. They chased one another playfully until they found their way to the large feather bed covered with lacy linens sporting fine embroidery. Scott's passionate embrace startled his wife making her a bit suspicious of his activities during his stay away from home. Unaware of her concerns, he lavished himself in her body, satisfying his needs for lust until he lay exhausted by his efforts. He released his hold of Olive and rolled onto his side, falling into slumber.

Scott did not wake until early the next morning. His wife was sound asleep in the bed beside him. Scott rose groggily and made his way into his daughters' room to visit the children he had missed the evening before. Their fragile faces warmed his heart, helping to dissipate the chilling experience he had been through in Little Valley. However, nothing could banish the photographs from his memory. Making his way back to his bedroom, the creaking wood floor stirred Olive from her sleep.

"Good Morning, Scott, did you sleep all right?" she asked, still groggy.

"Yes dear, I was quite tired. The trial took a lot out of me."

"It must have. You seemed different, somehow, when you came home yesterday."

"I did? Well, if you had seen what I saw, you would probably have the same look to you," Scott said in a serious tone.

"What was it, darling?" Olive asked, quite concerned.

"It was the Coldspring murders. Horrible deaths, with vivid pictures that I can't get out of my mind."

"That's awful, just ghastly."

"You have no idea, Olive. It was much worse than the newspaper let on. I forgot about the copy of the Randolph *Register* I bought at the station yesterday. I'll get it out of my bag later this morning. The judge sentenced the guy to life in prison, but I tell you, if it were up to me, I'd a hung him until his neck snapped like a twig." Scott spoke with an icy tone.

"Well, now, that's a lovely thought so early in the morning!" Olive remarked, reminding Scott that he was no longer in the company of men.

"Yes, I suppose it's a bit crass to hang someone before breakfast, eh?" he said laughing at his own wit.

"Oh, Scott, you can be such a cad!" Olive joked back, throwing her pillow at his head.

"Get up, woman! I am starving! I haven't eaten in forever," he ordered with a huge grin on his face.

"All right, Scott. Just let me put my robe on. I did not want to wake you for dinner last night. You seemed so in need of a good solid rest."

"Thank you, dear. Your passion was just too much for me. It wore me out," he said as he dropped back onto his pillow and feigned sleep.

"Ah, you are going to get a week of burnt meals if you keep that mouth going," Olive warned playfully.

"Never happen! You are the best cook in the county. And, besides, it would ruin your reputation." Scott went to her and wrapped his arms around her, hugging her tightly.

"I think you should go to court more often," Olive whispered. "It makes you quite affectionate, Mr. Winfield Scott Kenyon."

They made their way downstairs to begin their morning routine as the sun cast warm rays through the glass window in the kitchen. Olive prepared her husband's meal and quickly made her way to her babies' room to change their diapers and carry them downstairs for their morning feeding. With one arm wrapped around Dora, still nursing from her breast, and the other hand clasping a bottle for Morna who sat in the wooden high chair,

Olive's day of non-stop care giving was in full force.

The modest wealth attained by both Olive and Scott's shrewd business sense afforded the Kenyons a full-time maid who came every morning to clean the house, do the wash, and help with the babies. Although their farm produced respectable earnings from the production of milk, oats, and corn, it was their discreet ownership of oil-producing property in nearby Derrick City, Pennsylvania, that was filling their bank accounts with exceptional amounts of money. They had placed ownership of the properties in Olive's maiden name to conceal their holdings from needy friends and relatives. Scott was a private man and the wealth he was accruing would be for his children and grandchildren. He had no intention of squandering his fortune on those he could not personally regulate or instruct on how to use the money wisely.

Scott entrusted the mundane farming chores to young boys he hired in town. As hard-nosed and calculating as could be, Scott had a soft spot for those who'd had a harsh life and limited opportunities. The Randolph Children's Home had once asked him for a donation to help fund their home for orphaned children. But rather than throw money at the organization, he offered to employ boys interested in honest work. Scott interviewed each boy personally, and if he liked the way the boy handled himself, he gave the youth the opportunity to earn a decent wage. The boys plowed the corn and oat fields, chopped firewood, repaired broken equipment, milked the dairy cows, groomed the horses, cleared the manure from the stable and spread it as fertilizer for the crops, and handled anything else the Kenyon family needed. While this earned Scott tremendous respect for his service to the community, it also saved him a fortune in labor, making it a profitable endeavor for himself as well.

While Olive nurtured the children and tended her large garden and fruit trees, Scott was free to manage their businesses and travel into the town of Randolph to oversee his musical instrument shop.

Several months after the trial, Scott found himself the center of attention during a business lunch in town. The papers that morning reported that William Bourne had died in prison from what was listed by the coroner as heart failure, and as the foreman of the jury, the townspeople went to Scott for his take on the situation.

"Well, he got what he deserved after all," Scott replied to the repetitious questioning. Most people just nodded their heads in agreement and went about their business.

It was the beginning of the end of innocence across the country, with widespread communications equipment exploding throughout the land. The crimes that had previously gone unnoticed were suddenly being reported everywhere due to the emergence of local newspapers and the ability of reporters to travel swiftly by railroad across the towns and territories. The rise of industrialism in the north, due to Civil War efforts, spearheaded technological advances throughout the country. The various inventions of Thomas Edison and Alexander Bell were being funded by government grants, furthering the scientific revolution sweeping the nation.

Among the supporters of modernizing America, Winfield Scott Kenyon led the drive for knowledge by insisting on education as a means to improvement. He filled his home with a library of information recovered from his travels throughout the northern district. His awareness of current events encompassed an understanding of the power behind politics and he urged any man who would listen to become more involved in the democratic process. As a staunch New York Democrat, he encouraged his friends within the community to support the deconstruction of the south and reinstate freedom to those who had been enslaved. Regardless of his commitment to amass tremendous wealth for himself, Scott felt it was far more exciting to be victorious in his endeavors on an even playing field, rather than to simply dominate an unworthy opponent.

Out of his many ventures grew an enormous passion for the legal system, inspired by his involvement as foreman at the Coldspring murder trial. He joined the crowds that witnessed prominent cases if he thought they might determine the passing of amendments in Congress. While traveling home from a trial in New York City, his train was delayed in Salamanca. Recalling his first trial experience and the vicious depiction displayed in the photos taken by J.H. Blessing, Scott opted to stop by and see if the photographer had been truthful in his claim to have images of the murder scene that no one else had viewed. He smiled to himself knowing that his friend would be happy to see him, and more than pleased to lighten his own pockets for a portrait or two of his own.

When the brakes on the locomotive screeched, bringing it to a grinding halt, and the passengers eagerly disembarked, Scott sought out a local who could give him directions to the photography studio. Seeing no one who could guide him, Scott headed toward the center of the town. Salamanca was situated along the edge of the Allegany River where the Seneca Indians had once traveled in their handcrafted bark canoes.

As Scott walked the muddy, dirt streets, he looked into the windows of various shops. The third store had the words "Blessing Photography" hand-painted in script on the etched glass door. Bells hanging above the door tinkled brightly as he walked in. J.H. Blessing himself was in the back studio, smoking a cigar as he prepared a backdrop for a young woman eagerly awaiting memorialization by the camera.

"I'll be with you in a moment," J.H. called out without looking to see who had entered his store.

"No problem at all," Scott replied.

J.H. jerked his head around to confirm his recollection of the familiar voice.

"Winfield Scott Kenyon! Well, I'll be! Where in God's name have you been?" J.H. came around the counter to greet him with a hearty handshake.

"How are you, J.H.?" said Scott. "How have you been?"

"I'm better than ever, of course," J.H. answered, smiling.

"The train I took from New York City was held up here for repairs and I figured I was due for a visit after all this time."

"Well, I'm damn glad you finally got out here! Listen, I just have to finish up the young lady and then I'm done for the day. We can get some drinks and catch up. Whatta ya say?" J.H. offered.

"Sounds good. Do you mind if I watch you work?" Scott asked as he followed J.H. into the back studio.

"No, not at all," J.H. replied. Then, addressing his waiting client, an attractive young woman, he said, "You don't mind an audience, do you dear?"

"No sir, not at all," she responded, with a nervous smile and slight curtsy directed at Scott.

Scott watched as J.H. walked to the back wall and finished positioning the shades to accentuate the sunlight streaming in through the windows. "Please sit here, dear," J.H. motioned to the waiting customer.

The woman walked gracefully, as if her feet were hovering over the ground, and then she floated effortlessly down onto the soft, black velvet covering the large wooden chair. Her eyes closed briefly as she took a slow, patient breath to relax her body into a pose of beauty that could be captured by the famous photographer.

"You are stunning, my dear. Don't move!" J.H. whispered, adding an element of mystery to his request.

Motionless she sat, waiting for the puff of smoke to emerge from the flash pan. A tiny explosion popped as the photograph was taken, allowing her time to blink and flutter her large, green eyes.

"That was excellent! Give me a moment and I will prepare another shot," J.H. instructed

As he replaced the glass plate and readied himself under the cloak of the camera's viewer, he grew dissatisfied with the woman's expression and posture. "What is it you love more than anything in this world, Miss?" J.H. asked her matter-of-factly.

"Well, I'm sure I don't know! Mr. Blessing," she answered, obviously shocked at the intimacy of his question.

"All right then, let's pretend you know and make something up," he replied, one eyebrow raised.

"I suppose it could be moonlight dancing across the pond," she said demurely.

"That is very good. Very good indeed. You see what I am looking for is that moonlight in your eyes, do you understand?"

"Yes, yes, I understand completely," she said, quite pleased by the photographer's soulful insight.

J.H. returned to his post under the dark cloak behind the camera and was delighted with the woman's transformation. Her eyelids had lowered slightly, her mouth had softened, and her back had arched slightly, accentuating her cleavage. A subtle smile lifted the left side of her mouth and the enticing tilt of her chin gave the appearance that she was looking across time. J.H. waited for the moment when she exhaled, releasing the fantasy that resided in her delicate form, then he snapped the photo and came out from under the camera's cover.

"That's it. I'm sure we have it," he stated with glory.

"Are we finished so quickly, Mr. Blessing?" she asked, dismayed that her stage was no longer available.

"Yes, dear. That is why my prices are so very high. I am truly a master at my art." J.H. winked at Scott, who could not help but laugh aloud.

"Do not laugh, sir. This man is a genius. He has taken photos of the finest citizens in the state," the young woman snapped as she momentarily deviated from her usual propriety.

"A thousand pardons, madam," a bowing Scott begged with a sarcasm J.H. clearly understood.

"I'll have these ready for you sometime next week, probably not until Friday. If you stop in around noon, they will be ready for your approval. I will send the charge to your father," J.H. said, then laughed quietly, reacting to his friend's humor.

"Thank you so much, Mr. Blessing." The young woman rose from the luxurious setting, stepped slowly through the studio and waited for Scott to open the door.

"Here you are, madam," Scott said as held open the wood door, allowing her to pass through. The woman strutted past him with flirtatious dignity, the fragrance of her perfume wafting through the air. Once the door was closed, Scott turned around to look at J.H. in disbelief.

J.H. struck a match against the stone on the woodstove and lit his cigar in satisfaction of a job well done. He smiled at Scott and said, "One hell of a job I have here now, don't I? Hah! Wanna smoke, Scott?"

"Sure that would be perfect right now," answered Scott. "Who, or what, was that?"

"That, my dear Scott, was Sarah Fenton of the hoity-toity Fentons. Those kinds of folks are the ones that keep me in business!" J.H. laughed.

They lit their cigars and watched the smoke curl upwards, filling the room with a penetrating odor that quickly erased the flowery scent left by the young Sarah Fenton. J.H. picked up the exposed, covered glass plates and put them in his darkroom for development later. Scott watched his friend move quickly, with a precision and focus quite different from the character with whom he was familiar. Impressed with J.H.'s concentration, Scott smoked his cigar and observed the master photographer attend to final business in his studio, ignoring Scott's presence.

"All right, Kenyon," J.H. yelled out from the darkroom. "I'm just about finished here. We can be on our way in just another minute."

"Take your time J.H. I'm very impressed with your work ethic."

"Ethic? That sounds like a load of manure, Kenyon! Well, a man's gotta feed the family right?" said J.H.

"That is for certain, my friend. I've got three now."

"Three kids, eh? All girls, right?" J.H. laughed.

"Can you believe it? The next one better be a boy or I'll have to get a new woman!" Scott called out with a hearty laugh.

J.H. grabbed his coat and hat and Scott followed him out to the street. J.H. locked the front door and the two men headed across the bridge that spanned the Allegany River. They entered a small tavern that offered spirits and meals to wealthy patrons who craved the finer luxuries. A player piano filled the room with the sounds of fiddles and banjos, while distinguished men sat eating rich meats and drinking potent liquors.

"So what took you so long to get here, Scott? I thought for sure you would show up to see the photos I told you about."

"I've been busy with working, traveling and expanding the farmhouse. I've not had a chance to get out here, but I've got to tell you, J.H., those pictures from the trial have never left my mind."

"Well I guess I've just seen so much through the camera's eye that nothing really shocks me anymore. But that scene was definitely the worst I have ever witnessed."

"What else do you photograph?" asked Scott.

"Everything. Police work, news stories, school pictures, portraits, anything and everything that needs to be recorded for posterity." J.H. answered.

"Makes you a bit of an historian, doesn't it?"

"I suppose so," agreed J.H.

They finished their meal and enjoyed each other's company until Scott said, "So, how about you show me those missing photos you've been holding for me?"

"Be happy to, sport, I got 'em in the safe at the studio. Let me just square this ticket with the bar, and we'll go have a look." said J.H.

"Not this time! This one's on me," Scott insisted as he pulled out his billfold. Scott paid their bill and they made their way back across the bridge as the afternoon sun melted into the horizon and glistened across the thousands of treetops surrounding Salamanca.

As they entered the empty studio, the strong smell of the photograph processing chemicals and cigar smoke provoked an acidic sting in Scott's nostrils. His chest was pounding in anticipation of viewing the murder scene images. Memories of the trial flooded his mind and he wondered why his curiosity would not relinquish its desire for more vivid descriptions.

J.H. made his way to the back room to unlock his personal safe and share his treasures with his friend. As he walked towards Scott with the leather portfolio in his hand, he smiled with delight at the secrets he was about to reveal.

"It's funny that you took so long to visit me, and that you still want to see shots of people you never even knew," J.H. said as he unwound the leather cord that held the portfolio's flap closed.

"Something about that murder changed me, deep inside. I am different and I cannot stop wondering what really happened inside that farmhouse. I'm hoping what you have here might satisfy my mind," Scott answered.

"Well, sounds like to me like you have a fascination with the darker side of life," said J.H.

"Don't we all?"

"I suppose we do, but, at least you're honest about it. Most people wouldn't admit it," J.H. said with a hollow laugh. He pulled out the photos from the leather portfolio and handed them to Scott without saying another word.

Scott looked closely at the first picture. It was of Sophronia Omens' decapitated head. Scott's stomach tightened and his eyes closed as he took a deep breath and forced himself to focus on the bulging eyes and horrified look on her face. Disgust and rage filled his body as he flipped the matte image behind the stack and looked at the next photograph. The second shot displayed the mutilated pieces of flesh that remained of Caleb's body. His organs had been chopped and crushed into a pool of blood. Splashes of blood also covered the axe-scarred rocking chair. "That's enough for me, J.H. I can't look at the rest," Scott said as he handed the stack back to the photographer.

"Yeah, these are pretty gruesome, old boy. That's why I kept 'em from the authorities," J.H. said. "No need to be overly graphic. Simply gotta get the job done."

"Well, maybe he would have been hung if the judge were able to see those."

"Sure doesn't matter now, Scott. The son of a bitch is dead and gone."

"Why do you keep them?" Scott asked.

"Well, my friend, I suppose I have an interest in the dark side of man myself," J.H. answered. J.H. placed the photos back inside the leather portfolio and returned to the darkroom. In a bit, he brought back the newly processed portrait he had just finished in an attempt to lighten his friend's mood.

"This should cheer you up. Look at this lovely, young thing! She'll make someone a fine bride someday," J.H. said, handing Scott the photo.

Impressed by the talented artist's work, Scott said, "She looks even better in the photo than she does in plain sight. You really are a genius!"

"Thanks, pal! You gotta come back with your wife and kids.

We'll do a family thing for the Kenyon gang. It'll be a ball. I'll make you all look good, I promise."

"It's a deal. You are worth the small fortune you're charging for these. I'll swear it to anyone who asks."

"I'll hold you to that, Scott! Just send me a letter or telegraph and let me know what day you'll be here. I'll have my wife, Addie, make a feast for the lot of us," J.H. said with a proud grin.

The men shook hands and walked to the front door, a mutual understanding of both the violence and beauty of mankind lingered. As Scott walked out, he looked over his shoulder and gave J.H. a nod of respect, honoring their friendship and brotherly bond. The photographer watched as his friend hurriedly made his way down the bustling street in the direction of the train station. When the dark coat and top hat disappeared from sight, J.H. closed the door and locked it behind him. He lit a cigar and its overpowering smell filled the room. J.H. Blessing smiled to himself, supremely pleased with the man he had become.

CHAPTER SIX

J.H. FINISHED HIS CIGAR AND WENT ABOUT straightening his studio. Although photography was his passion, he was first and foremost a businessman. The Blessing family had not been able to obtain even a modicum of wealth and high social standing in the United States since the immigration of its first ancestor to North America in colonial times. J.H. intended to remedy that condition regardless of how it was accomplished. He possessed the uncanny ability to create opportunity whenever the need arose. And, no matter who crossed across his path, he could capture anyone's attention and manipulate the person without their awareness of what he was doing.

His meteoric rise began shortly after he arrived in Salamanca, New York, in early 1870. J.H. needed a bankroll to begin what he privately referred to as, "The Blessing Dynasty." He set his sights on Addie Huff, the daughter of a prominent Salamanca merchant. Her dowry, he surmised, would be ample enough to start him out in a photography studio.

Long before he began to court Addie, J.H. began a campaign of manipulation aimed at impressing Addie's father, Edgar Huff. J.H. convinced Edgar to try a novel advertising campaign that he guaranteed would bring new customers to Edgar's "Salamanca Dry Goods Emporium." Ads were placed in the Salamanca *Press*, the Randolph *Register*, and the Olean *Times*, promising a free tintype portrait, for one weekend only, to anyone who spent $2 or more in the store. Edgar would reimburse J.H. for the modest wholesale cost of producing the tintypes. The ad campaign was a huge success and brought in new buyers by the droves. Edgar netted a huge profit and J.H. established his photography business in that single weekend. From that point on, J.H. could do no wrong in Edgar's eyes.

His conquest of the merchant's daughter was as easy as shooting fish in a barrel. Addie succumbed without hesitation to the advances of the handsome, young photographer making a name for himself throughout Cattaraugus County. Their courtship lasted just a few months and the ensuing wedding was an impressive social event that brought out some of the most prominent members of Salamanca society. The expensive wedding gifts the guests brought filled the huge parlor of the farmhouse just outside of town that Edgar bought for the newlyweds. And, Addie's dowry proved to be more than ample. J.H. was set to become a mover and a shaker. He accomplished all of this in less than six months.

The night J.H. arrived home late from his afternoon spent with Winfield Scott Kenyon, Addie stood waiting for him at the front door to take his coat and hat and welcome his return with a kiss. She was his biggest fan and most dedicated handmaid, abandoning her privileged status to serve his every need. Although a housekeeper, two maids, and several farm hands maintained their house and farm, Addie prepared all the meals and kept herself on constant call for anything J.H. may need. She lived to serve her husband and no one else. Knowing that J.H. wanted children, she grew frustrated when her womb refused to ripen with child during their first two years of marriage. Fearful that she was unworthy of J.H., she prayed constantly for God's intervention. J.H. never noticed her insecurity. In fact, he never paid much attention to her once they were married. A wife to J.H. was no more than an additional piece of furniture in the house. He did, however love her in his own limited way. He found her to be a very suitable wife whose life's work was to be of service to him.

And she was. Addie rose quickly to her feet upon hearing his carriage pull into their carriage house. As the front door opened and J.H. stepped in, she smiled and took a breath of relief that her hero had made it home safely once again.

"Welcome home, darling! Did you have a good day?" Addie asked while she took his coat and hat.

"Yes, Addie, it was fine," answered J.H. distractedly as he made his way to his bedroom, skipping the meal he usually attended to immediately upon his arrival home.

"Are you not hungry, dear?" Addie asked.

"No, I ate earlier with a friend from out-of-town," J.H. called back over his shoulder as headed up the stairwell towards his bedroom.

Disheartened at the waste of a perfectly good meal, Addie went to the kitchen and removed his plate from the stove. She covered it with a towel, thinking he might want the food later, as an evening snack. To please him, she followed him up the stairs and began undressing herself in the hallway. By the time she entered his room, her clothes decorated the hallway's wood floor and her bare body shivered at the thought of his hands touching her skin. She knocked on the closed door gently and awaited his reply.

"Come in," J.H. announced.

"Since you already ate I thought you might have an appetite for something else?" offered Addie sheepishly.

He looked up to see her standing naked in the doorway, and a mischievous grin covered his face. He stood up from his desk and slowly walked towards, his desire rising once he saw her body tremble. Their lips met as he wrapped his arms around her waist, lifting her effortlessly. With no hesitation, J.H. dropped her body onto his bed and undid his trousers. Addie breathed deeply as her husband ravaged her body, pleasing himself with her soft flesh. In that moment, as he climaxed, their act of passion created a son whose soul would embody the artistry of his father and the self-effacing compassion of his mother.

Six weeks later, when Addie opened the front door to greet J.H., she had an extraordinary grin on her face.

"Well, don't you look like the cat that ate the canary, Addie. What's up with you today?"

"I am with child," she announced, joy palpable in her voice.

"Ah, I see! Well, now, that is wonderful news. I'm sure it will be a fine son. Let's get you inside, shall we? You need to be careful now that you are with child," advised J.H.

She threw her arms around him with the prospect of being a mother and at the opportunity to bear her hero's child. J.H. hugged her gently for a moment and then led her inside where he sat at the dining table awaiting his dinner. Addie scampered to the kitchen, retrieving his plate from the kitchen. He ate his dinner engrossed in the evening newspaper. As Addie watched her husband consume his meal, she could not help but wonder if he was really pleased to be a father. They had been together for two years, but J.H.'s work and ever-expanding bank account remained his priorities.

When they were first married, Addie assumed they would grow closer and more affectionate in time, yet J.H.'s abrasive manner and distant demeanor continued without consideration of romance or intimacy. Sadness and disappointment suddenly overcame her and she excused herself to avoid revealing her tears. "I'm going to get some rest now, dear. Just leave the plate. I'm sure one of the help will get it later," Addie said, walking away from the table.

"All right," J.H. answered without looking up from his paper.

Addie went to her small bedroom situated directly across the hall from her husband's bedroom. Unable to comprehend why she was feeling such intense dissatisfaction with the man she had taken a Godly oath to serve, she put on her sleeping gown and crawled into bed. The innocence of her youth seemed to vanish with the growing life inside her womb. The faith she had mastered was now replaced with confusion. As her eyes closed, weary from a long day on the farm, she thanked God for honoring her with a child and then asked forgiveness for the sinful anger she felt towards her husband.

J.H. left for work the next morning without seeing his wife. Normally, she rose early to prepare his morning meal. Instead, Catherine, their housekeeper, who possessed an uncanny ability to manage their home regardless of crisis or chaos, greeted him as he entered the dining room. After eating a light breakfast, J.H. jaunted off to work. He hadn't given Addie's absence a second thought, assuming she just needed her rest.

He stopped at the post office to check for correspondence and accounts receivable. He was pleased to discover that his friend, Winfield Scott Kenyon, had sent a letter. The message stated that Scott's wife, Olive, was again with child and that he planned to bring her and the three girls for their portraits at the end of the week. Thrilled to have yet another booking, and happy to know their friendship was alive and well, J.H. made his way to the telegraph office. He sent Scott a telegram confirming their appointment for a sitting.

J.H. returned home late, after a long day at the studio. Much to his surprise, Addie was not waiting for him at the door. J.H. made his way to the dining table and was greeted by Catherine, who took his coat and hat. "Would you like to have your dinner now, sir?" she asked.

"Yes. And bring me a scotch as well," J.H. demanded, irritated that his wife was not at the table. "Where is Addie?"

"She is upstairs, resting, sir," Catherine replied.

"Is she ill?" J.H. inquired, a harsh tone inflecting his words.

"No, sir, just tired. The baby is taking a lot out of her and she is feeling the physical strain."

"Well, I'll look in on her after supper. It seems the least she could do would be to welcome me home."

"Shall I wake her, sir?" Catherine asked.

"No, don't bother; I'm ready to read my paper anyway." J.H. did not try to hide his irritation.

Catherine disappeared, then returned with a plate of warm food for her employer. She placed the scotch down first, and then gently laid the plate in front of him.

"Will you need anything else, sir?"

"No," J.H. barked and he waved her off.

Catherine made her way upstairs to Addie's room. Once inside she sat at the edge of the bed, waiting for Addie to wake from her slumber. It worried the housekeeper when her mistress had failed to rise that day and asked for her meals to be brought to her bedroom. It was very unusual to see such depression in Addie, for she was normally an incredibly happy person. Addie woke and saw Catherine sitting quietly on the edge of the bed.

"What is it, Catherine?" Addie asked in a whisper.

"Your husband is home ma'am and he asked for you."

"Oh, I see. And what did you tell him?"

"I told him you were a bit tired today and that the baby was taking a lot out of you," Catherine answered.

"Well, I suppose that is true. Is that what you think?"

"Yes, ma'am, of course, what else could it be?"

"I have never had a baby before so I really don't have any idea," said Addie.

"Your husband said he would check on you later, after his supper."

"Really, now that is unusual. I don't know if he has ever been inside this room in the two years we've lived here." A hint of hope returned to her expression.

"Well, ma'am, I'll let you rest for now. Do you need anything?"

"No, Catherine, I'm fine. Please attend to Mr. Blessing's needs," Addie replied.

Catherine exited the room, leaving Addie to ponder the effects her absence had on her husband. As she snuggled into the pillows, she rubbed her belly to comfort the tiny creature growing inside her body. Suddenly her bedroom door swung open. J.H. walked into the room without hesitation or concern for his wife's slumber.

"So what is all this rest you are taking? Are you ill?" J.H. closed the door behind him.

"No, J.H. I'm just a bit tired," Addie answered without turning to face him.

"Sit up and look at me, woman! The least you can do is welcome me home from the bed that I afford you," J.H. barked.

"Welcome home," Addie said sullenly and rolled over to lift herself into a sitting position.

"That's better. Now let me have a look at you." J.H. walked closer sat on the bed to inspect her. "You look just fine to me. If this persists, I'll have a doctor look in on you. I want you better by Friday. I have a good friend coming to the studio with his family. His wife is with child, too, so you'll have something in common. You will travel with me to town on Friday. I want you to meet them at the studio."

"To your studio? Me?" Addie asked.

"Has your hearing gone bad, too, woman? Yes, you. To the studio. This Friday." J.H. stood abruptly. "Now get yourself well so I can have my wife back," he said, then left the room.

Addie smiled as the door closed behind him. She understood that even though her husband was brazen and callous, he loved her. She had never been invited to the studio before. J.H. kept his business private, even from his wife. This opportunity inspired her to spend the week making herself beautiful so she could create a grand impression on the family her husband obviously regarded highly.

When Friday morning came, Addie rose early to spend extra time on her hairstyle and to prepare a special breakfast for both her husband and herself. As they ate their meal in silence, she beamed with pride knowing this would be a day she would never forget. J.H. helped Addie into the carriage and closed the door behind her. The air seemed filled with magic as the horse pulled the carriage away from the house and headed towards town.

They arrived at the photography studio earlier than normal so that J.H. could prepare a special setting for the Kenyon family. He chose black velvet for the backdrop, a wood rocking chair for Mrs. Kenyon, and a small bench for the three girls. Assuming Scott would prefer to stand, J.H. left a small gap between the two pieces of furniture, which would make Scott the center of the photograph.

Addie watched in admiration of her husband's artistic process and stood far out of his way so as not to disturb his work. Addie was startled by the noise of the bells tinkling when the front door swung open, but J.H. was well attuned to the welcoming sound of cash-paying clientele arriving.

"J.H., my friend! Good to see you!" Scott proclaimed as he walked in.

"Scott, glad you could make it. These must be the ladies I have heard so much about!" he said with a bow. "It is indeed a pleasure to meet you, Mrs. Kenyon."

"Thank you, Mr. Blessing. It's wonderful to be here," said Olive. "We are so looking forward to having our portraits taken."

"And who are these lovelies?" asked J.H.

"This pretty little one is Edith, the oldest here is Morna, and the shy one standing behind her mother is Dora," Scott said.

"Well, it is wonderful to meet you all. May I introduce my lovely wife, Addie?" J.H. said, motioning for her to come out from one of the dark recesses of the studio.

"It is lovely to meet you, Mrs. Blessing," Olive said.

"And you as well, Mrs. Kenyon. You have a beautiful family," replied Addie.

"Do you have children?" asked Olive.

"We have one on the way." Addie's cheeks flushed with embarrassment.

"Congratulations!" Olive and Scott chimed simultaneously.

"Thank you. We are so thrilled," Addie said, regaining her composure. J.H. smiled and made his way back to his preparations on the studio floor.

"Are you ready for us back there, J.H.?" Scott yelled across the room.

"I will be, after a few lighting adjustments. Why don't you freshen up and get yourselves ready," J.H. instructed.

Scott guided his wife and children to the dressing mirror and checked his appearance in the large reflective glass. Satisfied that everything was in order, Scott strode over to the set J.H. had prepared and smiled at the opulent decorations the famous photographer had selected for the Kenyon family.

"Exactly what I expected," Scott commented.

"Yes, well, I have a knack for knowing what my clients want," said J.H.

"Well, aren't you the confident one, J.H." Scott said with a smile.

"Yep. Just call me Mr. Confidence, Scott, old man!"

Olive quickly tidied the girls and then tidied herself. She joined Scott, who was already in position in front of the velvet backdrop. She marveled at how the fabric shone with random patches of cobalt blue and black.

"Now, Scott, I thought it best you should stand in the middle, and Mrs. Kenyon, please sit with your youngest in your lap, the little ones sometimes have trouble sitting still. Then we'll have Morna and Dora on the bench together."

They all positioned themselves as instructed by the artist and awaited further guidance on to how to achieve the most attractive image. J.H. checked the shot through the lens and looked closely at each person's face. He made a few lighting adjustments and turned the two older children's heads just so.

Addie watched from a distance, beaming with pride. She had

never seen her husband at work and was amazed at his artistry.

J.H. looked again through the lens, and pleased with his ability to manifest illusion he readied his subjects. "Everyone looks wonderful. Are we ready, Kenyon family?" J.H. asked.

"Of course, J.H. Now, let's see what you can do," said Scott.

The photographer disappeared underneath the black cloak of the camera viewer and waited for the perfect moment to capture their essence. The girls wiggled on the bench for a bit until they found a comfortable position. Olive held her breath until she could no longer keep from exhaling. At the moment the entire family relaxed, the flash pan exploded and a small burst of smoke puffed into the air.

"Excellent!" J.H. said to the family.

"Just relax while I load another plate. Did I tell you that I'm the only photographer in Western New York who uses glass plate photography? It's the latest thing, Scott. It's a bit tricky, though. The plates are coated with an emulsion of gelatin and silver bromide. A bit more expensive, but I assure you it is well worth the extra cost."

Excited over being the center of attention, the Kenyon family beamed with pleasure. J.H. readied his camera and snapped a shot that captured their happy demeanor.

"That'll be the one," J.H. informed them.

"I'd like to do some individual photos as well," Scott stated.

"I had planned on it," replied J.H.

"Ladies, let's have you first," Scott said to his family.

"We should do the children while we still have their attention," J.H. suggested.

"Lovely. Let's start with Edith. She's getting a bit antsy," Olive proposed.

"Good choice, Olive. Let me make a few quick changes in the set," J.H. said.

The photographer removed the small bench and centered the

rocking chair in the camera's view. He motioned for Olive to bring Edith to the set and placed the child on the chair. When J.H. looked at her through the lens, it appeared as though Edith was staring directly into his eyes. He took the shot instantly, impressed by the young girl's relationship with the camera.

"She has something, this one. The camera loves her," J.H. said to his friend.

"Does she now? Well, we shall not tell her too much. Don't want to spoil her so young with ideas of grand beauty, eh?" Scott said.

"It's not so much beauty as it is a quality that the camera loves," J.H. explained. "It's quite unusual. Most of my subjects stiffen and shrink away from the lens. Edith seems to blossom in the spotlight."

"Shall we see how the others respond then?" Olive asked, hoping for the same response towards her older children's portraits.

Olive lifted Edith out of the chair and instructed Morna to take her sister's place. J.H. took individual pictures of each family member, bringing out the best quality of their respective characters. Scott stood for the photographer after his women were immortalized by the infamous J.H. Blessing. Distinguished and elegant, the proud gentleman held his head high for the artist to capture his best appearance. The pan flashed quickly, bringing their day of portraiture to an end.

"I think we got 'em all," said J.H.

"Shall we all go for late lunch?" Scott asked.

"That sounds wonderful, darling. We're all famished," Olive replied.

"I had planned on that," said J.H. "I've made arrangements for all of us at the inn. Just give me a few minutes to clean up shop. Then I won't need to come back to work until tomorrow."

"You all looked so lovely," said Addie. "I'm sure your portraits will be among my husband's best work."

"Thank you, dear. Do you have many of yourself at home?" Olive asked.

"We have a lovely shot of me on our wedding day," Addie said. "J.H. insisted on taking it himself."

The two women quietly bantered in easy conversation, which both found quite pleasant. Their opportunities to talk with other women had been rare for quite some time. Although Olive was far more confident and secure with herself than Addie was, she liked the fragile woman who seemed somewhat lonely and in need of a friend. Mrs. Kenyon decided she would take Addie under her wing. She felt that women should help one another garner as much personal power as they possibly could; the world was dominated by men.

"All right, everyone! I think I'm finished here," announced J.H. "Shall we go?"

"What about our portraits, J.H?" inquired Scott.

"Be patient, Kenyon! Rome wasn't built in a day, you know. It takes time to process the plates and print them. When they are ready, I'll deliver them to you personally in Coldspring. I'm even going to have them framed for you. Besides, it will give Addie and me an excuse to visit you in your neck of the woods," said J.H.

"And will there be an extra charge on the bill for the framing?" Scott joked.

"Aw, c'mon pal. You know I'm giving you a discount for all those girls," he jested.

"I accept most graciously, sir," Scott said with a gentlemanly bow.

"Shall we?" said J.H. as he gestured towards the door.

They left the studio and walked across the street to the Dudley Hotel, an establishment that provided lodging accommodations and refined dining for their customers. They enjoyed a large feast and spoke of the exciting changes occurring throughout the country.

New products, inventions, and political statutes were established daily, bringing massive amounts of information to modern enthusiasts. Survivalist living was becoming outdated, as etiquette, refinement, and education rose in importance. Winfield Scott Kenyon and J.H. Blessing were among the forerunners of the upper middle class, men who were working to further the prominence and wealth of their families by embracing the technological evolution.

As dusk fell, filling the sky with an electric, red sheen, the Kenyon family returned to the station to catch the evening train home. Pleased with the events of the day, Addie and J.H. Blessing walked back to their carriage. An atmosphere of contentment filled their dimly lit buggy as they traversed the dirt roads leading to their farmhouse just beyond edge of town. It was dark by the time they arrived and were greeted by Catherine and the stable hand, Thomas. Exhausted and ready for sleep, they kissed each other goodnight and retired to their respective quarters.

As planned, the Blessings arranged a trip to visit the Kenyon family the following week to deliver the portraits J.H. had personally framed. When they arrived the next Saturday afternoon, the entire Kenyon household treated them like royalty. The young girls clamored around the suede-covered portraits, eager to see their contents revealed. Scott led them into the parlor room where he planned on hanging the family portrait on the main wall. They all gathered around while J.H. held the photo and Addie unwrapped the leather ties.

"Are you ready to see yourselves?" asked J.H., teasing.

"Yes!" the girls squealed.

Addie pulled off the cover, revealing the beautiful family, bathed in a soft light that favored them all.

"It's glorious, Mr. Blessing! Thank you so very much!" exclaimed Olive.

"She's right, J.H.," Scott agreed. "It is indeed excellent!

Once again, I am completely impressed by your skills."

"Why, thank you, it was my pleasure. Shall we hang it here?" asked J.H., holding the portrait up against the wall.

"Just what I had in mind," said Scott.

"What about my picture?" Morna asked the photographer.

"He'll get to that in a minute, sweetheart," said Olive. "Just sit quietly and wait your turn while your father and Mr. Blessing hang this first."

The family portrait created a potent feeling of intimacy in the large Victorian room. Then they unwrapped each individual portrait, amazed at the beauty captured in each photo. Olive and Addie walked through the home, choosing locations to display the art, while Scott and J.H. followed with hammer and nail, appeasing their wives' fancy. When all portraits had been hung, they dined at the long table used only for special occasions. The families' bond grew stronger as they relaxed and revealed more of their personalities to each another. A rare sense of familiarity developed, for their world normally demanded properness before all else.

Even though it was quite a journey to see each other on a regular basis, after their dinner at the Kenyon's, Addie and Olive wrote letters back and forth to share their daily stories and experiences of pregnancy. This was Olive's fourth child, and although Scott desperately wanted a boy, she knew in her heart that she carried another girl. She shared this secret with Addie, who was also under the same pressure to produce a male heir to continue the family name.

As their bellies grew and they were able to manage fewer and fewer tasks, their letters became longer and more descriptive, providing an outlet for the stresses of maternity. Their husbands were not interested in, nor tremendously compassionate about the arduous process they were forced to endure. They lived during a time when it was a woman's duty to bear and raise children and they had no right to seek extraordinary care or concern from anyone, except each other.

Olive's water broke just before dawn on October 17, 1879. She woke with a shooting pain in her body, a pain unlike anything she had experienced during the births of her other children. Worried that the baby was in distress, she screamed and everyone in the house woke and raced to her room.

"Get the doctor. I want my father, now!" Olive yelled, as she stood framed in the doorway of her bedroom.

"What is it, Olive? Is the baby coming?" Scott asked in a panic.

"Yes, but something is wrong. The pain is different. Get my father NOW!" Olive demanded.

Shocked, and terrified by his wife's uncharacteristic demands, Scott dressed and rushed to the buggy. The half-dressed stable boy quickly fastened the carriage and the anxious father-to-be raced to the home of Doctor Oliver Guernsey, his father-in-law.

While they waited for the doctor to arrive, the nervous housekeeper, Victoria, went in to assist Olive. Serving as midwife for Olive's three other children, she felt capable of delivering the fourth baby until she saw the blood seeping between the legs of her mistress and pooling on the bed sheet.

"Ma'am, the bleeding, how long has it been like this?" Victoria asked in a panic.

"Oh, God! I don't know, Victoria! It won't stop! It won't stop!" Olive screamed.

"We need to get the baby out, ma'am. We can't wait for the doctor. I can see the head beginning to crown. I need to you to push the baby out," ordered Victoria.

"I don't think I can. Victoria, help me! You must help me!" Olive begged.

The blood began flow from Olive's womb with greater intensity and Victoria could no longer wait for her to push the baby out. She reached her hands into Olive and wrapped one hand behind the baby's head and the other on the skin beneath the baby's back. Victoria took a deep breath and prayed to God to give her the strength to save the baby. Olive screamed as her blood gushed onto the bed. As Victoria pulled the baby out of the womb, a loud cry was heard from both the mother and child. The little girl was alive!

Victoria cut the umbilical cord and handed the baby to Olive's young handmaiden, Rebecca. When Olive began to lose consciousness, Victoria screamed, "Stay awake! Don't sleep ma'am! You'll never wake up!"

"What happened?" Olive muttered.

"Ma'am, you need to feel the pain. You need to stay awake! I am going to pull the afterbirth out and then we are going to try to stop the bleeding," Victoria told her.

Victoria reached inside Olive's body once more and removed the placenta. Blood oozed out, covering Victoria's hands with the sticky, red substance, which she wiped on her apron. She dropped the remains in a bucket and plunged heavy blankets up against Olive's uterine walls. Pressing firmly caused Olive tremendous pain, but it kept her conscious and aware of what was happening around her.

"I must stop the bleeding or you will die. Do you understand me, ma'am?" said Victoria with tears in her eyes.

"Yes, yes, I understand. I'm not ready to die, Victoria. Where is Scott?"

"He went for your father. He should be back here any minute," Victoria promised. Just as the words left her mouth, she could hear Scott and Dr. Guernsey running up to the front door of the farmhouse. They burst in, flinging the door so hard its bang could be heard throughout. They took the stairs two at a time and ran into Olive's room. The first thing they saw was the blood-soaked bed.

"Get out of the way you stupid woman! What have you done while I was gone?" Scott screamed at Victoria.

"I can't move, Mr. Kenyon. I am trying to clot the blood, sir," Victoria answered without moving.

"What about the baby? You are killing the baby!" Scott screamed.

"Rebecca has the baby in your room, sir. I had to take it out. She would have been stillborn if I hadn't," snapped Victoria, completely forgetting her place as a hired servant.

"She? It's a girl? Another daughter?" Scott asked.

Dr. Guernsey took Victoria's place and removed the blankets to see what damage had been done.

"The delivery has torn her uterus. If I am going to stop the bleeding I am going to have to operate on her right now," the doctor stated without emotion.

"What?" said Scott as he staggered backwards in shock.

"Victoria, grab those clean towels and put the same pressure on her body as you were doing before. Get Rebecca in here to help you change the bedding under Olive. We need everything to be as clean as possible," ordered Dr. Guernsey. "I'm going down to the kitchen."

The doctor ordered Jennie, the cook, to start boiling several pots of water. He placed his surgical instruments into one pot as soon as hot bubbles formed. Waiting the prescribed time, he carefully lifted them out and wrapped them in a hot, steaming towel that had been boiling in a second pot. Praying that the instruments would be sterile enough, he went upstairs and ordered everyone but Victoria from the bedroom.

"This is going to be very bloody. Do you think that you will be able to stomach what you are about to witness, Victoria?"

"Yes, Dr. Guernsey. I think I can. I would endure anything for Mrs. Kenyon."

Satisfied with her response, the doctor retrieved a bottle of chloroform and an atomizer containing carbolic acid from his satchel. He soaked a small cloth with the chloroform and placed it over Olive's nose and mouth to render her unconscious. When the chloroform had taken effect, he sprayed his hands and Olive's abdomen with the carbolic acid to sterilize them both. Then he walked systematically through the interior of the tiny bedroom, using an atomizer to spraying the air with more carbolic acid.

"Victoria," he instructed, "try to hold your breath when I get near you. This spray will sear your lungs if you take in too much of it."

When Dr. Guernsey had finished sterilizing the room, he motioned for Victoria to remove the blood-soiled towels. Drawing a huge breath of air and releasing it fully, he mustered the resolve be necessary to perform the complicated, dangerous surgery.

The doctor looked skyward, used one hand to gesture the sign of the cross and then cut his daughter open from the umbilicus all the way down to her pubic hair. Once that was done, he carefully cut the rectus sheath so that he had access to the abdominal wall muscles. When those were exposed, he used his fingers to separate the peritoneum near the umbilicus and then used his scissors to lengthen the opening. Once the uterus was exposed, he lifted it out in order to examine it for rips. He discovered two places where the uterus had split – through the cervix and the vagina. Deftly, he sutured each of the tears with a single stitch and replaced the uterus back into its original position after making certain there was no damage to Olive's bladder. He closed the original incision with numerous stitches and stood back to survey his work.

"Well, Victoria, I've done all that I can do. Her survival now rests in the hands of the Lord. She will need constant observation for the next few days," he said, fatigue weighing down the words. "You missed your calling, Victoria. You would have made a wonderful nurse. Thank you for keeping the blood sponged so that

I could see to work. It saved me some very valuable time."

Victoria looked away as she blushed in response to the doctor's kind compliment.

Doctor Guernsey gave Victoria instructions for Olive's care and advised her on what to look for in the way of infection. Satisfied that he had done everything he could, he left the bedroom and encountered Scott pacing back and forth in front of the bedroom door.

"Is she going to be all right, Oliver?"

"I don't know, son. She's lost a lot of blood. It depends how strong her body is and whether or not there will be any infection," the doctor answered in a grave tone.

"She is a fighter, sir," said Victoria through the open bedroom door. "She'll pull through. I just know she will."

"Thank you, Victoria," said Scott. "Thank you for everything. Olive and the baby would both have died had it not been for your quick actions. Please forgive my thoughtless comments earlier. I was out of my mind with worry."

"I know, sir. Your love for wife is apparent to everyone you encounter."

"Victoria, clean her up with some more carbolic acid to disinfect the skin," Dr. Guernsey instructed, "and keep gentle pressure on her for an hour or so to make sure the bleeding doesn't start again. I will stay a while, until she regains consciousness. Now let me see the baby. We will need to let the child feed soon, even if Olive doesn't wake. Victoria, you will need to help the baby suckle her breast."

"Are you sure that won't hurt Mrs. Kenyon?" Victoria asked, forgetting her place once again.

"Who is the doctor here, Victoria? You or me?" Dr. Guernsey said icily. "Just follow my instructions, please."

"Sorry, sir," she answered sheepishly, casting her eyes to floor.

They made their way across the hall into Scott's room to find the tiny, freshly washed newborn asleep in Rebecca's arms. Dr. Guernsey inspected the child and found her to be quite healthy.

"What is my granddaughter's name, Scott?" The doctor asked, attempting to draw attention away from the grim circumstances that gripped the household.

"Good question, sir. I was planning on a boy. I was going to name him Bernard after the Irishman, George Bernard Shaw. My family hails from Ireland and I wanted my son to pay tribute to one of Ireland's best," Scott answered, attempting to hold back his tears.

"Well, this little lady is a miracle; that is for certain. She may be destined for great things, Scott," said Dr. Guernsey.

"We shall call her Bernice then, Oliver. Bernice, my little Irish princess," cooed Scott as he held his youngest child for the first time.

"I'm sorry to tell you, Scott, that Olive will never be able to have another child," said Oliver softly.

"That's not important. What matters is her survival and the life of this little angel," Scott said as tears flowed from the corners of his eyes.

They carried Bernice into her mother's room and as Olive slept, they all prayed for the Lord to save her life. The hours passed slowly and Victoria was able to get Bernice to feed from her mother's breasts as the woman lay unconscious. While the tiny infant suckled her first meal, Victoria held both Olive and Bernice in her arms with a loving embrace. The scene was overwhelming for Scott and he left the room and headed downstairs to the bar. Pouring himself a large scotch, he sat in front of the burning fire, lit a cigar, and let his thoughts drift away from the stress and calamity he was facing. As the smoke filled the house with a sugary smell, a calm silence blanketed the Kenyon's home and brought a moment of peace to the chaotic day.

When the baby finished nursing, Olive moaned softly, waking from her depleted state. Victoria handed Bernice to Rebecca and slipped out from between Olive and the pillows. The housekeeper stroked her mistress' hair and held her hand tightly, speaking words of encouragement and inspiration.

"You must wake now, ma'am. Don't you want to see your beautiful daughter?" Victoria whispered.

Olive's eyes opened, blinking to regain the memory of her whereabouts and recognize what was happening.

"Doctor! Dr. Guernsey! She's waking up!" Victoria yelled loud enough to be heard across the hallway.

The doctor rushed in and sat next to Olive, waiting for her to come into full consciousness.

"What happened, Father?" Olive asked, still dazed.

"You nearly lost your life, my dear."

"Where is the baby? Did the baby survive?"

"Yes, she is fine. Victoria had to pull her out to save her."

"Where is she? I knew it was a girl. Where is she?"

Rebecca walked towards the bed and placed Bernice next to her mother.

"Your husband has given her the name Bernice," Dr. Guernsey said.

"Well, hello, my darling," Olive murmured as tears trickled down her face. "Welcome to the world, little Bernice."

"I will go tell Scott that you are awake. He is downstairs. He's in a bit of shock," Dr. Guernsey said as he left his daughter to bond with the baby.

"Where are my girls?" Olive asked Victoria.

"They are all fine, ma'am. We kept them entertained downstairs in the parlor. Jennie played games with them until they fell asleep. We didn't want to bring them upstairs until we knew you were going to be all right."

"She is beautiful. Look at her full head of raven black hair.

Thank you, Victoria, for all you did for me," said Olive gently. "This child's a miracle."

"Are you in terrible pain?"

"Yes, everything hurts quite a bit. What happened exactly?"

"You bled terribly and the baby tore your womb. And when I pulled her out it made things worse, I'm afraid to say," Victoria said, holding back her tears. "Your father performed surgery on you to stop the bleeding. He saved your life."

"You both did," Olive said, clutching Victoria's hand.

Scott walked into the room and smiled at the sight of his wife and child. "I knew you would make it. You are tough as nails, Olive," he said with pride.

With fatherly authority the doctor stated, "Well, she still has a long way to go. It is going to take months for your body to heal, Olive. You must stay in bed until I say otherwise. Do you understand me?"

"I'll make sure she does," Scott answered for her.

"She will be in a lot of pain for some time, so she will need constant care. The stitches will not come out for a while, making it difficult for her to walk," Dr. Guernsey said to them both.

"Thank you, Oliver. Thank you so much," Scott said as he vigorously shook his father-in-law's hand.

"Get some rest, Olive. I will be back tomorrow with your mother. Stay in bed. And Victoria, put some of this salve on her once a day to help the skin heal." The doctor handed Victoria a small jar of yellow paste.

Scott walked the doctor to the front door. He thanked his father-in-law again and, as he turned back towards the house, breathed a sigh of relief acknowledging that death had literally been turned away at their doorstep.

CHAPTER SEVEN

THE FIRST FEW WEEKS OF BERNICE GUERNSEY KENYON'S life were marked by the uncertainty of her mother's survival. Olive was physically unable to nurture her youngest daughter the way she had done for Bernice's three older sisters. Victoria, the housekeeper, spent her days nursing her beloved mistress back to health, which left young Rebecca to care for the newborn. Scott was compelled to step up as a primary caretaker of his new daughter, and subsequently he bonded with Bernice in a way that had not been possible with his other daughters. He spent time every evening after dinner with Bernice nuzzled comfortably in his arms. They would sit in a rocking chair, absorbing the warmth of the parlor fireplace, until Rebecca came to fetch Bernice for bed.

By the time Olive had recuperated enough for her to leave the confines of her bedroom, Bernice was already profoundly devoted to her father. Olive longed to regain the feeling of closeness and intimacy with her family, yet her daughters had apparently realized that life existed without their mother. Saddened by the sudden diminishment of those bonds, Olive wrote to her new friend, Addie Blessing, due to deliver her first child in the next few days. Olive's letter was limited on the details of her trauma so as not to frighten the young mother-to-be. Her letter expressed a desire to continue their correspondence and share their intimate thoughts with one another.

Addie read Olive's letter immediately upon receipt. She was limited to waddling around the second story of her house alone, terrified at the thought of giving birth. She thanked God for her friend, Olive, who somehow understood exactly what to say to save her from her silly insecurities. As Addie sat down at the small secretary desk in the hallway to begin a reply to Olive's poignant note, a sharp pain shot through her belly, causing her to drop her fountain pen on the floor. A warm liquid was seeping through her cotton dress and leaking onto the satin-covered chair. Panic set in and she screamed for help. "Catherine! Catherine! Come quickly! I think the baby is coming! Catherine!"

The housekeeper came running. She slipped her arm underneath Addie's shoulder and helped her to walk to her room and over to the bed. She began undressing Addie.

"What are you doing?" Addie asked abruptly.

"Ma'am, have you forgotten that I have delivered quite a few children while in the service of others? We need to get you out of your soiled dress and into something lightweight so that you won't overheat," said Catherine using a particularly gentle voice.

"I'm sorry, Catherine! I'm just so nervous about delivering this baby! Do you think we should send for Mr. Blessing?"

"With all due respect to the master, I believe he is best left at work today, ma'am. We may have a surprise for him when he walks in the door this evening, if all goes well." Catherine removed Addie's boots and stockings.

"Oh, I hope the baby comes quickly," whimpered Addie, writhing in response to the latest contraction.

"Take slow, deep, breaths when the pain comes, ma'am. It will help you relax. Don't focus on the pain, either," Catherine advised.

Addie practiced slow breathing as Catherine removed her dress, pulling it over her head. She replaced it with one of J.H.'s summer sleeping gowns. As Addie smelled her husband's familiar scent, her body relaxed and her fear subsided. Catherine pulled Addie's long, silky hair away from her face, wrapping it in a soft cotton handkerchief.

"I'm just going to get a pan of water and some blankets. Keep breathing gently and I will be right back. How does that sound?" Catherine asked.

"That sounds fine," Addie answered haltingly. Her contractions had become even more intense.

Catherine returned quickly, bringing with her the supplies she needed to deliver a baby. She placed pillows behind Addie's back, under her hips and beneath her knees to keep her mistress's body in place during delivery. She hummed a soothing melody to create a peaceful atmosphere as she closed the curtains to keep out the morning light.

"How are you doing, ma'am?" Catherine asked softly.

"The pain is getting worse. It lasts longer, too," Addie yelped.

"That's a good thing, ma'am. It means we are getting closer to the delivery of your baby. It's going to slide right out. I can just tell." Catherine placed a few blankets beneath Addie's legs.

Addie's labor continued another two and a half hours. Tears were pouring down Addie's face as she struggled to cope with the pain of childbirth. Catherine massaged her mistress with oil and soothed her with by singing and humming. When the baby's head crowned, Addie shrieked and clenched her fists, tightening every muscle in a futile effort to resist the pain.

"Let yourself feel the pain. Don't avoid it," Catherine cajoled. "When you tighten your muscles, the baby stops moving down. Just breathe and, trust me, ma'am. It will be over very soon."

"I don't think I can," Addie yelled.

"Of course you can, ma'am. Just trust in yourself. It will be easier if you just endure the suffering. Let the pain guide the process. Your body knows what to do. Just breathe."

Addie let her head fall back against the mountain of pillows and attempted to distance herself from the pain that wracked her body. Thoughts of the wind blowing gently in the trees on a balmy summer's night filled her mind as her baby turned towards her spine and began its inevitable descent through her cervix. Catherine received the baby in one hand as it emerged from the vaginal canal. She took her knife and severed the umbilical cord. Everything was done with calm and ease. Then Catherine cleared the baby's eyes, nose, and mouth with a soft, damp cloth.

"Addie, you have a son," Catherine said, handing the baby to his mother.

"Oh thank you, Lord! Thank you!" Addie cried as she nestled her child in her arms.

"We are almost through here, ma'am. All that is left now is the delivery of what is called the afterbirth. That should happen within the next half hour or so. It won't hurt much, if at all, ma'am.

Addie held her baby in her arms as she awaited the expulsion of the afterbirth. Fifteen minutes later Addie's ordeal was over and Catherine removed the blankets that were now heavily soiled. She continued to hum as she moistened a small towel she used to clean the blood from Addie's legs. When she finished, she placed a clean blanket underneath her mistress and gently cleaned the baby, still wrapped in his mother's arms.

"Let's just get him cleaned up a bit more and we'll give him a fresh blanket as well. How does that sound?" Catherine said with a smile.

"Thank you, Catherine," Addie replied.

"I told you this one was going to slip right out. What are you going to name him?"

"Mr. Blessing wants to call him John," said Addie.

"That's a fine name."

"Yes, I think so, too. I think it will be John Lynn Blessing. How does that sound?"

"It's very grand. A wonderful choice, ma'am." Catherine

answered, as she wrapped the baby in a fresh blanket and returned him to his mother.

"Your father will be home soon, Johnny. He will be so happy to meet you," Addie whispered to her baby.

Addie and John nuzzled in the bed as Catherine opened the curtains slightly. She gathered the soiled linens and instruments, then spent a moment watching mother and son lie peacefully together, both fatigued by the birth experience. The afternoon light faded and Catherine opened the curtains completely to reveal a landscape freshly dusted with snow.

At five p.m. J.H. guided his horse and sled into the carriage house of the Blessing home. Arthur, the stable hand, was waiting to take the reins from J.H.'s gloved hand. "Good evening, sir," Arthur greeted his master with a mysterious suspicious smile.

"And to you, Arthur. You seem to be in exceptionally good spirits today," J.H. replied with curiosity.

"How was the travel through the snow today? Not too troublesome, I hope, sir."

"No, but we're going to need a new gelding for next winter. Jake here has been struggling a bit. I think his snow days are coming to an end."

"Yes, sir," Arthur answered, taking Jake into the stable after freeing him from his heavy harness.

J.H. opened the front door to find Catherine waiting there to take his coat and hat. Puzzled by her glow, J.H. suddenly realized what must have happened. "The baby has come!"

"Yes, sir," Catherine said with a tremendous smile.

"It's a boy, isn't it?" J.H. grinned.

"Yes, sir," Catherine answered.

"Yahoo! They're upstairs?"

"Yes, sir. In Mrs. Blessing's bed, sir."

J.H. ran up the stairs two steps at a time. He reached the bedroom door and stopped. He stood there, frozen, entranced by the sight of his wife and child sleeping. For a moment, he forgot his male pride and felt only humility and gratitude. From beneath the shrewd businessman's facade emerged the soul of the artist whose heart was filled with awe at the splendor of life's most sublime moment. He stood, tears rolling down his cheek, his hands grasping his heart. Emotions, which had been banished so long ago, came flooding back. He looked away, shook his head, and wiped the evidence of vulnerability from his face. He walked into the room and sat on the edge of the bed. His quiet presence woke Addie from her slumber.

"Welcome home," she whispered as she peered up at her husband.

"What have you been up to while I was away today, hmmm?" J.H. smiled coyly.

"I guess the baby wanted to surprise you," Addie replied.

"Both of you did! How are you feeling?" asked J.H. softly.

"I'm, well… a little tired. Catherine was amazing. It all happened so quickly after waiting for several hours. It was over almost before I knew what happened. Then our little John was in my arms," she smiled.

"Good. Then I'm glad I wasn't here. Birth is a woman's realm. So, we like the name John?"

"Yes, John Lynn Blessing. It sounds strong, don't you think?" Addie she said, reaching for her husband's hand.

"I do," he nodded.

"Would you like to hold him?"

"No, no! He's fine where he is. I would like to take some photographs. It may wake him, but he's a Blessing. He'll get used to the spotlight."

"That sounds lovely, dear," she whispered as her eyes closed.

J.H. watched her drift back to sleep, then he made his way downstairs. He found the servants waiting patiently, ready to celebrate the arrival of the newest member of the family. They had poured the master a whiskey and prepared his finest cigar, placing both upon a silver tray in the dining room. The smell of roast beef wafted through the house as J.H. sat, king-like, at the head of the dining table.

Catherine brought him his supper. He gently took her hand and looked up at her. "Thank you, Catherine. I know you made things easier for Mrs. Blessing," J.H. stated with utmost gratitude.

"My pleasure, sir," Catherine bowed. "Enjoy your meal, sir."

J.H. ate slowly, savoring each mouthful. He watched as snowflakes fell outside the dining room window. This was the most beautiful day he could remember and he was looking forward to capturing the memories with his camera. When he finished eating, J.H. went back upstairs to photograph his family. The maid followed, holding candelabra in her hand. Without waking Addie or John, she placed it on the nightstand. J.H. attached the camera to its tripod in preparation of photographing the peaceful tranquility of the moment. The flash of light woke Addie.

"What's going on?" she said in a sleepy voice.

"I just had to memorialize this event, Addie, dear." J.H. whispered back.

Baby John woke, too. He simply opened his eyes and presented himself to the camera. He didn't make a peep. When his father took another photo of him, the baby responded without fear, merely blinking at the flash, then continuing to pose.

"Why isn't he crying?" J.H. asked his wife, concerned. "Is something wrong with him? Don't most babies cry constantly?"

"He cried earlier, then I fed him and he stopped," Addie said defensively. "Nothing seems to bother him. He's a peaceful child."

"Well, I guess he gets that from your side of the family," J.H. joked.

John continued to pose for photos until his tiny eyes could no longer stay open and he fell back into a quiet sleep. Addie was soon to follow, leaving J.H. and Catherine to tuck them in.

The new father took the plates to his downstairs darkroom and worked into the night. He wanted to have a portrait ready for Addie by morning. Just as he was settling into bed, the newborn began to wail. He jumped to his feet and ran across the hall to find Addie nursing baby John.

"Are you two all right?"

"Yes, darling, we're fine. Go back to sleep," Addie answered.

J.H. returned to his bed, collapsing into a deep sleep. Catherine tended to Addie and the new baby early in the morning, changing both their sleepwear and the bedding. Addie had moved to a large chair near the window, cradling her new baby.

"Do you think you are strong enough to make it downstairs, ma'am, or shall I bring your meal to the bedroom?" Catherine asked.

"I think we are ready to go downstairs. Will you carry him?" Addie asked.

"Of course, ma'am."

Addie slowly descended the stairs to the dining room. She gasped with delight at the large photograph of baby John and herself, sleeping by candlelight. That portrait was to become Addie's most cherished possession, reminding her always of the miraculous gift of life the Lord had bestowed upon her. J.H. was a difficult man, but his ability to please her when she least expected it made the difficulties seem insignificant.

When J.H. finally came downstairs, ready for a long day of work, he was greeted with adulation and gratitude. "The portrait of Johnny and me is magnificent, darling! Thank you! You are truly a genius! I would bestow a kiss of gratitude on you, but, alas my prince, I am too tired to stand after yesterday's ordeal."

"Good, I'm glad you like it. I'm sorry, dear, but people will be waiting for me outside the studio if I don't leave now, so you'll have to manage without me today. And, let me come to you for that gratuitous kiss, my darling." J.H. bent down and kissed Addie goodbye.

"We'll be here waiting for you. Be safe in the snow," Addie whispered in his ear.

Mother and son watched from the window as the sled disappeared into the distance. Catherine brought a blanket, wrapped John tightly, and Addie and her baby sat in front of the fire, warming themselves.

"Catherine, would you take him for a bit. I would like to write to my dear friend, Olive, and tell her of our news," Addie requested.

Catherine took Addie's place in the warm chair, enjoying the moment with the tiny infant. Addie walked cautiously over to the drawing room across the hall and sat at the large wooden desk. She wrote:

~22~December~1879

Dearest Olive,

Little John has arrived! He is healthy and well. He is just beautiful and behaves so well! I can't wait for you to see him.

I am so grateful that the birth is over. I had no idea how painful it was going to be, however Catherine's wonderful guidance made it easier, indeed. We can compare our birthing experiences when we next see one another.

How are you and Bernice doing? Are you able to care for her by yourself yet?

I was so sorry to hear that this would be your last child. Is Scott very upset that he will not have a son? Has it caused any troubles for you in your marriage? I certainly hope not.

I miss you terribly and as soon as we can, we must plan a visit. Maybe you will want to update your family portraits for the parlor display? It would be an excellent spring if we could see one another in person at that time. Don't you agree? Please write soon and tell me how your family is getting along.

Have a Merry Christmas & Happy New Year!!
Best Regards,
Addie

Olive was thrilled to receive the letter and shared her friend's joy of motherhood. Olive's body was healing faster than anyone expected, yet her sadness refused to relinquish its hold. The secrets she held in her heart could not be shared with her household, but she took a chance and decided to reveal her dark thoughts with Addie. As she sat down to write the letter, Olive prayed to God that her young friend would not abandon her or judge her for expressing the sorrows and fears with which she was consumed.

~2~January~1890
Darling Addie,

Thank you so much for your wonderful letter, and congratulations on your new arrival. I have enclosed a blanket knitted for you to keep you and Johnny warm on these cold winter nights.

I have found myself desperate to confide in someone, and your letters are my only remedy for the sadness that tortures me. I know this will sound ghastly, so forgive me in advance if I offend you in any way.

My girls are wonderful. Bernice is the most independent child I have ever encountered, and Edith is absolutely in love with her. Morna and Dora are inseparable. They go everywhere together and spend their days playing quietly with their dolls.

For all intents and purposes, my life is perfect and I have nothing to complain about, yet my dreams have turned to nightmares and I am unable to stop crying. Every time I go to sleep, I dream that a man is chasing me around the house, attempting to kill me. I wake up trying to scream but no sounds will come out and I am always holding my throat. It has gotten so bad that I find it very difficult to fall asleep these days. I fear that I am losing my mind. What do you think?

I am so sorry to burden you with this nonsense, but I just don't know what to do. Hopefully, the spring will bring new joy to my life. I have never felt this kind of sadness before and nothing except your words have made me smile in months.

Thank you for your friendship. It means the world to me.

Yours Truly,

Olive

Revealing her secret on the cotton paper seemed to ease Olive's suffering, and as she stamped and sealed the letter with wax, she sighed. She feared her revelations would injure her cherished friendship with Addie. Scott carried the letter and gift into town the next day and dropped them at the postal station. Although he had not been aware of his wife's suffering, something seemed dysfunctional, something was wrong, but he could not figure out what. He reviewed every aspect of his accounting and business transactions to confirm that his holdings were secure and that the imbalance did not stem from work-related issues.

The only change of late had been the birth of his daughter Bernice, so he decided it must be the baby who was in need. He considered her capacity to comprehend that she almost died at birth and he often wondered whether the near-death experience had an effect on her. Whenever he went home, he made sure to go directly to Bernice before checking on any of the other family members, and to hold her in his arms for most of the evening. The other children were quite jealous of their father's affection for Bernice, yet none of the girls was brave enough to question his favoritism of her. Edith found comfort in both her mother's and Victoria's presence, while Morna and Dora clung to each another for affection. All in all, the household was in dire straits emotionally since Bernice's birth.

Scott and Bernice were inseparable, but Olive's attempts at bonding with the infant were rejected. Olive was forced to abandon breastfeeding because Bernice grew more and more agitated as she lay in Olive's arms. A wet nurse had to be employed. Scott, enthralled with his connection to his child, spent less time in town and more days at home with Bernice. While Olive took pleasure in her husband's newfound joy for fatherhood, the heartache she experienced became more potent with every moment shared between Scott and tiny Bernice. The other children suffered the agony of their mother's depression, seeking comfort from the maids and from each other. As Olive's nightmares continued their emotional stress, Olive's body became frail, which compelled her to allow Bernice to sleep in Victoria's room.

On the first evening Olive spent alone in her room, the dreams of terror mysteriously ceased. For the first time since the baby was born, Olive was free to rest peacefully. She did not wake until late the next morning, and although her body was not strong, her spirit had revived and her smile returned. When she made her way downstairs to attend to her family, she greeted them all with a joy and enthusiasm she had not felt for months. Relieved to have his wife back, Scott handed Bernice to Victoria and embraced Olive.

"You seem much better this morning, Mrs. Kenyon," Scott said as he kissed her cheek.

"Yes, I feel wonderful," replied Olive.

"I have a surprise for you," Scott whispered.

"What is it darling?" she asked with excitement.

"A letter from Mrs. Addie Blessing," he announced with exuberance.

"Wonderful, I can't wait to read it," she said, a bit worried about the response she was would receive from Addie.

"It's in my case. Shall I get it for you now?"

"That would be fine. I shall read it and get a cup of hot cocoa. Who else would like some cocoa?" she asked her children.

The girls squealed with delight at the prospect of warm, sugary chocolate in their bellies and they encircled Olive, hugging her in thanks. She embraced them with a familiar joy that warmed her heart. The dark cloud that had been lingering over the Kenyon farmhouse dissipated like fog in the morning sun.

Olive sat down to read the letter from Addie and the steam from her drink rose slowly. The cup warmed the hand she wrapped around the ceramic mug. Olive sighed with relief when she read the salutation assuring her of the true friendship she shared with Mrs. Blessing.

11~January~1880

My dearest friend Olive,

Please know that you are free to share any and all feelings you have, no matter how sinful or frightened you may judge yourself as being. Remember, we are like sisters. Nothing can break our bond. I am sorry for your troubles, but keep in mind the Lord only gives us as much as we can handle, and you, my dear, can withstand anything! We will talk of these things when we next see one another in person.

Everything on the farm is going well. J.H. has been at home quite a bit this winter since the weather has been so harsh, but mostly he spends his time in his study and I snuggle with the baby. More and more I have been calling him Lynn. He just doesn't seem like a John or a Johnny to me. J.H. doesn't seem to care either way. It's as if he is interested only that his son will carry out his legacy. The bond between father and son is not really a priority to him. However, I'm sure that will change as the boy gets older.

At one time, I was deeply in love with J.H. I still am, yet somehow the love I now feel for Lynn overshadows what I feel for my husband. I am no longer a prisoner. Does that make sense? I feel free for the first time in my life, yet I have more responsibility than ever. It's an interesting journey to be a mother. That is for certain.

I do hope to see you this spring, Olive. I miss you so much and feel closer to you than ever. Please send my love to your family and write as often as you can.

Your friend,
Addie

The tranquility of that morning marked a new era in Olive's life. Her brush with death had transformed her. Although it left her body quite fragile, her spirit was stronger. The remaining winter months were some of the very best that the Kenyon family would ever experience. They spent the evenings laughing with the children and singing hymns and popular songs as the late night fire crackled, its warmth permeating the crisp air of the farmhouse.

Olive's passion for life had returned, inspiring her to pursue her role in the community as a schoolteacher. As her body grew stronger, so did her determination to educate the youth of the nation and inspire them to live far beyond their expectations. She decided to apply as a music teacher at the Randolph Central School for the upcoming fall semester. When she announced this to Scott, he was surprised, but supported her efforts to make herself of service to the community.

"Then do it you shall!" Scott pronounced with one forefinger pointed into the air at her declaration to return to work.

"Thank you, Professor Kenyon!" Olive joked. "Seriously, though, we have plenty of help here for Bernice and Edith. And Morna and Dora are going to school this coming fall."

"Excellent! And I can take Bernice with me into town now

and then!" he laughed as he jounced Bernice on his knee, much to the infant's delight.

"Darling, be careful! She's just a baby!"

"Aaah, she won't break! Besides, I want to make sure she's a tough cookie so I'm starting out early," Scott said, laughing.

Olive never quite understood the connection between Bernice and Scott. Perhaps her illness and nightmares had pushed Bernice away, straight into her father's arms. A bond between the two was forged the night of Bernice's birth and Olive knew there was no undoing it. As the child's mother, this was difficult for Olive to accept, yet her first thought was for her daughter's happiness. She was rewarded for her selflessness every time she heard the laughter Bernice shared with her father.

The spring rains of 1880 flooded the lush landscape bringing forth bountiful foliage and new life everywhere. Upstate New York was finally feeling the effects of the cultural explosion as the city of Buffalo became a hub of modernization. The culture was a brilliant combination of the wild, freedom-loving pioneer spirit mixed with the inescapable sophisticated lifestyle sweeping the land through the advancement of technology. Women in the western world had begun to fight not just for their husbands' freedom from oppressive European tyranny, but also for their own personal rights. Specifically, they petitioned and lobbied for the right to experience a life outside of the home.

When Olive regained her health, she convinced Scott to take them all to see the Blessings. The trip would allow them to update their family portraits and rekindle the friendship they had developed with J.H. and Addie. Scott agreed enthusiastically, for he had not seen J.H. in quite some time, and looked forward to a long and much overdue evening of drinking and smoking. The Kenyons arranged to meet their friends the first week in May, when the flowers bloomed and the humidity of summer was still at bay.

The screech of the metal brakes echoed through the station as the train came to a halt. Scott held Bernice in his arms, instilling in her a lifelong love for train travel. The tiny infant was alert and happy as she lay safely cradled in her father's arms. Olive held Edith while the child slept, and Victoria patiently sat between Morna and Dora, who were prone to dizzy spells brought on by motion sickness.

The Kenyon family was greeted with warm cheers and exuberant embraces interlaced with tears and heart-felt giggles. Olive and Addie walked arm-in-arm, carrying children and baggage across the brick streets as the sun reflected luminescent light from the store windows. When they arrived at the Blessing studio, Olive and Scott noticed newly painted portraits of esteemed clients, evidence of the Blessing's prominence in the community.

"Your studio looks marvelous J.H!" Scott remarked.

"Thank you. I felt it was time to step my game up a notch. Got a family now. Gotta make myself respectable," J.H. said with a grin.

"We would like to have an extra portrait of your family to hang on our wall. If you don't mind," Addie asked Olive and Scott.

"It would be an honor," said Olive.

"C'mon over here ladies, see what I have set up for you this time," J.H. instructed.

The Kenyons sat on plush satin couches covered in fox furs and pillows, a bit awed by the luxurious textures. Victoria straightened the girls' dresses and fixed their hair before removing herself from the setting, while Olive made herself comfortable on the lavish pillows.

"Let's have one of just the ladies, eh?" J.H. said with a wink.

Scott nodded in agreement, with pride for his family but a hint of sadness for the absent heir to his namesake. Quietly, the photographer began taking the photographs that would become magnificent portraits for the Kenyon family parlor. When all the portraits were finished, the Blessings and the Kenyons walked through town, drawing attention to themselves by their fancy dress and expensive luggage. The Kenyons opted to spend the night at the Dudley Hotel in order to avoid traveling twice in one day with an infant and their other young children. J.H. had reserved a large table for dinner at the hotel restaurant.

While Addie and Olive spoke of childbirth and caring for their children, J.H. and Scott secluded themselves at the far end of the table to discuss the more worldly matters of politics and business.

"I can't believe how many immigrants they are letting into this country. We're going to be the only homegrown men left if they keep things up at this rate," J.H. commented quietly to Scott.

"The Asians are coming in by the thousands, eh?"

"The Asians, the Irish, and anyone else who can get on a boat and survive the journey," remarked J.H.

"I hear we have a treaty with China, keeping their numbers down, but not too low so that we don't lose the cheap labor."

"Well, Scott, it seems to me this world is going to hell in a hand basket, even though we have killed off most of the wild native types."

"Yes, well, I'm not sure how I feel about that," said Scott. "Not that I agree with their savagery or strange ways. But killing them all, it just doesn't sit right with me somehow."

"Well, you always have been a little soft, old man. That's why the lord blessed you with so many women," J.H. smirked.

"Yeah, yeah, yeah. By the way, where's your boy?"

"He's at home with the help. Thought it best to leave him be for the evening. Getting to work on the second one though; need to keep the family growing eh?" J.H. laughed as he elbowed his friend.

"Our wives are thick as thieves over at the other end of the table, J.H. We did that," Scott remarked.

"Hah, well let's drink to our cunning!" J.H. bellowed as he lifted his glass.

The men toasted each other and drank, and then stumbled out of the restaurant to have a private smoke. Olive and Addie looked at one another, both equally embarrassed about their husband's public drunkenness, yet somehow accustomed to the men's abrasive charms. The women continued their conversation.

"So I've decided to return to teaching," Olive told Addie.

"Really! How exciting! Won't you miss the children?" Addie asked.

"Well, I am going to take Morna and Dora with me, and Edith is quite content to be with Victoria and her dolls. And Bernice is permanently attached to her father's arm anyway."

"Won't you miss them though?" Addie persisted.

"Of course. But I just need to do this. I don't exactly know why. I just have to do it," Olive said.

"Well, I think it will be wonderful. It is too bad we don't live closer to each other, Olive. I would love to spend more time with you. We always have such lovely conversations."

"That is such a sweet thing to say, Addie. Thank you. I feel the same way as you. Maybe one day I will be able to talk Scott into moving out here near Salamanca. If I catch him on the right day, or if I figure out a way for it to make him more money, he'll do it in a snap," said Olive.

"We'll have to work on that then," Addie laughed as she hugged Olive.

The families celebrated long into the evening and then bid each other good night. They decided to meet again the next day for a late lunch, prior to the Kenyons' departure. Addie promised to bring her infant with her so that Olive could meet Lynn in person. J.H. and Scott, somewhat sober, shook hands firmly and returned their attention to their wives and children.

Lunch on the following day flew by as Olive and Scott took turns holding Lynn, while J.H. beamed with pride as his heir basked in the attention and affection of the Kenyons. J.H. promised Scott he would deliver the portraits in person as soon as he had time to steal away from his busy schedule.

When they finished their meal, the Blessings walked the Kenyons to the train station, wishing them all the best tidings and speedy return to their quiet home in Coldspring. Olive blew kisses to Addie as the train pulled away on the metal tracks. Addie waved Lynn's tiny hand as if he, too, were bidding dear friends farewell.

Chapter Eight

The train's engine roared as it left the Salamanca Station carrying the Kenyon family swiftly back to Randolph. Life was moving along faster and faster in the northeastern farm state of New York. The former pristine territory once populated only by those accustomed to living off the land, was becoming saturated with modern miracles. Rumors flew that Thomas Edison would be moving to New York City. His inventions were creating a shift in consciousness, rattling the beliefs and lifestyle of the masses. Technological transformations were entrancing the farming communities with new gadgets that sometimes exceeded their capacity to understand and accept.

The Kenyon family was a dynamic force within the social structure of the town of Randolph. Their ability to adapt was a key factor in raising their status from simply "well bred" to "intellectual gentry." Although Morna and Dora certainly were not beauties, they excelled in their school studies. Even though they were the youngest in their school classes, they proved that women were capable of tremendous intellect and value to the community beyond housewifery and motherhood. Olive continued to teach and explore new musical concepts, while Scott made his mark acquiring real estate and honing his legal expertise by attending prominent trials held throughout the state of New York. Their household thrived on the family's desire for knowledge and mastery of their world.

When Bernice was six years old, Scott decided to take her to court to watch a trial with him. He had concluded that Bernice's mind was ripe for development and he wanted to acclimate her early to professional society. He was keen on encouraging his daughter to develop her cunning and wit. Olive disagreed completely and found it highly inappropriate that a young girl be exposed to the adult world. Both Scott and Bernice dismissed Olive's opinion.

"Bernice is plenty old enough to make her own decisions, Olive," Scott scoffed.

"Do you want to go with your father to court?" Olive asked Bernice.

"Yes, Mama," Bernice said with a soft tone and firm intent.

"Why do you want to go to the trial?" Olive asked.

"To see what justice is all about," answered Bernice.

"What do you think justice is, Bernice?" Olive asked.

"I think it's when you don't behave well, you get punished for it."

"Well darling, I don't see what you need to go to court for. You are obviously brilliant and already know all about justice," Olive stated.

"Yes, but it's time for me to learn more. If I just do the same things over and over, I'll never learn anything new," Bernice stated matter-of-factly.

"There's my girl!" Scott pronounced, ignoring his other three daughters sitting at the dining table next to him.

Bernice finished her meal in silence. She was aware of her sisters' pain whenever her father showered her with special treatment. She generally attempted to divert attention away from herself by lowering her head and removing herself from the conversation. The tiny girl saw her mother sigh with relief at her sensitive response, which served to bond Olive and Bernice in their respective roles in the household. While Bernice was to be Papa's girl, it was very much her responsibility to soften the effects of that privilege on the others in the home.

Scott and Bernice embarked on their grand adventure early

in the spring of 1886 by taking the train to Buffalo. They crossed magnificent landscapes of lush, green forests and even greener pastures that stretched as far as the eye could see. Bernice watched silently as the vast space liberated her imagination and inspired her to focus on a larger scale of existence. As the train pulled into the bustling Buffalo Station, Scott lifted Bernice into his arms and disembarked. Scott found a porter to gather his luggage and walked briskly through the crowds towards the center of town, to the hotel room he had reserved via telegram.

They spent the evening over a quiet meal, rarely speaking for they had no need of meaningless chatter. They were much alike in that both relished the absence of noise. When morning came, Bernice prepared for her day with her father. She put on her dress all by herself and combed her hair to the best of her ability. Scott woke to find his daughter ready to depart, which caused him to laugh. He was enjoying the enthusiasm his daughter brought to the adventure. He made ready his appearance and together they walked through town until they found a bakery where they bought pastries. Continuing their walk to the courthouse, they munched their sweet breakfast, broad smiles on their faces and sugar crumbs covering their lips. As they arrived at the courthouse steps, Scott wiped Bernice's mouth and fingers with his handkerchief, then did the same for himself.

"Now, darling, remember what I told you. Not one word, no matter what happens, all right? It's very important that no one disturbs the courtroom after the judge takes the bench."

"Yes, Papa," Bernice answered.

"And if you have to use the water closet to relieve yourself, what do you do?"

"I pull on your sleeve three times," Bernice responded.

"That's my girl. Are you ready to see what justice is all about?"

"Yes, Papa," Bernice said, smiling.

"Good, let's go then."

Scott held Bernice's hand and together they walked through the large entrance and past the crowds of people waiting for the courtroom door to open. Scott made his way to the front to greet the bailiff, whom he had befriended on his many trips to the Buffalo courthouse.

"Good to see you, Thomas," Scott said boldly reaching out his hand to the large, bearded, uniformed man.

"Scott Kenyon! Good to see you as well. And who is this?" Thomas asked.

"This is my youngest, Bernice. Say hello to Thomas," Scott instructed Bernice.

"Nice to meet you, sir," Bernice replied in a small but potent voice.

"Nice to meet you, too, little lady. Is your mama meeting you here to take you shopping for the day?"

"No, she's with me today, Thomas," Scott answered for his daughter.

"Really? You're taking her in there? You know it's a murder trial, right?"

"Yes, I know. She's young, but I prefer not to shelter her from the world. Trust me, Thomas, she will be fine," Scott assured him.

"Well, I'll see if I can find you some seats, maybe off on the side, eh?" Thomas suggested.

"That would be very kind, but if it's at all possible, we would love to have something dead center, so we can get the entire view," Scott said, shaking Thomas' hand and passing him a silver dollar.

"Not a problem, I'll see what I can get for you folks," Thomas answered, forgetting the young girl as he began planning where to spend his unexpected pocket money.

Scott and Bernice were seated in clear view of the judge and the witness stand, enabling little Bernice to sit on her father's lap and watch the faces of those who were confronting justice. As the trial began and the attorneys accused, defended, and vindicated their statements, Scott watched the speakers as well as his daughter's reaction. He was amazed that she did not tire, cringe, or become disinterested in the endless diatribe that took place before her. His instinct about his daughter once again proved to be the most accurate method of making good decisions.

The defendant was accused of murdering a bystander after a failed bank robbery turned into an exchange of gunfire between deputies and three bandits. Two of the defendant's accomplices were killed, and the accused maintained it was his associates who had shot and killed an elderly gentleman innocently waiting in line at the bank.

The trial wore on, breaking only for the luncheon hour. By mid-afternoon, the prosecution and defense wrapped up the trial with their equally eloquent and convincing summations for the jury. When the jury retired to make their decision, Scott carried Bernice outside for some fresh air. They shared a snack and smiled at one another, inspiring the young girl to tell her father what she thought about the situation. "Daddy, I think the man was telling the truth," Bernice said softly.

"Which man?"

"The man who was crying. The one who everyone is mad at."

"Why do you say that?"

"Because I can just tell," Bernice said.

"Well that's not a good enough reason for justice."

"Why not?"

"Because there is something called evidence, and without evidence, there is no justice," Scott explained.

"What is ev-dence?" Bernice asked, attempting to repeat her father's word.

"Hmmm. That's a tough one to explain. Let me think. Ah, yes. Do you remember when we found honey all over the rug in the front room?"

"Yes," Bernice replied.

"Well, we found the evidence all over Edith's face and hands, remember?"

"Because Edith had honey on her face and hands, you knew it was her who spilled the honey?"

"Yes, the honey on her face was the evidence that convinced us that Edith was the guilty party," Scott concluded.

"Oh," Bernice answered, unsure of the new concept.

"Come, let's go back inside."

They watched the jury return, the foreman stand to declare the defendant guilty as charged, and set the matter before the judge for sentencing. The prisoner was ordered to stand before the judge. Realizing that the imminent death sentence was more than a six-year-old might be able to handle, Scott rose quietly from his seat and led Bernice out of the courtroom. The judge paused long enough for the little girl to leave the room, thankful for Scott's discretion.

It was early evening and little Bernice was exhausted from her long day. Her father carried the sleeping girl back to her hotel room and tucked her into bed. He had a meal brought to his room and enjoyed a strong scotch and a cigar on the balcony after he dined. His thoughts drifted back to the conversation he'd had with his daughter where she insisted on the defendant's innocence, yet the twelve educated men of the county were convinced of his guilt and sent him to his death. Scott scratched his head and pondered who was more accurate in their assessment of the situation. He realized no one could know the truth except the bandit and his Creator, yet he tended to side more heavily of the opinion of his six-year-old daughter.

When the train rolled slowly out of the Buffalo station back towards their home in Randolph, Bernice nuzzled her father's neck as he held her in his arms. She said she enjoyed the experience and thanked him.

Scott pondered how the innocence of America would soon be lost to those who had the power to define the laws. From that day on, the main topic of conversation between Bernice and her father revolved around the law. Regardless of the context of the situation, Scott had an ability to put a legal spin on the discussion, presenting the conclusion as a concept of justice. These discussions heavily influenced Bernice's development as a young girl, emphasizing her differences with her sisters and friends. While Bernice was able to excel at chores and music lessons, her heart was not satisfied with feminine recreations. She longed to play in the creeks with the boys from the farm next door, chasing after frogs and grasshoppers until the sun went down. Olive, however, would allow no such impropriety from her daughter, regardless of her husband's inclination to turn his youngest daughter into his only son.

Discouraged by her limited freedoms, Bernice spent every moment she could with her father when he was home. Scott was often gone in those days, dealing with his real estate ventures or attending trials. While he enjoyed his daughter's company and wished to further her education, he succumbed to his wife's resistance to bringing Bernice on every trip. Olive insisted that Bernice attend school at an early age, along with Edith and her two older sisters, which provided her with the opportunity to experience the world through books. Her mother's persistence paid off. By the time she was nine years old, Bernice was an avid reader who spent her days in the school library searching for information on the legal system. Her profound intelligence isolated her from the other children, yet they gravitated to her for leadership and guidance.

One afternoon in the library, Bernice met a young boy

struggling to understand the meaning of a certain word. He silently mouthed the letters, attempting to break down the syllables into manageable sounds, yet his efforts were thwarted. Bernice sat down next to him and introduced herself.

"Hi, I'm Bernice Kenyon. Nice to meet you," she said extending her tiny hand.

"Yes, you are Mrs. Kenyon's daughter. I sit three pews behind you on the right. My name is Orla," the boy said quietly.

"Orla? Oh, yes, Orla Black, right?" Bernice asked.

"Yes," Orla replied.

"I remember from roll call."

"Uh, huh."

"Are you having trouble with a word?" Bernice asked.

"Yeah, sort of," Orla responded, embarrassed that she had noticed his struggle.

"What word is it?"

"This one here," Orla pointed.

"Evidentiary. Yeah, that's a tough one, all right," Bernice stated in a tone she had adopted from her father.

"Evidentiary," Orla repeated. "What does it mean?"

"It means that the thing in the paragraph that you are reading has to do with evidence of some sort," Bernice said plainly.

"Yeah, so?"

"Look here, Orla Black. You asked me what it was. Don't make it seem like I forced it on you."

"All right, all right. Sorry. It made me feel stupid that I didn't know what it was. That's all," Orla muttered and continued reading his detective magazine.

"Apology accepted, Orla."

The interaction caused Orla and Bernice to become friends and after that encounter, they often sat together in the library, studying their books and occasionally commenting back and forth. It was far from a sweetheart romance; no innocent sparks of passion were exchanged or even considered. They were simply two peas in a pod, quite content to be friends without the recognition of the difference between their sexes.

While it often disturbed Olive's sense of appropriate behavior that Bernice took up with boys instead of girls, she was lenient with her daughter's friendship with Orla because she could keep a close eye on them both without being noticed. Scott was simply pleased that his daughter was such a committed student and unwavering in her focus for achieving academic success.

When Olive wanted to expand her own career by applying for a teaching position at the Chamberlin Institute in 1889, Scott gave her his full support. Although very few women taught at the college level, the subject of music was considered a feminine art, which made it acceptable for a lady of her stature to be employed as a professor.

In the fall of 1890, Olive was accepted for employment at the Chamberlin Institute as its first female professor, leaving her children to be educated by others at the Randolph Central School. Her position made it possible to eventually enroll all her daughters in the institute, furthering their experiences and providing them with the credentials for future occupations as teachers. Both Olive and her husband had become profoundly driven people who exposed the American work ethic to their children. However, it was only Bernice who embraced it completely. The two oldest girls, Morna and Dora, performed beautifully on the piano and maintained satisfactory marks in all their studies, but they lacked the stamina to endure the demands that accompany labor-intensive or intellectual undertakings. As the middle child of the Kenyon bunch, Edith was far too interested in watching the butterflies dance through the garden and land inches away from her small fingers, to have been tempted by the spoils of politics and commerce.

With the responsibility of her family's reputation squarely

positioned on her shoulders at such a young age, Bernice became wise beyond her years. There were times when even her mother turned to Bernice for advice. When the question of how to convince Scott to see her point of view arose, Olive went directly to Bernice and enlisted her as council. Bernice's advice always worked, making Olive extremely fond of their "girl talk."

When Scott decided that Bernice was ready to learn how to ride, he insisted that she command a horse just as a man would. Bernice took to her lessons with joy and tremendous talent, for it gave her the opportunity to be out of the house, free from feminine propriety, and liberated by the speed of her large, gray gelding. Bernice and Shadow spent hours together under the apple trees, munching the tangy crunch of the fresh fruits and feeling the cool breeze blow through their long locks.

The freedom of galloping through the grass into the woods and across the streams satiated Bernice's need for raw, untamed power and allowed her to return home with a lighter heart and more generous attitude towards her sisters. While they, too, were given the opportunity to ride and have their own animals, none of the other Kenyon girls was particularly interested in the smelly creatures. Dora was terrified of them. Morna thought they were very dirty. And Edith simply preferred a carriage ride. Scott joined her occasionally, however his traveling had become even more extensive, and Bernice was allowed to join him at trials only on family vacations or during the summer months.

Time spent alone in nature was the perfect balance for the youngest of the Kenyon ladies. Bernice worked so diligently at empowering her mind that her imagination would go a little crazy if she did not spend time away from her books. Even Olive would insist that Bernice go for a ride across the farm whenever anxiety in the house caused bickering among her four teenage daughters. As soon as Bernice left, the arguing would cease, and by the time she returned no one remembered there had been a disagreement.

The fire that burned in her spirit was so intense, that often only a blaze of speed across the northern territory would soothe Bernice's need for adrenaline.

It was a curse and a gift to have the soul of a conquering warrior embodied in a sensitive, petite form. But it was Bernice's feminine intuition that guided her to victory. Her goal was to achieve balance and harmony wherever she went, but the continuing explosion of technology and information brought chaos as well as wisdom into her world.

Just before the turn of the century, America had been a collection of men who fought to free themselves of tyranny and to claim land for their own, yet they were constrained by their own physical and emotional dysfunction. They were like wounded soldiers who had seen far too many deaths in battle. Anger and disease permeated the city of New York—from its docks to its neighborhood gangs. Immigration laws were increasingly restrictive due to the rampant cholera epidemic spreading from rags left aboard steamships by sickly passengers. Wealthy first class travelers, crossing the sea in private vessels, were protected from the filth killing the unprivileged.

This division of class structure made its way across the Atlantic from Europe and Asia onto the land of the new world. The upper class brought along their comfortable trappings of entitlement and freedom. They traveled in polished carriages and wore finely stitched clothes, while the impoverished begged, borrowed, and stole whatever they could to survive. As the separation between the rich and the poor increased, it became essential to establish and record family lineage. Winfield Scott Kenyon and Olive Guernsey Kenyon were fiercely dedicated to furthering the prominence of their ancestry and their power within the community. The family portraits taken by J.H. Blessing were among their most cherished possessions, along with the journals and memoirs of historical data recording the contributions made by their familial relations. The Kenyon girls were continuously reminded to take pride in their personal histories and to carry themselves with dignity and assuredness everywhere they went.

No one took this more to heart than Bernice did. She felt it was her duty to uphold the names and reputations of her forefathers. In school, she spent ample time studying the notable families of the community and made sure to acquaint herself with the children of socially esteemed parents. Although she found it cumbersome to tolerate people she did not care for, being deliberately social provided her the opportunity to acquire a political acumen that brought her tremendous success. When she turned thirteen, the children and their parents who made it onto her birthday party guest list were the most influential citizens in upstate New York. Planning for her party became such an event, that extra help was brought in for the evening, and an entire redecoration of the Kenyon home was required. The week prior to the party was a whirlwind of chaos and the household preparations consumed Olive's attentions so thoroughly that she elected to take the week off from work.

While none of the other Kenyon girls had received such an extravagant production for their entrance into womanhood, Bernice assured her sisters that her birthday party was just an excuse for their parents to rub elbows with high society and to prove themselves righteous in the eyes of the wealthy. The jealousy of her sisters subsided after they all received new dresses for the party. Exquisite silks from China were sewn into ruffled gowns, making the Kenyon girls into living versions of the hand-painted dolls they had collected since early childhood. They cooed and sighed at the sight of themselves immersed in luxurious fashions and easily forgot that the celebration was directly associated with the thirteenth birthday of their baby sister.

As a member of the Daughters of the American Revolution, Olive Kenyon was assured the respect and social graces provided to those of historical importance. Olive's mother was Lephe Bent Guernsey, the daughter of David Bent, who had fought as a Captain in the Revolutionary War. This decorated veteran left behind a legacy of honor and leadership that inspired his progeny to strive for glory and the ensuing power it brought to them. Olive made sure her Bent family heritage was displayed in the parlor, with tribute to the Revolutionaries who liberated themselves into freedom by way of America. Without the slightest hesitation, Olive went through life holding her head high, proud of her membership in the D.A.R. Her family walked the land with dignity and sovereignty.

To accent the portraits and historical documents, Olive pinned ribbons throughout the parlor and placed fresh flowers in glass vases to encourage her guests to tour the room. The housemaids and additional help spent two days scouring every inch of the farmhouse, bringing the home to a respectable sparkle and shine. On the morning of the party, the Kenyon girls woke with excitement and scampered around the house investigating the decorations their mother worked on far into the night. Red, white, and blue bouquets sat atop lace doilies on every table, and from the chandeliers dangled the same patriot-colored ornaments. Across the threshold, leading into the main dining hall hung a freshly painted wood banner with the words "Happy 13th Birthday, Bernice!" written in a royal blue script. Olive had colored the hand carved sign herself, and spent considerable time that morning scrubbing the blue stains from her fingertips.

With the household in a flurry of activity, breakfast was served in the kitchen to maintain the cleanliness in the dining area. Bernice knew she would be the center of attention for the evening's celebration, but felt sad that no one wished her a happy birthday that morning. She realized acting sullen would be a bit immature, so she hid her disappointment. Her suspicion that the party was being given for her parent's social status rather than as a celebration of her birth had become apparent. The convincing speech she had made to her sisters to ease their envy was all too true. She sat at the kitchen table, eating breakfast, but all she could muster was a subtle smile.

"Bernice, darling, happy birthday!" Scott burst out.

"Thank you, Daddy," Bernice replied and her smile grew larger.

"Happy Birthday, Bernice," her sisters all chimed in.

Olive came around the corner with a small birthday cake, singing "Happy Birthday" to Bernice and encouraging her family to join in. Teardrops filled Bernice's eyes and her doubts subsided as the embracing love of her family warmed her heart and filled her need for reassurance of their affection. When the song ended and they all cheered, Bernice wiped the tears from her eyes and took a huge bite of the frosted cake. She gave everyone a taste of the special treat, sharing the sugary sweet wonder Victoria had made especially for her. They barely had a chance to savor their breakfast dessert before the invited guests trickled into the house. The party was under way!

CHAPTER NINE

SCOTT, OLIVE, AND BERNICE STOOD AT THE FRONT door greeting guests as they arrived in waves of small groups bearing gifts. Bored by the need for such formal etiquette, Bernice was reminded by her mother that this was a small price to pay to those who honored her by attending her gathering. Responding immediately, the young girl stood strong, showing high regard for her mother's social refinement and character. Guests were thanked immediately for attending and even more so upon receipt of gifts. She received flowers, candy, trinkets, and gold coins. When all of the guests on the list had been accounted for, Bernice was free to roam and enjoy the rest of the day.

Her first mission was to sneak into the kitchen to sample the fare that would soon be served in the main dining hall. In need of an accomplice willing to risk the repercussions for such inappropriate party behavior, she looked to her friend, Orla, standing nearby with his father. Orla was attempting to look interested in the endless political discussions. Bernice walked right up to them and with the most gentle, innocent voice asked Mr. Black if he wouldn't mind her borrowing his son for a moment.

"Well, of course not, Miss Kenyon, and happy birthday to you today," Mr. Black replied.

"Oh, thank you sir. We won't be long," Bernice said sweetly, pulling Orla by the arm of his coat, forcing him to move quickly.

"I think she likes him, what do you say?" Mr. Black asked the crowd gathered around, listening to his social lecture. The group of men laughed and nodded in agreement and then encouraged Mr. Black to continue the debate on the effects of politics on the American Judicial System. Without notice of where Orla and Bernice had gone, Mr. Black returned his attention to the conversation, unaware of the secret mission the twosome was undertaking.

"Where are you taking me this time, troublemaker?" Orla asked.

"C'mon! I'm starving. Let's get a taste of the food in the kitchen. We don't have to wait," Bernice insisted.

"Oh! Yeah, I'm in!" Orla whispered.

"You stand guard outside. The cooks will give me the food and you just let me know if anyone is watching. Then we'll go into the back study and take turns so we don't get caught," Bernice ordered.

"Well don't you think someone is going to notice we're gone?" asked Orla.

"Nah, there's too many people here and dinner isn't served for another hour, so we have plenty of time."

Orla agreed and they executed their plan with finely tuned precision, as only close friends could. Thrilled with her performance, Bernice enjoyed the first spoils of the victory. As the butter-drenched potatoes slid down her throat, she sighed in utter delight. Laughing, she attempted to devour the tender pieces of beef she had discreetly acquired, without spilling the warm gravy on her blue silk gown. Orla peeked his head around the door, exposing lips and a chin covered in gravy. Bernice laughed loudly at Orla and nearly choked on her roast beef.

"Are you done eating yet?" Orla asked, through his gravy-covered lips.

"Just about. What happened to taking turns as lookout?"

"Sorry, I couldn't wait! The smell of the roast beef was far too powerful for me."

"I can see that you're a little piglet! Come here and let me clean you up," ordered Bernice.

As she dabbed at the gravy on Orla's chin, they forgot themselves and looked deeply into each other's eyes. However, the brief prospect of intimacy was broken abruptly when drops of gravy fell from Orla's chin onto the wood floor. Once again, Bernice burst into laughter, covering her mouth with her hand to muffle the noise lest someone discover them. Orla, indignant, snatched the napkin from her hand and finished the job himself.

As they readied themselves to return to the party, neither said anything about their brief jaunt into the realm of romance. Yet, underneath their silence, they both cherished the love they had for one another, if only as friends.

Dinner was called at 8:15 in the evening. As the bells for service rang, the many servants escorted the guests to their seats. Olive made sure that J.H. Blessing sat next to Scott, keeping Addie within whispering range for herself. The children were positioned so they could sit together and chatter during the meal without disturbing the adults. The multitude of guests gathered in the dining hall filled the Kenyon house with boisterous laughter and hearty conversation that lasted further into the evening than expected. With the presidential election just three weeks away, talk of the candidates dominated the adult conversation. When dinner was over, the men retired to the drawing room for a more serious discussion of the election and its possible ramifications on the Democratic Party in New York.

The presidential race was between the incumbent Republican president, Benjamin Harrison, and former president of the United States, Grover Cleveland. The last election had left the Democratic Party with some bitterness. Grover Cleveland, running as the incumbent Democratic president in the 1888 election, had won the popular vote by more than 100,000 votes. However, his victory had been snatched away when the electoral votes were cast. Grover Cleveland had garnered only 168 electoral votes, against "Little Ben" Harrison's 233 electoral votes. There was bad blood over that election and the staunchly Democratic Cattaraugus County wanted revenge that year, like so many other Democratic voters across the United States.

Addison Crowley, Vice President of the State Bank of Randolph, continued the conversation once the Kenyon's drawing room doors shut them off from the rest of the house. "Do you think those damned Republicans will steal the election away from Grover again?" he asked Scott, who was the head of the Democratic Precinct in Cattaraugus County.

"Hell! Anything is possible with those scallywags! We need to be sure that we get complete support for Grover Cleveland from every Democrat in the county. I have received word from the National Democratic Party Office that this election will be far different from the last. They have galvanized the support of Democrats from all over the nation. With such a united front, we can't lose. I say we toast to the party's victory right here and now!" replied Scott.

This rousing speech drew a hearty "Hear, Hear!" as every person sitting in the room raised his glass to Scott Kenyon.

While the gentlemen remained behind the closed doors of the drawing room, the ladies enjoyed the spoils of the decorated parlor while sipping tea and coffee and reminiscing about being thirteen themselves. Olive and Addie sat across from one another, engaging in silent conversations comprised of brief looks and an occasional raised eyebrow. Their friendship was a special bond that allowed them complete understanding of the other person's thoughts without speaking a word. It empowered them in social situations, enabling them to direct the conversation any way they wished, unbeknownst to the others in the room. Occasionally, Olive focused an ear on the young adults socializing in the front sitting room on the other side of the woodstove. She laughed when she heard the girls giggle, lapse into complete silence, and then erupt into loud laughter. "What a wonderful thing to be young. I wish I could remember what it felt like," Olive said to Addie.

"You don't remember?" Addie asked.

"No," Olive answered, surprised. "Do you?"

"Of course I do, Olive! You just work too hard my dear," Addie said stroking Olive's forearm.

"You may be right, Addie. I have been working a bit much of late."

With four teenage daughters, a farmhouse to run, a husband to care for, and a full-time teaching career, Olive's life had become a whirlwind of activity that required her focused attention every moment of the day. It was a rare pause when she could sit back and reflect on what she had accomplished but she truly enjoyed the family and the successes she labored so intensely to create. While the party continued to flourish, Olive was able to relax and simply enjoy the evening for a change. Bernice walked into the room to ask her mother a question and was surprised to see Olive in such a relaxed state. Bernice paused, not wanting to interrupt the rare tranquility, but her presence in the room was a distraction that pulled Olive out of her reverie and back into her role as hostess.

"Hello, darling," Olive said. "What do you need?"

"Father said he has a special present for me and wanted me to remind him, but I don't want to go into the study," Bernice answered.

"That's probably a very good choice, my dear," Olive agreed, with a small grin. The other ladies laughed.

"Should I just wait until tomorrow?" Bernice asked.

"No, I'll have one of the male help go into the study and he can pass the reminder to your father," Olive said, solving the dilemma.

"Thank you. Sorry to interrupt," Bernice said. The she smiled and quickly left the room. She returned to the front room where her friends were gathered around several plates of cookies, chocolates, and other delectables.

"Well, Bernice, who is going to be sent into that den of wolves to tell Papa it's time to for you to open his gift?" asked her sister, Edith.

"Mother is going to get one of the male help to do it," Bernice pronounced, receiving a nod of understanding from every child in the room.

Immediately their focus returned to the card game begun in Bernice's absence. Using candy as bets, they played poker in an attempt to retrieve all of the cherished sweets through gambling. A small circle was formed to shroud them from intruding adults who would not approve of such inappropriate behavior. Bernice was dealt in and she ended up winning the hand without even needing to draw a single card.

"Can you believe the luck of this girl?" Orla shouted across the circle, angered by his loss of the large walnut-studded brownie.

"Oh, take your darn brownie, you spoilsport!" Bernice retorted, tossing the baked good back to her friend.

"Thanks, B!" he exclaimed, shoving the chocolate square into his mouth.

"You really are a refined fellow, aren't you Orla?" Lynn Blessing asked the boy sitting across from him.

"Sure am!" Orla mumbled, laughing at his own impudence, while crumbs bounced down the front of his shirt.

Edith looked at Lynn shyly and smiled at his gentle wit. Something about that boy was magical to Edith. Nothing he could do or say would bore her even if it revolved around an activity in which she had absolutely no interest. Lynn never seemed to notice her fondness for him, as he was far too interested in his own dream world that revolved around nature and art. Lynn's eyes revealed the kindness in his soul, something his father J.H.

Blessing considered a weakness. Edith sat and stared dreamily at the younger boy, which made Lynn nervous. Bernice watched her sister enviously, as she had yet to find a boy that could make her feel like that. However, as her eyes lingered on Edith's goofy grin, Bernice's heart filled with happiness for her sister.

Orla was shuffling the deck to deal another hand when the door opened, prompting the boy to quickly conceal the cards behind his back. Victoria entered the room and announced that Mr. Kenyon was presenting Bernice with a gift in the living room.

"Come right this second, dear," Victoria insisted, craning her neck over the children, hoping to see what Orla was hiding.

"I'm on my way, Victoria!" Bernice said as she and the rest of the children followed the housekeeper down the hall.

The entire party was gathered in the parlor to witness this last event. The late hour was beckoning them all to bid farewell and be on their way home. Bernice entered the room to find her father waiting in the center of the room with a large, flat, rectangular box tied up with a bright green bow. Blushing from the attention, she walked towards her father who bent down and kissed her on the cheek as he whispered in her ear. "Happy Birthday, Bernie. You're gonna love this."

"Thanks, Papa," Bernice said as she gently hugged him.

Scott took his knife out of his pocket and cut the ribbon for her. She stepped forward and reached out her delicate hand to lift the top from the box. She pulled off the top layer of tissue and stared in disbelief. Then, slowly, Bernice lifted the pearl-handled revolver from the box. Bernice did not know how to react. She had asked for the gun, but never in a million years did she think her father would give her such a gift in the presence of their guests! Olive stood motionless, having absolutely no idea how to react to her father's inappropriate gift. Just as Scott recognized his social gaffe, Bernice spoke up in an effort to stop what she felt was about to turn the successful party into a complete disaster.

"Oh, Papa! Thank you so much," Bernice said with feigned femininity, "but, whatever shall I do with such a thing?"

The silence was overwhelming until Addison Crowley piped up and saved the day. "I know quite a few Republicans that you could use it on, Bernice," he said with a wink.

The guests roared with laughter and the inappropriateness of the gift was quickly forgotten. Olive quickly ushered Bernice away from the gun and towards the front door so she could begin thanking all of her guests for coming and wish them a safe journey home. Olive shot Scott a stern look on her way out of the room, but his intoxication prevented him from recognizing that his wife was angry. Scott followed his wife and daughter to the front entrance and shook hands with the gentlemen he had entertained for the evening. When all the guests had departed and made their way to their respective carriages, Olive shut the door with a tremendous sigh of relief, thankful that her duties as hostess had come to conclusion. She grabbed her husband's arm, forgetting she had been upset with his unconventional gift for Bernice, and they made their way towards the staircase. As they climbed the steps to the second floor, Scott looked down at his daughters huddled together in the parlor and smiled at the cherubic faces that gazing up at him.

"Good night girls, I love you all," Scott said with a drunken wave.

"Good night, Papa," they answered in unison.

"Get to bed soon, girls. Don't forget we have to attend Sunday services tomorrow morning," Olive reminded them.

"We will, Mama. Thank you for the wonderful party," Bernice said.

The servants rushed around, cleaning up the mess left behind by the party guests, while Bernice, Edith, Morna, and Dora lingered in the parlor. With their parents gone, the girls giggled among themselves as they discussed the evening's excitement.

"Edith, it seems to me that you have a crush on someone," Bernice said to her older sister in a playful, singsong tone.

"Oh, Bernice, shush up! Don't say that out loud. You are going to ruin the magic of my unspoken romance," Edith answered with a dreamlike, wistful smile.

"My apologies, Edith. I shall never speak again of your torrid love affair until it comes to blissful fruition," Bernice whispered, with Shakespearean resolve.

"Why, thank you, my dearest sister," Edith replied in an affected English accent, her nose in the air.

Morna and Dora looked at one another, wondering what in the world they were talking about. Bernice looked at her oldest sisters and, realizing their naiveté, lowered her eyes as she stifled a laugh. She tapped Edith on the leg to see if she too had witnessed the shock in their sisters' eyes. Edith took note of Morna and Dora's blank looks and poked her tongue out at them in an attempt to distract them by silliness. The Kenyon girls burst into laughter, forgetting the drama of love and returning their attention to their lovely gowns.

"I don't think we are going to have another party like this for quite some time," Morna said with regret in her voice.

"Why do you say that?" asked Edith.

"It just seems like Mama is getting tired, and Papa is just crackers sometimes. I mean really, Bernice! Buying you that crazy gift!" Morna said.

"Morna, for your information I asked for that crazy gift! In fact, I am going to learn to shoot it, too. I'm going to shoot it tomorrow. And, furthermore, you little miscreant, don't you ever say anything bad about Papa again," Bernice barked at her sister.

"She didn't mean it like that, Bernice," Dora said meekly, speaking for Morna who was so frightened she hid behind Dora's back.

"Never again, Morna. I mean it! You'll be sorry if you ever

do it again," Bernice said as she advanced angrily towards her sister with her fists clenched at her side.

"All right, you two. That will be enough!" Edith interjected. "I think we're all tired. Let's get to bed. Come on, girls, follow me."

The four teenagers made their way upstairs, waving goodnight to the housemaids still finishing their duties. They changed into their sleeping gowns that had been laid out on their lace-covered bedding. As their bodies sank into their beds and they drifted off in slumber, their dreams combined memories of past and future moments.

Morning light came quickly, but it was kept hidden by the heavy, velvet green curtains that hung across the windows of their bedrooms. Exhausted by the previous night's festivities, the Kenyon girls slept late, forgetting their duty to attend church. They were jolted awake by the sound of their mother's loud voice.

"Ladies! This is unacceptable! We have to leave for church now!" Olive bellowed, her hands on her hips, as she stood in the hallway between their rooms. "Good gracious! You all look a mess. Well, I'm just going to have to tell everyone you were all too overwhelmed by the party. None of you will be attending church today! I insist!"

"Thanks, Mama," Bernice whispered, knowing that her mother's demanding tone was a façade to appease her father.

"No problem. I'll see you at lunch," Olive whispered back, winking and smiling at her precious and sleepy children.

Olive and Scott were well received at the church that morning, and the absence of their children was accepted as due to legitimate fatigue. The sermon seemed to take longer than usual for Olive. Her failing health worried her as she prayed to the Lord to forgive her for her sins of selfishness and anger and save her soul so that she might one day be free in Heaven with her creator. Her connection to the Divine was something she never questioned.

Olive believed that faith was a personal journey and she never sought to impose her beliefs on others. Scott, however, simply used the church to advance his political and social stature. His faith in God was real, but there was a side to him that flew directly in the face of those beliefs.

Later that evening, Bernice learned of her father's hidden persona when she asked him if he would teach her to shoot her new revolver.

"You really want to learn? Or are you just trying to make me feel good about my gift? Because I don't want to waste my time teaching you something you don't really want to learn," Scott told his youngest daughter.

"I really want to learn," Bernice replied with a stern look.

"All right then, let's go outside," said Scott.

"On a Sunday, Scott? Is this really appropriate?" inquired Olive.

"Woman, just be still now. We'll be back before supper," Scott said, silencing his wife. "Come on with me kid," he said, grabbing Bernice by the arm.

She followed him quickly, putting on her boots, and grabbing her coat on the way out the door. She noticed a slight shift from how she had been treated up until then. The gentle, kind man she knew as her father became an aggressive, sharp, abrasive creature who demanded action and accepted nothing but success. Frightened, and a bit unsure of herself, she pushed away the feelings making their way up her chest and into her throat. Instinctively, she knew crying would be the worst thing she could do.

Clenching her fists and driving her tiny, sharp fingernails into the soft skin of her palms distracted her thoughts. They walked briskly to the far edge of the cattle gates and Scott picked out a tree. He took a red napkin from his pocket, stretched it around the trunk, and tied it in a knot to secure its position.

Without speaking, he started to pace out from the tree with Bernice running to keep up with him. When he counted out twenty paces, Scott stopped abruptly, turned sharply, and stared his daughter squarely in the eye. "Guns are very dangerous. They are for men. Do you understand?"

"Yes, sir," Bernice answered firmly.

"I realize your body is fragile and weak since you're a woman, but you were born the strongest of my four girls, making you the protector of the bunch. I'm sorry I have to treat you like a man. I know it's not fair, but it's the best thing I can do for you. Do you understand?" Scott persisted.

"Yes, sir," Bernice replied as her nerves calmed and her understanding of her father's behavior became clearer.

"I left the choice to you. I figured if you wanted nothing to do with the gun, or if you were just doing it to please me, I would bust my ass to find you a good husband. But you wanted to learn, and I believe your desire is sincere, so with that I'm going to teach you everything you'll need to survive in a man's world. Do you understand?" Scott said sternly.

"Yes, sir," Bernice replied, having absolutely no idea what her father was referring to. However, she recognized the need to go along without more specifics.

Scott slipped the bullets into the gun's chambers and locked the load into position. "Stand here. You can keep your legs spread out evenly or put one in front of the other, whichever one feels best to you."

"I like my right one back," said Bernice.

"That's fine. Now, I'm going to stand behind you because when you pull the trigger the gun is going to throw you backwards."

"All right," Bernice said, even though her arms were shaking.

"Now wrap your right hand on the bottom here, but don't put

your finger through the trigger yet," Scott explained as he stood behind her and placed her hand around the revolver.

"Like this?" Bernice asked.

"Yes, that's good. Now, put your left hand underneath the right one to steady your grip in order make the best shot," Scott continued as he lined up her aim with the marked tree.

"It's heavy," Bernice said.

"Yes, I know that, Bernice. We can get you a smaller weapon if you really need it, but for now we'll work with this one."

"Yes, sir," Bernice said.

"Now, gently slip your right finger over the trigger and don't pull it yet. Just put it there. Very good. When I say so, I want you to squeeze the trigger back slowly and fire the gun. Don't jerk the gun towards you as you fire. Just pull it slowly and steadily. That way you'll get a better aim. I'm going to hold it with you because there's a lot of power here and I don't want either of us getting hurt. Are you ready?"

"Yes," said Bernice as she planted her feet firmly in the ground and stared at the red cloth on the tree in front of her.

"All right. Now. Just squeeze it slowly," Scott commanded.

Bernice's petite finger strained as she focused intently on following her father's instructions. When the gun went off, her arms flew in the air and her small body shot backward into her father's chest. Scott's strong body absorbed the force of the blow, so she was able to experience the explosive power without incurring injury. The sharp report of the revolver echoed throughout the empty valley. Stunned at the violent power of the gun, Bernice remained limp in her father's arms until he pushed her onto her own feet and demanded another attempt.

"That wasn't too bad for a first try, but you completely missed your target. Now you know what it's like. Try to hold your body still so the shot doesn't throw you so far back. Go ahead and gently squeeze the trigger again," Scott insisted.

Sweat glistened on her forehead as she concentrated all of her energy on battling the tremendous kick produced by the firing of her new pistol. The bullet exploded out from the barrel, again throwing her back against her father's body, but not quite as hard as the first time.

"Yes, that's it. Much better," Scott encouraged her.

"Shall I do it again?" Bernice asked, pleased with her performance.

"Absolutely, and lets work on aim as well this time. What you are trying to line up is that small point at the end of the barrel with whatever it is you want to hit. You are looking for a level line of the barrel and the barrel's sight to the target. Do you understand?" Scott asked.

"Yes, sir," Bernice replied, empowered by holding such raw power in her hands. She took her stance, locked her shoulder, and wrapped her young fingers around the handle of the revolver. Her focus narrowed as she aligned the sight level with the center of the red cloth in front of her. Taking a deep breath, she exhaled and squeezed the trigger with a comfort and familiarity that was beyond her experience. As the bullet flew out of the barrel and across the empty space to the tree, Bernice knew she was a shooter. Scott, too, could feel the perfectness of the shot and he held her tightly, with fatherly pride, as Bernice struggled to keep her balance.

"That was it!" Scott exclaimed.

"Yes, Papa, that one was easier," Bernice agreed.

"You're a natural, girl! No wonder you wanted to learn how to shoot. Do you know how hard that is? I bet you hit the target, too! Shall we go see?" he asked, clearly elated by her talent.

"Sure," Bernice answered, impressed more by her father's reaction than actually hitting the tree.

They walked together to the tree Scott had marked with the

red cloth and upon inspection discovered that the third shot had indeed hit the target, torn through the fabric and implanted the bullet deep within its trunk. A satisfied smile covered Bernice's face as she watched her father untie the knotted material from the bark. Scott smiled, too. The tough attitude he had adopted at the beginning of their practice faded and was replaced by a soft manner.

"I think that's quite enough for today, Bernice, but we need to practice all the time to stay sharp. And, if you are truly dedicated, I will buy you a pistol that is more appropriate for a lady of your size. To be perfectly honest, I had the revolver in mind for myself, but it'll be a good learning weapon for you to use for practice," Scott said matter-of-factly.

"So you bought my birthday present for yourself?" Bernice asked teasingly.

"Yeah, well, what are you going to do about it? You're just a woman, right?" Scott teased back.

"I'll give you 'just a woman,' Papa!"

"Ha, ha! That's my girl! You're going to get a lot of ribbing about being 'just a woman' now that you intend to tote pistols and act independently. Do you understand what I'm saying?" Scott asked in a serious tone.

"I think I understand as much as I can without having had the experience," Bernice answered honestly.

"Well, that's a good start. All I am saying is, your life isn't necessarily going to be an easy one. I'm counting on you to look after your sisters when your mother and I are gone," Scott said with utmost sincerity.

"What do mean, Papa?"

"Look Bernice, we're going to try and get them all married and taken care of, but there are no guarantees in life, you know. I'm just saying that I'm counting on you to be the provider of the lot. Your mother and I aren't going to live forever, and it's better that we speak of these things now while you're young, rather than spring it on you later," said Scott.

"Are you ill, Papa?" Bernice asked.

"No kid, you're getting this all wrong. Just try to understand. I don't have a son. If I did, we would not be having this conversation. But, I don't, so we are. It's the way of the world. Sometimes we have to make sacrifices for the good of the whole. I'm just trying to tell you that at some point you may need to make the choice of putting the welfare of your family before your own happiness. Do you understand?"

"I guess so," Bernice answered, unsure of the responsibilities she was expected to shoulder.

"Don't worry about it for now. We'll have plenty of time to figure it all out later. Until then, just be happy you put a hole in your mother's napkin. I really did not think you would hit it; otherwise, I would have brought out something that if it got ruined, it wouldn't upset her. We'll just tell her I did it, that way she can blame me," Scott said, laughing.

"Wouldn't she blame you anyway?" Bernice asked, laughing along with him.

"Yes, yes she would," Scott agreed.

They walked back to the house together with Bernice emulating her father's stride. The cool evening air of autumn prompted them to quicken their pace and before they knew it, Bernice and her father were racing one another to the kitchen door. When Scott arrived first, he grabbed the handle and pulled the door open allowing Bernice to squeeze by him. Olive's stern face halted their progress. As the gust of wind from their abrupt entrance subsided, Scott burst out laughing.

"What is so funny, Mr. Kenyon?" Olive said. "I am preparing Sunday dinner and the two of you burst in here like the fire brigade!" Olive barked.

"Oh my love, you are too beautiful to be so serious," Scott

whispered in her ear as he enveloped her in his arms.

Olive smiled as she returned her attention to the stew simmering on the stove. Without looking up, Bernice quickly removed her jacket and boots, washed her hands, and helped her sisters set the table, silently shifting the attention away from her entrance and towards the meal at hand.

Bernice's talent as peacemaker and diplomat was well honed by the time she arrived in high school, making her extremely popular with both teachers and other students. No matter what the situation, Bernice could offer a fair solution or remove the intensity of the circumstance with a matter-of-fact calmness that quelled even the hottest of tempers.

CHAPTER TEN

THE NEXT FEW YEARS FLEW BY AT the Kenyon residence. One-by-one the Kenyon girls emerged from their adolescence. Edith graduated from high school with honors, followed in succession by Dora and Morna. The older sisters had garnered exceptional reputations due to their scholastic achievements, but none of them held a candle to their baby sister, Bernice. Despite their academic achievements, not one of her sisters put their skills to use. They lived their lives like princesses in a European court. Dora's feigned physical ailments assured her that she would never have to work outside the home. Morna simply hemmed and hawed whenever the topic of gainful employment arose. Edith volunteered her services once a week at the Western New York Home for Homeless and Dependent Children in Randolph.

Scott Kenyon was disgusted with the three older girls and it drove him to push Bernice even harder. The prediction he had made to Bernice years earlier regarding protecting her three sisters was right on the mark. No suitors lined up at his door asking for their hands in marriage. In fact, no young men came around showing even mild interest in any of them.

Graceful and surreptitious, Bernice glided through her teenage years with catlike elegance coupled with clever strategy. Every day she demonstrated to her father that she was clearly in charge of her destiny. That attitude came at a price for Bernice, however. Although she enjoyed the company of others, she never felt free to be herself with anyone. She was a chameleon.

Edith, Morna, and Dora meanwhile developed close ties with other women who were content to sit in circles gossiping and whispering. Bernice would rather die than sit in on one of their gatherings. She disdained their behavior for they were doing absolutely nothing with their lives.

It was Bernice's secret pleasure to exit the house in a huff whenever she was irritated by the blathering of her sisters' feminine conversations. What she liked best was to create a bit of a scene for the hired boys to watch. She would stomp out onto the front porch in her boots, clomp down the steps, and strut to the stables. Pulling her large, gray gelding away from its straw-filled box, she would gallop out of the barn, her skirts flying behind her. A sly grin would cover her face as she barreled past the boys, leaving them in a cloud of dust. The display of independence magnified her liberation from the dullard women she left behind and created an emotional high that satiated her need for excitement. Wild as the eagle that soared above her head, Bernice tasted this freedom as often as she dared. Only when the light of day waned and heralded the coming of night would she turn her magnificent steed towards home. Bernice often galloped back to the farmhouse, arriving just before suppertime. She became quite adept at slipping back into the household undetected.

While Bernice had no trouble hoodwinking her mother and sisters, her father was wise to her maneuvers. He watched with pride as his daughter came and went secretly through back doors and upstairs windows. Scott said nothing of her actions until he caught a glimpse of the way the working boys ogled her as the setting sun shined through her dress, exposing the shapely form that lay beneath it. Realizing that his youngest daughter was becoming a woman and therefore an object of men's desires, he took it upon himself to instruct her further on the ways of the world. He determined that their Sunday target practice sessions would give him the perfect opportunity.

"You're getting better every time," Scott said one day, complimenting Bernice on her shooting.

"Still intend to get me that woman-sized pistol you promised five years ago, Papa?" Bernice asked with a smirk.

"No, but I am still waiting to claim that man-sized revolver you've got now, Bernie!"

"Oh, nonsense, Papa. I can't believe that you are still complaining about that after all these years. You just want to switch weapons on me so that I don't outshoot you anymore."

"Madam, you wound me!" Scott said as he touched the back of his left hand to his forehead and pretended to swoon.

They both laughed at Scott's antics and Scott selected that moment to deliver the speech on sex and reproduction that he had prepared for his daughter. Current mores prevented him from being graphic, so he planned on hinting at the fact that men were sex-starved beings who wanted nothing more from women than to satisfy their sexual urges and move on to their next prey.

"So, Bernice," Scott began. "I've noticed you have a habit of sneaking out of the house without anyone realizing you are gone. That's pretty impressive," Scott said, blandly.

"You're not mad?" Bernice asked, worried that a punishment would be forthcoming.

"Well, I don't see any harm in it as long as it remains discreet and you don't get yourself into any trouble," said Scott.

"So, you're not going to tell Mama?"

"Of course not! That's the last thing I would do. I think you should know that by now," Scott said as he readied his next shot.

"Yes, you're right. I do know that," Bernice admitted.

"Then don't ever ask me that again," Scott said, sharpening his tone as the blast exploded out of his gun.

"Yes, sir," Bernice responded sheepishly.

"I think it's time you understand that even though you have been exposed to more of the world than any other woman your age, you have still been protected from some of the harsh realities of the world. Do you understand?"

"Yes, sir," Bernice answered with a stronger voice.

"There are things that you need to understand about men, Bernice. Things that most women don't ever learn, or at least not until it's too late for them."

"All right," Bernice said. The topic piqued her interest.

"Men only care about themselves, Bernie. They will tell you they care about you, but really, they only care about the pleasure you provide for them. It's just the way of the world today. Women care about everyone and everything, and men pretty much care only about themselves – until they get married and start a family. Do you grasp what I'm trying to tell you?" Scott asked.

"I suppose," Bernice answered, having a hard time believing her father was speaking these words to her.

"That doesn't mean a man doesn't care for his children or his wife. I am simply trying to explain to you that until that family is in place and the house is in order, it does not occur to a man to care about the needs of others. You get what I'm trying to tell you?"

"You're telling me that until I marry a man he doesn't really care about me?" Bernice replied uncertain of her understanding.

"Exactly. So, when a man is being nice to you it's because he wants something from you. Now do you understand?" Scott said, firing his pistol once more.

"I guess so, Papa. That's sad though, because some of my friends are boys and it seems to me that they have a genuine regard for my well being," Bernice responded, a bit disappointed at the lesson her father was giving.

"Well, Bernie, I'm sure they do some have regard for you. I'm just trying to explain that these boys out here, working in the field, and most of those men you see when we take trips to court, they all have private agendas that don't really have your best interest at heart. It's not that they wish you harm, it's just that you have a lot to offer and they might want to take advantage of you, without wanting to provide you with something worthwhile in exchange."

"I think I understand, Papa," Bernice said as she discharged her pistol at the target.

They said nothing more about the topic that day, as if some secret had been sufficiently exposed and further discussion was unwarranted. However, her father's words haunted Bernice. She slowly built a wall around herself to keep men at a safe distance. After that, whenever she passed by the hired boys working in the fields, the innocent flirtations they once shared ceased and were replaced with an icy glare that warned them to keep their distance. Proud and strong, she carried her head high, feeling protected by the wisdom her father had shared with her. She felt empowered now that she understood the motives that lay behind the actions of men.

Bernice continued to retreat into intellectualism to supplant her growing emotional and sexual desires. Rather than waste her time seeking out potential husbands, she spent her time with the intellectuals of Randolph. She always carried a newspaper in her book bag and kept a close eye on the national and international events shaping history. She was quick to bring her knowledge into classroom discussions and schoolyard debates. She was a tremendous fan of the underdog and there were plenty of those in the years following the panic of 1893. When reports surfaced about the American economy had been saved by J.P. Morgan and the Rothschild family, plenty of people celebrated the charity of the robber barons that helped bail out the American government. However, Bernice felt it was the duty of the unethically wealthy to save the country and since their acts were self-serving, the men were undeserving of the accolades being heaped upon them.

In her young eyes, the glory of the United States was far more important than the success of just one or two families. Bernice's ancestors had fought and died in the American

Revolution in order to secure freedom for all the people of the American colonies. Watching her fellow citizens suffer from the recent economic hardships was hard on her. She was adamant when she assured others that the Union would improve because, after all, they were Americans.

When opportunities arose for Bernice to speak her opinions about the state of affairs in political or economic arenas, nothing could dam the flow of the passionate patriotic diatribe that spewed from her silver-spooned mouth. Her teachers and classmates were taken often aback by her lengthy lectures on honor and responsibility, yet they were simultaneously entranced by her intelligence and the eloquence with which she spoke. Only the resonant sound of the school bell marking the end of class silenced her speeches. Sometimes, even the loud bell did not cut short the lecture she delivered with profound wisdom and insight. Bernice became infamous throughout town for her vocalizations about truth and liberty. She refused to allow her opinions to be quashed merely because she was a woman.

One day, when her teacher sent a note home to her parents suggesting that Bernice find additional outlets for her speechmaking, her father laughed. "Bernie, what in the world have you been talking about in school?"

"Well, I just stand up and tell everyone what I think," Bernice answered.

"What subjects do you speak about?"

"Anything! Everything!"

"Bernice, please, we are having dinner. Keep your voice down," Olive said, exasperated.

"Sorry, Mama," Bernice responded quietly, but with irritation.

"More specifically then, Bernice, what exactly are you lecturing everyone about?" Scott persisted.

"I talk about what I read in the papers and what I hear at the trials we attend. And about how we live in this time of amazing invention and how no one seems to have any pride anymore in this great country of ours. And how we have lost our faith in our fellow American!"

"Well, that is certainly understandable. Where else is a young girl to discuss such things if she doesn't discuss them in school? Don't you agree, Olive?" Scott asked with pride as he turned to his wife.

"Yes, dear, of course, I do. Unfortunately this note from her teacher says Bernice is becoming so aggressive in voicing her opinions that's she's a distraction."

"Oh, to hell with all those hoity-toity, pseudo-intellectual educators, Bernie! Don't you ever change. You are ahead of your time, my dear, and far more intelligent than most of the people I know," said Scott. "Just keep your mouth shut so the teacher can continue to delude herself that she knows more than you do. All right?"

"Yes, sir!" Bernice answered happily.

Hearing about his daughter's intellectual prowess made Scott feel the time he had spent on Sunday afternoons with Bernice had been well worth the effort. The tiny seeds of masculinity he had implanted within her mind had sprouted into a veritable grove of tall, powerful oaks. Pleased with his success, he began taking Bernice on even more trips to Buffalo and other cities to further expose her to a man's world. Scott felt free to discuss politics, economics, and social reform with Bernice, as if she were his equal.

In the summer of 1897, Scott took Bernice on a trip to New York City to tour the newly opened Morningside Heights campus of the prestigious Columbia College. Scott wanted Bernice to rub elbows with some of the nation's brightest students.

As they left Grand Central Station in Manhattan and made their way through the towering architecture and burgeoning masses, Bernice was awed by the energy of the booming city. It was the first time she had been to the City and the intensity, noise and chaos of the crowds was intimidating. Because of her youthful appearance and affluent attire, Scott held her arm as they walked in an effort to protect her from thieves and hooligans that might attempt to prey upon her. He quickly ushered Bernice towards a horse and buggy and gave the driver instructions to take them to the Gilsey Hotel at the corner of Broadway and 29th Street. The man loaded their belongings onto the back of the carriage and the black colt leapt to a trot at the sound of the whip's snap. Although Bernice was separated from the crowd by the window of the buggy, she could feel the excitement of people.

Unaffected by the noise and the pandemonium of the City, Scott read his paper and relaxed as the carriage transported them to their hotel.

"Have you stayed in the Gilsey Hotel before, Papa?" Bernice asked.

"No, but J.H. Blessing recommended it to me because it is frequented by young people and artists and he thought you might enjoy yourself in that kind of environment. It's located in the theater district," Scott answered without looking up from his paper.

"Oh! That sounds wonderful," Bernice replied.

"I think we should have dinner at Delmonico's. Your mother feels I am spoiling you, but I explained to her that these trips are for your worldly education, not simply to lavish you with luxury."

"So we're not going to be lavished?" Bernice asked as she batted her eyelashes and looked up with a mock frown.

"Oh, please, Bernice! When have we ever traveled and not had the best of everything?"

Bernice returned her father's smile and leaned back into the musty, service-worn, leather seats. Soon, the driver stopped outside the Gilsey Hotel and opened the buggy door for Bernice to exit. She accepted his assistance, stepping onto the ground, noticing that the driver was trying to flirt with her. She turned her head and disregarded his presence. The hotel doorman immediately stepped to her aid as her father paid the driver. Once inside, Scott went to the front desk while Bernice wandered the richly decorated lobby, making sure to keep within her father's line of sight. Although he was insistent upon her independence, whenever they traveled together, he protectively kept Bernice under close watch.

Scott had requested a suite so that Bernice could have her own room adjacent to his, yet not isolate her entirely. They followed the bellman to their suite, which was decorated in rosewood and walnut, a richly veined marble fireplace, tapestries, and bronze-gilt chandeliers. Once inside their rooms, they waited in the sitting area for a snack of coffee and sweets before dressing for dinner.

Lighting a cigar and adding a bit of brandy to his coffee, Scott sighed contently as he stared out the window at the busy city below him. "Sometimes it is so nice to get away from the farmhouse. I try to get your mother to travel with me, but she loathes the city. She says it makes her nervous. If it were up to me, we would travel often, but she won't have it."

Bernice munched on a sugar cookie. "I know. That's why I'm surprised she keeps talking about moving from Randolph to Salamanca. What are your thoughts about that, Papa?"

"Well, it puts us a lot further away from the rural life we are used to, but I would probably make a fortune if we sold the farmhouse now. I know it would make your mother very happy if we did move there. She's been talking about moving to Salamanca ever since you were a baby."

"Really? I had no idea she has been dreaming about it for such a long time," Bernice responded, surprised at her mother's patience.

"The thing about your mother is that she always gets what she wants. It may take some time, but she always wins. That's why we never argue. That, and because I go out of town quite a bit," he said with a hearty laugh.

"So, do you think we are going to move, Papa?"

"I don't see why not. You've finished school, so there is little that holds us to Coldspring and Randolph now. And I've been thinking about selling the shop in Randolph, anyway."

"Hmmm, Papa. It sounds like you've already made up your mind to move."

"Well, it does seem like an opportune time to do it, my dear. We will see what happens. For now, let's focus on our little adventure in the big city, shall we?"

When they finished their mid-afternoon snack, Scott said he was tired after the long train trip from the station in Salamanca and wanted to rest. Not being tired in the least, Bernice walked downstairs to explore the grandeur of the Gilsey Hotel. She stepped gracefully onto the Persian carpet that covered the lobby floor and slowly traversed the perimeter of the room. She stopped at each of the large paintings that graced the rosewood walls. Suddenly, the back of her neck tingled. Discreetly, she turned her head to the side to survey the room and was startled by the nearness of a gentleman who had approached silently and stood staring intently at her. He was dressed effeminately and wore his hair unstylishly long.

"May I help you, sir?" Bernice asked.

"I beg your pardon, Miss! I am writing a play and I was simply observing the way you lost yourself in your perusal of the lobby art. It struck me that one of my characters might do the same thing if she were to find herself in your circumstance. Then I considered the fact that you might very well be the manifestation of the character I have created, but then I just recently created the character. So, how could that possibly be? Unless, of course, I have merely tapped into a character that already exists in life and simply written on paper what has divinely been created already."

"I see," Bernice responded, believing the man might be mentally unbalanced.

"Do you? Do you really see? What do you see? What does the world look like through your young eyes right now?" the man asked with a penetrating stare.

"Well, sir, to me the world is a place of unlimited potential inhabited by cowards who think mostly of their own happiness as opposed to the greater good of humanity," Bernice stated haughtily.

"Hmmm, well that kind of kills my theory that you are the character in my play. I'm afraid that she would never be so pessimistic."

"I don't see my perspective as pessimistic at all! I think it's quite practical and entirely honest."

"Really? Well I will have to think about that for a while. Would you care to join me for a drink, mademoiselle?" the man asked.

"Thank you, but I really don't think that would be proper. I am waiting for my father and he would not appreciate me spending time with a strange man in some hotel bar," Bernice answered in a self-righteous tone.

"Would it change things if I told you that I was quite famous?" the man said.

"I'm sorry sir, but I don't recognize you as such," Bernice replied as she stuck her nose in the air and turned her head slightly away from the stranger.

"Well, then! Allow me to introduce myself! My name is Oscar Wilde, playwright extraordinaire! Please, let me assure you that I have absolutely no intention of seducing you or otherwise offending your honor. I am in town to promote the revival of one of my plays. It is currently playing up the street from this fine establishment. I would simply enjoy the presence of your company while I imbibe in spirits and ready myself for my journey back to France."

"France? You don't impress me as being French, sir," Bernice said, trying not to display her interest.

"No, I'm not. I am originally from Ireland."

"Really? Most of my ancestors are from England and Ireland."

"As are most of the best people in this town. Shall we?" Oscar suggested, stretching out his arm and pointing to the entrance to the hotel bar.

"We shall," Bernice responded, wrapping her arm in his, a bit nervous, a bit hesitant.

"I promise you that I shall be on my best behavior. Which may or may not be a good thing!" Oscar whispered as they strolled towards the lounge together.

Bernice laughed as the outrageous man with long, dark hair escorted her into the bar. Although imbued with the mores of the Victorian era, she secretly yearned for wild adventures that might involve steamy romance and international intrigue. Oscar's invitation was far too tempting to ignore. And, although she did not know the work or character of this Oscar Wilde fellow, she sensed his intentions were sincere and that he would behave in a manner that would not soil her good name. With a fresh dose of adrenaline coursing through her veins, Bernice walked into the crowded room and was pleasantly surprised to see the patrons turn their heads and raise their eyebrows as she walked by with Oscar on her arm. Recognizing that he was indeed a famous person, she was delighted with her decision to join him.

They sat down on leather-covered chairs at a small, round table and were immediately attended to by a waiter. "We'll have two glasses of Grand Marnier, warmed, please," Oscar said without asking Bernice what she would like to drink.

"At once, Mr. Wilde," the waiter replied.

"You see, I told you I'm famous," Oscar said.

"It does appear you have quite a following at this establishment," Bernice stated without giving him the satisfaction of recognition.

"You know, you remind me of myself at your age. What did you say your name was?"

"I didn't, Mr. Wilde. Let me correct my poor manners. I am Bernice Guernsey Kenyon. And I am very pleased make your acquaintance, sir," Bernice said with a demure smile.

"Charmed, to be sure, Miss Kenyon," Oscar said with a polite bow of his head. "It's an odd thing to find someone who is so like me in so many ways."

"Really? And how is it that we are so similar?" Bernice asked.

"There is a certain air of confidence about you that is balanced by an equal measure of irreverence. I like that."

"Well, I'm not sure if I should thank you for that comment or slap you in the face and leave in a huff, Mr. Wilde!"

"Ho, ho! And with a fine spirit, too, I see! So, tell me, oh, high-spirited one, what brings you to the City? You are with your father, I think you said. Is it business? No, of course not. Pleasure, I'm assuming. But where is the rest of the family? Is there more to your family? Is he really your father? Or were you just putting on a show to get rid of me quickly?" said Oscar a bit breathlessly.

"Yes, I am with my father. Yes, there is more family and they simply do not care for travel. Yes, this trip is for pleasure and my, you do ask several questions simultaneously!" Bernice responded, laughing at Oscar's odd mannerisms.

"Well, life is too short to merely ask one question at a time, don't you agree?"

"That was only one question."

"You're just wonderful, darling! You don't miss a thing do

you? I bet you frighten most men. You do, don't you? They want you, but they wouldn't know what to do with you if they had you. Am I right?" said Oscar.

"Well, I have spent far too much time studying to be bothered with wondering what men think of me. I suppose some men might be intimidated by me, if they had the opportunity," Bernice said, emphasizing the word "if."

"I see," Oscar said, raising one eyebrow.

Their drinks arrived and although Bernice had tasted liquor at family functions and various parties, she had never before sat in a bar sipping fine liqueur with a foreign gentleman. She worried that her father would not approve, but that did not prevent her from enjoying the moment.

"A toast, to long lost friends, new acquaintances, and chaotic coincidence," Oscar proclaimed as he raised his glass to meet Bernice's.

"Yes, Mr. Wilde. To all of that," Bernice replied as she clinked her dainty beveled glass to Oscar's.

A strange silence fell between them as they suddenly became aware of each other's secreted sadness. Oscar looked at Bernice then averted his stare in respect for her privacy, while attempting to keep his own thoughts hidden. Abruptly, he checked his silver pocket watch and hastily swallowed the liquor remaining in his glass. He rose swiftly and threw several notes onto the table to cover the cost of their drinks. Shocked by Oscar's sudden withdrawal, Bernice lowered her glass to the table and dabbed her lips nervously with the silk napkin.

"I am so sorry, my dear, but my time here is finished. I must be off to my next destination. It was lovely to meet you and I will forever be inspired by your exquisite presence in the lobby," Oscar said as he bowed grandly.

"It was a pleasure," Bernice said, attempting not to stumble over her words.

Oscar raised his arm to acknowledge the rest of the bar patrons and then quickly exited the dimly lit room. Taken aback at the whirlwind experience, Bernice sat alone at the table with her drink. Finally, she looked around to see if anyone had noticed her embarrassment and was pleased to discover the crowd was far too consumed in their own discussions to have taken notice of her. With a slight grimace, she consumed the rest of her liqueur, placed the glass on the table, and discreetly exited the barroom. The Grand Marnier had made its way into her bloodstream, warming her face and putting a slight swagger in her step. She walked back through the hotel without much thought as to what anyone thought of her. She decided to keep her experience with Mr. Wilde to herself.

As she reached their rooms, Scott opened the door. "I'll meet you in the lobby in half an hour?" he said.

"Give me forty five minutes," she answered.

Bernice closed the door behind her father and allowed herself to swoon into the rich interior. She sighed and laughed out loud at her experience with the famous Mr. Wilde. Still reveling in the experience, she filled the bathtub and slipped into the water, giddy with pleasurable thoughts. She wondered about Mr. Wilde's sudden departure. What a strange, strange man, that Mr. Wilde. I must research him when I get home, she mused.

Time passed quickly as she relaxed in the warm water, but her internal clock sent out the alarm that she would be late for dinner with her father if she lollygagged any longer. She stood, toweled off, and slipped into the silk gown packed specifically for their night on the town. She twisted her long brown hair into a soft knot that provided a more mature look. Just as Scott's patience was about to wear thin, Bernice appeared at his side in the lobby.

"You look lovely, Bernie," Scott said forgetting his impatience.

"Thank you, Papa. So do you. Shall we go? I'm quite famished."

They arrived at Delmonico's just in time for their dinner reservation and were immediately seated at a table close to the club's famous dance floor. The waiters were plentiful and gracious, attending to each patron as if he or she was the only customer in the establishment. Scott ordered a scotch for himself and suggested that Bernice might enjoy a glass of champagne. She accepted his offer without thought of her previous alcohol consumption. When the sparkling white wine arrived, she drank it as if it were cool water on a hot day. Surprised at her ease with the strong taste of the spirit, Scott watched her behavior closely to see how much of the Irish tolerance for spirits she had inherited.

"So Bernie, what would you like to have for dinner?"

"I will try their famous tenderloin steak. How about you, Papa?" she answered firmly.

"That's a marvelous suggestion. I'll do the same."

"Shall we have a toast?" Bernice offered.

"Why, of course we should. To you, my dear," Scott said, lifting his glass in her honor.

"Thank you, Papa. Here's to me!"

They tapped their glasses and emptied the contents. Scott looked at his daughter with fresh admiration of her strong spirit. The waiter returned and Scott placed their order for dinner. Then the band assembled on a small stage and began to play.

"Shall we have a dance while we wait for our meal?" suggested Scott.

"It would be my pleasure, sir."

Bernice and her father twirled and stepped as the band played the newly released "Arbutus Waltz." Delmonico's was the only restaurant in America that offered dinner and dancing. This innovation was not lost on the young and impressionable Bernice Kenyon. She was enthralled with the experience.

When the waltz ended, they returned to their table to find the first course of their meal waiting. All evening the champagne flowed and gourmet delicacies were served, until neither Scott nor Bernice could eat another bite. They left the restaurant after a wonderful evening of dancing and dining, fully realizing that this was a night they would cherish for the rest of their lives.

Supporting his daughter on one arm, Scott used the other to hail a horse and buggy to carry them back to their hotel. Exhausted from a day full of exciting new experiences, Bernice fell asleep leaning against her father. When their carriage arrived at the Gilsey Hotel, Scott gently woke his daughter and guided her through the lobby and up the stairs. She stopped just before closing the door to her bedroom. "Goodnight, Papa. Thank you for tonight. This has been the best day of my life!"

"Let's pray there will plenty more! Goodnight, Bernie." Scott said, and turned to enter his own bedroom.

It was late morning before either of them woke. Bernice was the first to venture out of her bedroom, fully expecting to find her father waiting for her. To her disappointment, he was still asleep. Gently, she knocked on his bedroom door. "Papa, are you awake?" Bernice asked quietly through the closed door.

"What? Yes, I am now, Bernie. What is it?"

"Nothing, I was just wanted to see if you were awake. It's nearly ten o'clock, Papa."

"Oh, my! Well, give me a moment to wake up and get dressed. I'll meet you downstairs in the restaurant," Scott instructed her.

"All right. But, I don't feel very well this morning, Papa." Bernice confessed.

"It's from the liquor. Just have some whiskey with coffee and some food and you will be fine. It's called 'taking the hair of the dog that bit you,' dear. Trust me. It works," said Scott, chuckling.

Bernice dressed and went downstairs, irritated by the noise in the hallways and brightness of the lights. She kept her head down and walked without ruffling her dress. She entered the hotel dining salon and found a table in a quiet corner. A cheery waiter arrived to take her order.

"Good morning, miss! You look famished! What may I bring you to start this fine day?"

Wincing at the waiter's loud voice, Bernice spoke softly, "Coffee with whiskey, bacon, and eggs scrambled, rye toast and marmalade, please."

"Right away, Miss," the waiter responded, surprised at the call for liquor so early in the day from such a young woman.

Bernice waited impatiently for her drink to arrive and when it came, she sipped the harsh coffee to ease her discomfort. The smell of the whiskey made her stomach churn, so she added milk and sugar to mask the odor and flavor. By the time she had drained her cup, the effects of the hangover had eased, and when her breakfast was delivered, she found it surprisingly appetizing and enjoyed crunching the bacon and the buttered rye toast. By the time Scott finally appeared, her hangover was gone and she greeted him with a smile.

"Hello, Papa. How are you feeling?"

"A little befuddled, I must admit. Judging by your spirits, I see my remedy worked wonders," Scott said, still struggling to find his strength.

"Yes! Thanks to you, Papa. You should get one yourself."

"Yes, Bernice. I absolutely intend to do just that. Where is the waiter?" He raised an arm to draw attention to his table.

The waiter arrived promptly and raised one eyebrow when Scott requested precisely the same drink as the young lady. The waiter hurried away and hurried back with the coffee and whiskey, placing it gingerly in front of the well-dressed patron.

As the spirits made their way into his bloodstream, Scott relaxed and enjoyed his breakfast as well as the company of his beloved daughter.

"Papa, what time does our train leave tomorrow?"

"Around six in the morning," Scott answered.

"I see. What are we going to do after breakfast today?"

"Tour Columbia College. So, I think that we had better get a move on, don't you agree?"

"Yes, Papa. I do," said Bernice.

They finished their meal, exited the hotel, and stepped out onto the sidewalk of New York City. The doorman hailed them a carriage.

"Where to, Sir?" inquired the driver.

"Do you know where the new Columbia campus is located?"

"Yes, sir! A beautiful location if I may say so myself, sir. And it's not too far from here. It's up on Broadway and 120th Street. Anywhere after that, sir?" the man asked, hoping for an additional fare.

"No, young man. Just the college campus today, please."

Bernice watched intently as they rode through the bustling streets of Manhattan. The crowds amazed her. The city seemed so vibrant and alive in contrast to the sleepy, rural streets of Randolph.

Eventually the carriage pulled up to a huge, red brick building with a copper-sheathed roof. Bernice noticed that the cornice separating the second and third floors was inscribed with the names of some very famous men, American statesmen and scholars such as George Washington, Alexander Hamilton, Abraham Lincoln, and Daniel Webster. Tears of pride welled up in her eyes, prompting her father to give her a little hug. They spent the rest of the morning and part of the afternoon touring the college campus.

"Oh, Papa! Isn't there some way that I could attend a college like Columbia?" Bernice asked as they were leaving.

"No, Bernice, I'm afraid not. Columbia, like most American universities, is for men only. The only universities that allow women are too far from our home in Randolph. Your mother and I have discussed this and would fear for your well-being if you were so far away from our protection. I'm sorry, dear, but we must find some other solution. We can discuss possibilities when we return home," Scott said, closing the subject.

It was early evening before they returned to the Gilsey Hotel. Famished, they ate again at the hotel restaurant and then climbed the stairs that led to their rooms. The gaiety of the prior evening had taken its toll on them and they retired early.

As the sun rose over the East River, Bernice and Scott were boarding the train bound for Randolph, bidding farewell to the magical city of New York. By the time the train lurched out of Grand Central Station, Bernice's thoughts concentrated on one thing and one thing only: how would she convince her parents to allow her to attend an American university? Hours later, as their train pulled into the tiny Randolph station, she still had not formulated a plan.

CHAPTER ELEVEN

THE TRAIN TRIP HOME PROVED TO BE remarkably uneventful in direct counterpoint to their stay in New York City. Bernice and her father arrived at the Randolph Station in late afternoon. One of the stable boys was waiting for them with a carriage and he drove them back home. When Scott saw Olive was standing on the front porch waiting for them, he became alarmed. He jumped from the carriage and strode towards his wife.

"Olive, darling! What is it? What's happened? Is everyone all right?"

"No, no, no, Scott! You misunderstand! We have received wonderful news while you two were away. Bernice, dear, come here. You won't believe what has happened!" Olive exclaimed.

Bernice hurried to the porch. "Whatever are you talking about, Mother?"

"I believe the good Lord has heard your prayers, Bernice. Come inside where it is at least a little cooler, and I'll tell all."

Once inside the parlor, Olive, flanked by her smiling daughters, Edith, Morna and Dora, said, "Oh, my! Where to start? That's the problem. Well, I guess anywhere will do. Right after you two left, the Chamberlin Institute Board of Directors held their monthly meeting and you will never believe what they voted to do!" Olive said, pausing to catch her breath.

"For the love of God, Mother! Spill the beans, would you? What in the world is it?"

"Bernice, the board of directors has voted to allow women to attend all of the courses offered at the Institute! And they will begin accepting applications for the fall semester immediately!

You and your sisters will be in the first class of women to attend the Institute as regular students. This is a huge victory for the Suffrage Movement here in Cattaraugus County! Can you believe it?"

Silence filled room. Bernice finally spoke up. "I must be dreaming, Mother. I thought you just said that I would be attending regular classes at the Chamberlin Institute this fall. I cannot believe it! I simply cannot believe it!"

By the end of the evening, it was decided that all four girls would attend studies at the Institute. Edith, Morna, and Dora applied for the Teachers Normal Course. Bernice grudgingly agreed to enroll in the Teachers Normal Course, but also applied for admission to classes that offered instruction in modern business. Although it was most uncommon for a woman to have an interest in the financial aspect of business, it was becoming popular to have female secretaries and receptionists working in the field of commerce.

The Chamberlain Institute was nearly fifty years into its history by the time Bernice enrolled at the progressive liberal academy. The school had been endowed and funded by Judge Benjamin Chamberlain, who had not attended formal educational facilities himself, yet found it pertinent to maintain the school in his will. Originally known as the Randolph Academy, the title was changed to honor the financier who built a beautiful boarding house to increase the prominence of the growing institution. Teachers and students came from afar to participate in the academic developments taking place within the small, yet esteemed place of study. Located within a farming community, the Institute brought a cultural explosion of refinement and intellectual enlightenment to an area that was particularly hungry for it. Although Bernice maintained her residence at the family farmhouse in Coldspring and thus did not experience the independence of living with her peers at the boarding facilities, she flourished among the freethinking students exploring ancient and modern wisdom.

At the turn of the century, the nation was undergoing a major societal reconstruction to accommodate new lifestyles permeating America. With the youth of the country at the forefront of this evolution, secondary schools and universities became hotbeds of enthusiastic insight and investigation. No longer satisfied with a political system based on financial monopolies of the wealthy and powerful, new voices of progressive thought and actions were heard throughout the land. Citizens of the United States were regaining the optimism ripped from them when the 1893 depletion of gold reserve terrified the populace.

The enthusiasm of an empowered upper class filled the Chamberlain Institute with a student body aware of their ability to influence, transform, and participate in the development of the country. Bernice was among the few women who gathered outside the boarding hall every afternoon. There she would discuss the politics of business and how to succeed in a world run by capitalism.

"Gentlemen, please," interrupted Bernice. "Do you really expect to accomplish anything by shouting your opinions at one another? It is obvious that the only solution is to use both of your ideas to unite the forces trying to influence the powers that be." Bernice addressed her words directly to Bill Dobbs and Teddy Clark, the young men who had been arguing incessantly over how to keep the voice of the people alive in government.

"What are you saying exactly, Bernice?" said Teddy.

"I'm simply stating that you are both right. Teddy, you want to get a common man into office in order to have internal forces working for us, while Bill feels such an act would leave the masses vulnerable to that individual's integrity. Am I correct in my understanding?" she asked.

"Yes." The men agreed.

"So, why not have the unions represented internally under contract so that the voting populace can control the advocate and have the power to remove anyone from authority if we feel their actions don't serve our needs?"

"That is a lovely idea in theory, Miss Kenyon, but in actuality, the possibility of positioning that sort of hierarchy is entirely fantastic," Bill retorted snidely.

"Well, not necessarily, Bill," said Teddy. "What Miss Kenyon is suggesting is strategy, regardless of the structure, and that, my friend, is exactly what the farmers and working men have been without all these years!"

"Teddy, you worry me when you take up sides with a woman! I say we retire to the Men's Dormitory where we can discuss this matter privately amongst us men," Bill responded, effectively cutting off Bernice from further interaction.

The small crowd of young men cheered Bill's suggestion and made their way into the dormitory leaving Bernice outside. Her frustration with being a woman in a man's world fueled a fire of ambition. Bernice wanted to compete fairly, on an equal level with men, but it was apparent that she would not be granted that opportunity. It was on a warm, spring afternoon that Bernice committed herself to achieving equality with men, no matter the cost or sacrifice. The passion that blossomed that day transformed Bernice from girl to woman. A merciless work ethic replaced the delicate manner that had kept her power hidden. Scott and Olive noticed the change as their youngest daughter developed an increasingly aggressive demeanor. They assumed, incorrectly, that her exposure to higher education was instilling her with self-confidence.

Bernice spent her spare time reading books and newspapers in an effort to keep abreast of the political and economic developments around the globe. Her sisters and mother, concerned that Bernice was becoming a social recluse, attempted to draw her away into more social behavior. But Bernice was not inclined to participate in what she deemed "superficial events." Eventually, they all gave up and Bernice was allowed to become a ghostly figure in the Kenyon household.

When Bernice had exhausted the supply of books available in the Institute's library, she began perusing book lists from New York publishers. In one such list, she came across a volume containing true life experiences recounted by criminals incarcerated the New York penal system. When she obtained a copy, she was appalled to discover the filthy conditions of the prisons, as well as the brutal treatment meted out by prison personnel. She wondered how many of the inmates contained in the nation's prisons might actually be innocent. And, of those who were guilty, how much of their behavior was a result of their environment. Reading a newsletter distributed by the New York Prison Association, she came across a statement made by Gideon Haynes, a retired warden of a Massachusetts prison in Charlestown. Bernice was relieved to learn that someone in the country had dedicated his life to the betterment of mankind. As a result of these readings, Bernice developed a lifelong interest in the rights of men and women who had entered the wrong end of the legal system.

Without neglecting her educational duties, Bernice took it upon herself to research stories written by inmates throughout the country. Their tales of inhumane treatment, deplorable living conditions, and severe punishment spurred her to correspond with those who extolled the virtues of rehabilitation versus punitive incarceration. A strong desire arose in her to become a champion of the downtrodden. She understood, finally, that her life had been one of privilege and she vowed not to waste that privilege; she would not ignore the plight of those less fortunate. Her life's work would be advocacy for those who could not speak for themselves.

As her time at the Chamberlain Institute was ending, Bernice searched for a job that would allow her to hone her administrative skills and serve as a humanitarian. Although she received many offers due to her exceptional academic record, she delayed accepting any of the proposals. Instead, she sent out inquiries to local law enforcement agencies, jails, prisons and courts of law. One morning, as she searched through her mother's desk for blank parchment paper, Bernice uncovered a box filled with correspondence from Addie Blessing. Without a thought to her mother's privacy, Bernice sat down at Olive's desk. The letters spanned almost twenty years. She selected the most recent one:

26~June~1901

Dearest Olive,

How are you my dear friend? I miss you so much! Everything here is flowing right along as usual. Lynn is working with his father in the studio as J.H.'s protégé. Honestly, I feel he has far more sensitivity and artistic ability than his father and I believe he will gain even more renown as a photographer. Please keep that between us, though. I would never want my beloved J.H. to think I have lost my admiration for his genius.

Harry is doing well in school and, although he has no interest in art or photography, he has his father's keen mind, which will serve him well in any endeavor he chooses.

Little Bess is the darling of the town, always surrounded by a gaggle of girls chattering away about something or other. I feel we won't have any trouble finding our daughter a good husband.

Speaking of husbands, have you had success finding a husband for Morna or Dora? I always keep my eyes open for any possible suitors for those lovely girls. Your last letter noted that Morna was playing the organ at church every Sunday. That is wonderful! Edith, I'm sure, has been swarmed with offers for marriage, but don't let her accept any quite yet. I know Lynn has deep feelings for her and would one day love to offer her his hand in marriage – when his profession has been properly established, of course.

And what of Bernice? Has she found a suitor yet? I'm sure she will. She is so bright and so very talented! I am surprised no man has swept her up off her feet and claimed her for his own.

The house on River Street that you have had your eye on has been recently been offered for sale. I agree that it would be a perfect place for you and your family. It is surrounded by such beautiful gardens in the spring, and there is ample space for your future grandchildren to play in when they come to visit you and Scott! I know you would be so happy there and I would be so happy to have you so close to me!!

Please write soon and visit even sooner if you can.

Love,

Addie

Bernice was reminded of the conversation she'd had with her father years ago in New York City regarding her mother's dream of living in Salamanca close to her dear friend Addie. Bernice was just closing the desk drawer when her mother walked into the room.

"What are you doing in here, Bernice? Are you rummaging through my things?" Olive demanded.

"I was just looking for some parchment, Mother."

"And have you found what you were looking for?"

"No, I didn't. I stumbled across some of your letters and couldn't help but read one of them."

"I see," Olive replied icily.

"Forgive me, Mother. I didn't mean to invade your privacy. It was thoughtless of me. But now that I have read the letter, I realize that Mrs. Blessing really wants you and Papa to move to Salamanca. What do you think about that?"

"Well, I have been trying to get your father to move there for years. Salamanca is a magical place to me and I would love to spend the rest of my days there," Olive replied, forgetting her daughter's transgression.

"And what does Papa say about that?"

"He says one day it might be a good idea," Olive replied, letting out a sad sigh.

"I would love to see the house on River Street. Have you seen it in person?"

"Yes, I came across that house one day when Addie and I walked up River Street to meander along the Allegheny River. I just wish I could get your father to take a look at it. I know he would fall in love with it," Olive said, a twinkle in her eye.

"How are we going to get him there?" asked Bernice.

"How are *we* going to get him there? Are you willing to help me with this?" Olive said with growing excitement.

"Of course I will, Mama. Your happiness means everything to me."

"Well, how about finding a good, young man and marrying him? That would make me very happy," Olive said with a Cheshire cat grin.

"How about we move onto something with a better chance of success, Mama? I'm far from ready for marriage. You know that," Bernice said, laughing.

"Well, if anyone can convince your father to move to Salamanca, it's you, Bernice. He absolutely worships the ground you walk on. I would be eternally grateful for your help. However, that doesn't mean I'm going to let up on finding you a respectable suitor."

"I wouldn't think it would, Mama! After all, I get my strong will from you, contrary to what Papa might think."

"You're a good daughter, Bernice. I love you dearly," Olive said softly.

"And you're a good mama. And I love you, too," said

Bernice as she kissed her mother's cheek.

"Leave Papa to me. He is mere putty in my hands! No one knows him better than I do, with the exception of you!"

Bernice contemplated the best approach to get her father to view the large estate on River Street in Salamanca. She considered appealing to his shrewdness for financial gain, but lately the fiery ambition that had once pushed him towards wealth seemed to have been replaced by a mere simmer of satisfaction for his past success. By putting herself in her father's shoes, pretending she was a powerful man of fifty-seven with a family of grown children and a flawless reputation in the community, Bernice concluded that he was motivated by simple pleasures and enjoyment of life. She carefully planned her approach. In order to appeal to his masculine ego, she knew he must never know she was trying to influence him.

The next evening, Bernice went to her father after dinner as he sat smoking his cigar on the front porch. She watched as he rocked back and forth in the old porch swing. "Hey, Papa. I see you're enjoying the sunset this evening."

"Yes, I am, Bernie. Why not sit down and join me?"

"I think I will, Papa. Thanks. By the way, I haven't found a good place to start work yet, but I will soon."

"I know you will. Take your time and find the right opportunity. There's no rush, Bernie. Enjoy this time. It's special."

"Yes, Papa, I will."

"It's a beautiful evening isn't it? Glad it's not too cold yet. I don't tolerate the cold like I used to, Bernie," Scott said, staring off into space.

"Yes, I guess that's a natural progression. You know what, Papa? I think Mama seems to be slowing down quite a bit these days. Have you noticed?"

"Yes I have. I worry about her health quite a bit. Her body

has never been as strong as her will, but fortunately, she has no intentions of leaving us anytime soon. I can assure you of that."

"Oh, I agree. I was just thinking about how great it would be if we could do something special for her. I mean she has taken such good care of us for all these years and never really asked for much in return," Bernice spoke carefully.

"That she has," Scott agreed.

"The only thing I ever remember her asking for was to live in Salamanca to be closer to the river and her friend, Mrs. Blessing," Bernice mentioned casually.

"I suppose you are right," said Scott, striking a match to relight his cigar.

"Well, maybe one day you'll be her knight in shining armor and whisk her off to her dream house in Salamanca," Bernice suggested.

"Hmmm, never thought she needed that," Scott said, blowing a puff of smoke across the night sky.

"Every woman needs that, Papa, in some form or another."

"Really, even you, Bernie?" said Scott, surprised by her statement.

"Okay! Most women, then."

"Ha! You're a real corker, Bernie!" Scott laughed.

"Well, what can I say? I take after my father," Bernice said as she leaned over to kiss him goodnight.

"Oh, I see. You're turning in early?"

"I'm going to do some reading first. Good night, Papa! Sweet dreams," Bernice whispered as she walked into the house.

"Goodnight, Bernie," Scott said, looking over his shoulder to see her walk through the door.

Pleased with the seeds she planted, Bernice headed upstairs to her room and smiled knowing it would not take too long for her father to realize what he had to do. As she lay in bed, she stroked the quilted spread her mother had sewn for her so many years ago.

Her fingertips played over the stitching as she imagined what it would be like to live in Salamanca and how happy it would make her mother. Bernice felt that her father would come to appreciate the lifestyle that town life offered. Eventually, she drifted off to sleep.

The next morning Bernice could not stop thinking about the house on River Street. She was sure her father needed to buy it and move the family there. When she arrived at the breakfast table to share the meal with her sisters, she was surprised to see her mother and father waiting for her.

"Good morning, everyone," Bernice said, curious about what would come next.

"Good morning, Bernie," Scott said. "Sit down. There is something I want to talk to you and your sisters about."

"Yes, sir," Bernice answered, somewhat nervous by the strident tone of her father's voice.

"I have made some decisions that will affect all of you and although they may be difficult to accept, I hope you all are willing to listen before reaching any hasty conclusion," Scott announced, looking each woman in the eye.

"What is it, Scott? Are we in financial trouble?" Olive asked, growing concerned with the seriousness of his manner.

"No, dear. We are more than solvent, I assure you. I've been doing a lot of thinking lately. It is no secret that I am getting up in years and I feel it is time for me to slow down my lifestyle and settle into a more enjoyable pace of living. In order to do that, I have decided to sell the farmhouse, the business in Randolph, and find us a new home somewhere in the town of Salamanca. I realize this is sudden, but I have been thinking about it for nearly a decade and I know your mother wants this. But it's up to you girls to make this move work well for all of us."

"Really, darling? Are you sure this is what you want?" Olive asked, tears filling her eyes.

"Absolutely sure!" Scott said. "I sat awake until dawn letting it roll around in my mind and I just know this move will be the best thing for all of us. This farm property place will sell instantly. I've have had several lucrative offers over the past few years. I'll contact some people as soon as we are ready."

"Well! This is so sudden! I just feel dizzy. I mean, Papa, this is just so much for me to absorb," Dora whimpered.

"Yes, I agree Papa! This is such a shock. Are you sure this is the best thing, really? I suppose if you think it is best, it must be. We have so much to do! It's overwhelming. Our whole life is here. How will we move everything? What about the school? Where will we teach? What about our friends? This is so sudden!" Morna said frantically.

"Oh, it will be fine Morna and Dora. Don't you worry. You won't need to do a thing," Bernice snapped, rolling her eyes at the dramatic reaction of her sisters.

"Well! I think it is wonderful, Papa! I can't wait. I'm so excited, I want to start packing right now!" Edith squealed.

"Yes, I thought you might be somewhat pleased at the idea. I'm sure the Blessings will be happy to have you over for supper as often as you are available," Scott smiled, implying his awareness of Edith's not-so-secret crush on Lynn Blessing.

"Oh, Papa! Stop! You're making me blush," Edith giggled, burying her wide smile in her napkin.

"All right then! I will plan a trip for your mother and me to visit some homes in Salamanca as soon as possible. I think this is something she and I should do alone," Scott said, placing his hand on Olive's and glanced in her direction.

Overcome with emotion, Olive squeezed Scott's hand firmly as tears flowed down her face and laughter burst from her mouth. Bernice felt the tremendous love between her parents. Morna and Dora, oblivious to anyone else as usual, spent the rest of the morning meal whispering to one another. They kept their upset hidden from the rest of the family. Edith positively glowed after hearing the news, sure that Divine Providence had intervened on her behalf. Moving to Salamanca would bring her closer to the man she loved. Lynn Blessing was all she could think about these days.

Olive immediately rang up Addie on their new telephone and upon hearing the news, J.H. immediately went out to set up appointments for the Kenyons to view various properties available for purchase in Salamanca. He had photographed nearly every family in the town of Salamanca and had intimate knowledge of almost every business opportunity in town.

Olive's first priority was to view the house on River Street that she had fallen in love with so many years ago. The stunning home was a Victorian beauty. Nothing would make her prouder than to be the lady of such a fine house. Her dreams of social prominence and respectability had manifested beyond her fondest desires. The house on River Street would embody all that and more. Scott noticed Olive's preference, which inspired him to move quickly towards the purchase of that property. Over the years, he had conquered nearly every mountain he set to climb, and now it was imperative for him to fulfill the desire of the woman who was the object of his deepest affection.

The letters Bernice had accidentally stumbled across revealed how close her mother was with Addie Blessing and explained the way the two women had worked to manifest their dreams. Bernice knew her parents would return from Salamanca having bid a fair price on the house her mother cherished. She asked her mother to speak with Mrs. Blessing about possibilities for a job in Salamanca.

"Of course I will, Bernice! By the way, thank you for influencing your father's decision to move to Salamanca."

"Oh, think nothing of it, Mama. All I did was plant a seed in Papa's mind. He watered it and made it grow. I guess he was thinking about it all along. I just gave him a gentle push in the right direction at the right time. It's called synchronicity, Mama," Bernice said, happy for her mother and excited by Olive's cheerfulness.

"Oh, I hardly think your influence was as minimal as you say! I know what leverage you hold over your father. I've been watching you two for years, Bernice, my dear," Olive said with a laugh.

The synchronicity of the day's events continued when the mail was delivered and Bernice received a letter from the Western New York Home for Homeless and Dependent Children in Randolph. They were interested in hiring her to fill a recently vacated secretarial position in the principal's office. Bernice struggled with the decision to accept or reject their offer. She knew she would have to set up residence in Randolph in order to accept the position. It would be far too difficult to commute back and forth from Salamanca five days a week. With so much change afoot in the Kenyon household, she also worried that her lodging elsewhere would be too radical a change for her family. What swayed her in the end was the opportunity to interact with the juvenile delinquents being rehabilitated at the home. Early the next morning she found her mother sitting at the kitchen table sipping her morning tea.

"Good morning, Mama."

"Oh my goodness, darling! What are you doing up so early?" Olive asked.

"I haven't slept, Mama. I received a letter from the Children's Home in Randolph. They want me to start work there immediately," Bernice said softly.

"That's wonderful dear, but we are moving to a new town. I don't see how you can seriously consider their offer," said Olive.

"Yes, Mother. I know. But I want to accept their offer and stay in Randolph by myself."

"I see," said Olive, stunned by her daughter's statement.

"It's not that I don't want to be with you and the family, Mama. But my gut that tells me I should do this," Bernice said with heartfelt passion.

"Well, I am not the one you will have to convince. Your father will never stand for one of his girls living alone in town!"

"I can always stay with someone. I don't have to be alone. There is always a solution to any problem, Mama. Please support me in this," Bernice pleaded.

"Why the Children's Home, Bernice? There are so many other fine opportunities for you to choose. I am sure that J.H. and Addie can find you a wonderful position elsewhere in Salamanca."

"Mama, I really want to do this and I need your support. It will make a big difference with Papa. You know it will," Bernice insisted.

"I'll stand firm with you, Bernice, but I am not happy with your decision to leave home. I'll agree to it, but your father will never allow it. Mark my words, dear. Never!"

"All right. Let me talk to him. If I need you, I'll bring you in on the conversation. Thank you, Mama. Trust me. If Papa gives me his consent, you will not regret it."

Bernice pounced on Scott as soon as he entered the kitchen for his morning coffee. As she began her request, she realized she was not a free woman after all. Further, she understood that her father might as well be her jailer. To ask him to release his hold on her seemed, for the moment, impossible. Yet, nothing could deter her from attempting to wrest herself away from him. As Scott sat down at the kitchen table Bernice looked her father directly in the eye and said, "Papa, I'm going to take a job here in Randolph at the Children's Home. I need you to help me figure out where I'm going to live."

"All right," Scott answered without looking away from the

cup of steaming coffee his wife placed in front of him.

"You aren't going to disagree with my decision to leave home?" Bernice asked.

"No, Bernie. I've known all along that this moment was inevitable. I am only surprised it has taken you so long to ask for your independence. I know that you are more than capable of taking care of yourself, dear. If it were any of your sisters sitting here asking the same question, the answer would be absolutely no. They don't have your inner strength. You'll do just fine. And I have a great solution in mind for a place to hang your hat."

"You do?" asked Bernice in a tone that betrayed her astonishment.

"Yes. I do. I have calculated the proceeds from my proposed sale of the farm and the shop in Randolph. And, if I get my asking price for both, I will be able to pay cash for the house in Salamanca as well as for a house for you in Randolph. There will be plenty left over for your mother and me to live comfortably the rest of our lives. What do you think of that, Bernie?" Scott asked with big grin.

"Oh, Papa! You are the most wonderful man in the world! Thank you for having such confidence in me. I wouldn't be the person I am if it wasn't for your constant guidance! Oh, I can't wait to tell my sisters! This is just the absolute end! The absolute end!" Bernice kissed her father on the cheek and ran out of the kitchen.

Olive stood frozen in the middle of the kitchen, her mouth open in disbelief. When she recovered from her shock, she grabbed a towel from the stove and swatted her husband on the back.

"Hey! What the hell was that for?" Scott bellowed, nearly spilling his coffee.

"Why in the world would you ever give her permission to leave home, you big oaf?"

"Because if it weren't for Bernie reminding me how desperately you wanted to move, and how much you deserved it, I may never have made that decision. I just figured tit for tat. She earned it. She'll do just fine, Mother," Scott assured her.

"Well! I can't imagine she should live by herself. That is far too dangerous!"

"Well, I have a solution for that, too. Morna and Dora can share the house with her. What do you think of that?" Scott asked his wife.

Her reaction surprised him. His wife sank into a kitchen chair, buried her head in her hands, and wept.

"For the love of Pete, Olive. Now what's wrong? I thought that having the other two girls with Bernice would make you feel better about the whole thing. Honestly, I will never understand you women!" Scott rose and walked over to Olive to comfort her.

"Oh, Scott! Our house will be so empty. I don't know if I could bear the silence. We've had these girls with us so long, I can't imagine life without them," Olive said between sobs.

"Now, now, Olive. Calm yourself. It won't be all that bad. You know, this marks the major difference between men and women. The man wants to push his little birds out of the nest as soon as they are ready to fly. The woman wants to keep them under her wing for as long as possible. Let your babies fly, darling. They will be fine. Trust me."

"You may well have something there, my dear. Well, I guess I have no choice but to accept your decision, Scott. I hope you are right about this. I doubt that Morna and Dora will be happy with your decision, though," Olive said as she wiped away her tears with her apron.

Scott and Olive left for Salamanca by train the next day to meet with an attorney who would draw up the necessary paperwork for the River Street house. Upon their return, Scott successfully brokered deals for the Coldspring farm and the shop in Randolph. There was no turning back once he had formally accepted these offers. Olive tendered her resignation with the Chamberlain Institute and it was accepted with regret. Her outstanding work ethic would be sorely missed. Olive was overwhelmed by all the changes taking place so quickly. Morna and Dora were also having problems.

"Oh, Mama! Whatever shall I do when I have one of my attacks?" cried Dora.

"Really now, Dora! Don't be absurd," Scott interjected. "You'll have your sister, Morna, by your side constantly. Where's your pioneer spirit, girl?"

"Oh, Papa! I will surely perish without my mother's care. How can you do this to me?"

"Dora, listen to me carefully. You and your sister Morna are going to live with Bernice in Randolph and that's the end of it. Attack or no attack, you're going. Do I make myself perfectly clear?" Scott asked sternly.

"Yes, Papa. You do," Dora replied sheepishly, recoiling from her father and clutching Morna's hand for support.

Scott stomped out of house muttering in disgust. He encountered Bernice who was walking up to the porch.

"Hi, Papa. What's wrong? You look angry."

"Oh, it's those two pantywaists, Morna and Dora. If I have to listen to them whine one more time I'm going blow like a stack of dynamite! It's sickening, I tell you. Just sickening!"

"Now, Papa. You can't expect them to embrace this change without some resistance. They'll get over it soon enough. Morna and Dora just take a little longer to accept things. Remember the advice you gave me years ago – it takes all kinds of people to fill the world? I think that applies well here, don't you? Bernice said, watching him intently.

Scott's shoulders slumped with her advice. "Well, I suppose you're right. I certainly can't disagree with myself now, can I?"

"Good. Now let's talk about my search for a house in Randolph. I think I've found the perfect place for us, Papa. It's on Main Street, near downtown. It has three bedrooms, a large enough parlor, and a great kitchen for Morna. I've come to fetch you so that you can do the haggling with the seller if you approve of my choice."

"Okay. Yes. Let's go into town right now. I need to get away from the house and those two spineless wonders. I love them dearly, but honestly Bernice, they try my patience!"

Scott and Bernice drove the buggy into Randolph where they met with the owners of the house Bernice had picked out. After inspecting the property, Scott conferred with Bernice and agreed that the house would serve them well. True to his nature, Scott launched into an extensive bargaining session with the seller and emerged with a sound deal. The sale was contingent upon his receipt of the monies he would receive from the sale of his home and his business. They consummated the deal with a handshake. A man's word was his bond. Having secured a home for his daughters, Scott was now free to concentrate on moving the rest of his family to Salamanca. Within the month, the Coldspring household had been moved to Salamanca, and Bernice, Morna, and Dora were settling in to their new home in Randolph. Olive had been so busy with the preparations for the move that she had no time to reflect on the major changes taking place in their lives.

Soon a new rhythm developed. Olive wrote to her daughters every week, even though telephones had been installed in both houses. Olive preferred to write because it helped her to pass the time. It was a habit she kept for the rest of life. Bernice left it to her sisters to keep up the written communication with their mother and father, preferring to stay in touch by phone.

Morna and Dora eventually accepted their fate and grew accustomed to their new life in the Main Street house. While Bernice worked in the offices of the Children's Home, Morna and

Dora began giving music lessons from home. Morna taught piano and organ, while Dora gave lessons in the mandolin, a very popular instrument at the time. Dora would accompany Morna to church every Sunday in order to hear her sister play the church organ during services at the Grace Episcopal Church.

Bernice plunged into her new duties as secretary to the Children's Home principal. She rapidly discovered that the home's records were in severe disarray. Drawing upon the discipline she learned at the Institute, she began the long and arduous task of creating order from the chaos she'd inherited from her predecessor. The other secretaries resented her presence when they realized Bernice was all business and no play. She demanded excellence from them, a new requirement. As a result, the women resigned from employment, one by one. Bernice made sure they were replaced with educated women who did not balk at implementing her directives. Within two years, the home's office was operating at peak form. Mr. Dean Waite, her boss, turned over the duties of hiring and firing office staff, once he realized Bernice was an excellent judge of character.

By end of her third year of employment at the Children's Home, Bernice was depressed. The challenges her position once offered her were gone. The office was capable of running without her direction. Every day seemed like the one before, and tomorrow would be just the same as today. Her life was an endless stream of monotonous events. Plus, her position did not offer the satisfaction of interacting directly with the young children who lived there. One day she concluded that she needed to move on.

When she tendered her resignation, Mr. Waite became angry. "Miss Kenyon! What can I do to make you change your mind? Do you need more money? I'm sure that the board of directors would approve a salary increase for you. Name your price and, if it is within reasonable limits, I will seek their approval immediately!"

"No, Mr. Waite. Money cannot sway me from this decision.

It is time for me to move on. I have fulfilled all of my goals here and there is simply no challenge left in my position. My decision is final. Thank you for all of the kindness that you have shown me over the past three years. I especially want to thank you for the confidence that you have shown in me. It has not gone unnoticed," Bernice said with firm resolve.

"There is nothing I can do to dissuade you from tendering your resignation?" he asked.

"No, sir. There is not. May I suggest that you consider promoting from within to fill my position? There are a few girls on your staff now who could run this office quite competently."

"Very well then, Miss Kenyon. It is with sincere regret that I accept your resignation on behalf of the board of directors for the Children's Home," Mr. Waite said reluctantly.

Bernice left the following week without saying goodbye to anyone. It was her preference that Mr. Waite should tell no one on the staff about her resignation. She was too private to open herself up to the inevitable questions. She could only imagine their shock at discovering that she was already gone. However, excitement over the prospect of obtaining a new position with a new employer lifted her spirits. Bernice again applied to every law enforcement agency, jail, prison, and court of law in the county. Having done so, she sat back and left her fate to divine providence, sure that something exciting would come her way.

Chapter Twelve

Bernice found life at home far too mundane and needed something to occupy her mind. Her simple, yet momentous decision to terminate her position with the Children's Home had been made at a time when women were in demand for positions in the white-collar work environment. Within a week of Bernice's job inquiries, employment offers poured into her Randolph home. Unfortunately, the offers either paid too little or did not offer her the opportunity to work directly with the public. She began to doubt that she would find the right position unless she was willing to relocate far from her rural home in upstate New York.

Early one Thursday morning the telephone rang. Morna, who distrusted the device and hesitated before she lifted the receiver, found an excited Addie Blessing at the other end of the line asking to speak with Bernice.

"Oh, Bernice! I am so glad I caught you at home," Addie began. "Sorry to have rung you up so early, but J.H. insisted that I call you first thing this morning. While he was photographing the court clerk's family late yesterday evening, J.H. learned that a court stenographer had just been fired and there was a job opening at the Cattaraugus County Court in Little Valley! What luck, eh? The girl was apparently not proficient at stenography and made many crucial mistakes in recording trial testimony. J.H. told the man you were available for hire. Can you get to the courthouse right away? Today? The court clerk is considering another woman for the position, but I know you are far more experienced."

"Oh, absolutely, Mrs. Blessing, I can be there! This is wonderful news indeed! Thank you for calling. And please thank

Mr. Blessing for putting in a good word for me! I will leave for Little Valley immediately. Whom do I ask for when I get there?"

"When you reach the courthouse, go to the Clerk's office and ask for Mr. Elmer Kelly. He's the court clerk. He is expecting you sometime today. J.H. took the liberty of assuring him that you would be available this morning. And you are quite welcome, my dear. I'm sure your reputation at the Children's Home will precede you. J.H. said Mr. Kelly has heard of your work at the Home and is very interested in speaking with you. Good luck, dear. And be sure to call us as soon as you can to let us know how your interview went!"

"Yes, I will, Mrs. Blessing. Thanks again. I will be sure to call you back later. Good bye!"

"Yes. Good bye, Bernice," Addie said as she rang off.

Bernice sprang into action as soon as she hung the telephone's earpiece back on its cradle.

"Morna! Morna! Where are you?" Bernice hollered up the stairwell.

"I'm in Dora's room, Bernice. She's had another of her attacks. Oh, dear. I think they're getting worse!" Morna called down.

"Oh, for crying out loud, Morna! Dora has at least one of those a day and they haven't killed her yet. Come to the top of stairs, will you? I need you, right now!"

Bernice heard a muffled response from Dora, and then Morna appeared dutifully at the top of stairs, visibly flustered. Bernice issued a string of commands as soon as Morna appeared.

"J.H. Blessing has secured me an appointment for an interview with the court clerk in Little Valley. I have to get there as soon as I can! Go into my room and fetch my dark gray work dress, matching hat, and a pair of black shoes. Brush the dress and hat and give my shoes a quick polish. I'm on my way to the livery stable on Main Street to procure a horse and carriage. I will need those items ready when I return. Any questions before I go?"

"Yes! Which shoes, Bernice? I swear I've never seen a woman with so many shoes in my life! You know there are a lot of people in this world who can't even afford one pair let alone fifty or sixty like you!"

"Morna! This is no time for your blathering. Just pick one pair out and get them polished up. Now, go! Honestly, I don't know how I've tolerated you all these long years!"

Bernice returned to the house a half of an hour later with the horse and carriage. Morna had managed to pick out the right dress with matching shoes and was just finishing the coat of polish on the shoes when Bernice marched in the front door.

"How's this, Bernice? Did I get the right dress and shoes? Oh, dear, if I didn't, it will only take me a minute to run up and replace them."

"Morna, how many times do I have to tell you to stop your groveling? It's unbecoming of you. I'm your sister not your wicked stepmother. Thank you. The dress and shoes are exactly what I wanted. How's Dora, anyway?" Bernice asked.

"Oh, her attack subsided right after you left. I think she'll be fine now."

"What a regular miracle, eh? Yet another spectacular recovery by the indefatigable Dora Kenyon!" Bernice snorted sarcastically as she climbed the stairs with her dress on her arm and her shoes in her hand.

Within minutes, she descended the stairway again, carrying her hat and purse and hurried out the front door to the waiting horse and carriage. She climbed onto the carriage seat, jerked the reins and the buggy lurched off to Washington Street.

It was an hour's ride at a decent clip to Little Valley from Randolph. Bernice took advantage of the time to rehearse what she would say to Mr. Kelly he asked about her duties at the Children's Home. She guided the horse down Main Street through the villages of Randolph and East Randolph. Near the outskirts of East Randolph, she turned onto Jamestown Road and that led her through the town of Napoli.

She turned left on Fair Oaks Road and took it all the way into Little Valley. In Little Valley, Bernice turned left on Eighth Street, then right on Court Street and hitched the horse and buggy in a small gravel lot across the street from the brick courthouse. As she dismounted from the carriage, the bell in the courthouse tower rang out, marking the eleventh hour of the day. Plenty of time before lunch, she thought as she hurried up to the courthouse doors. Once inside, she bore right and walked into the Office of the County Clerk. She informed the secretary at the front desk that Mr. Kelly was expecting her. She was asked to wait; Mr. Kelly would come for her.

"Welcome, Miss Kenyon. I am Mr. Kelly. It's good of you to come on such short notice," the man said as he grasped Bernice's hand and gave it a gentle, polite squeeze.

"My pleasure, Mr. Kelly. It is good to meet you, sir." Bernice replied.

"Please. Step into my office where we can speak privately," he said, indicating the direction. Mr. Kelly closed the door behind him and walked around his large, wooden desk to sit down. Bernice took a seat in one of the two chairs facing the desk.

"Now, Miss Kenyon, did Mr. Blessing explain to you what position is open?"

"Actually, sir, it was Mrs. Blessing who rang me up and told me about the opening. Mr. Blessing was probably engaged with clients and far too busy to contact me himself. I believe you have a position open for a court stenographer."

"Yes, that's correct. Have you had any training in shorthand, Miss Kenyon?"

"Yes, sir. Extensive training I might add. I am a graduate of the Chamberlain Institute where I received excellent training in all aspects of secretarial duties. I used my shorthand skills often during my employment at the Children's Home in Randolph where I have been employed for the past three years."

"Yes, I know. Mr. Blessing reminded me of your employment at the Home. I hope you don't mind but I took the liberty of ringing up Mr. Waite and inquiring about your employment there. Whatever did we do before we had the telephone?"

"Things moved a little slower then, Mr. Kelly. I only wish more people could afford to add a telephone to their homes and businesses. I'm glad that you had a chance to speak with Mr. Waite, sir. I trust that you found everything to your satisfaction?"

"Oh, yes, indeed I did Miss Kenyon. Mr. Waite was obviously dismayed with your departure from his office. May I ask why you decided to terminate your employment there?"

"Yes, sir, you may. When I first started with the Home, I found the offices in a state of complete disarray. It took two years to straighten the mess out and for Mr. Waite to replace key personnel with qualified employees. Once that task was completed, there was really no challenge left for me. I informed Mr. Waite of that when I tendered my resignation. He was quite understanding, I must say."

"Yes. I got the impression from him that you are sorely missed. He stated that he would hire you back in an instant. He gave you a glowing recommendation, too. In view of that I would like to offer you the position if you think it might be something that would hold your interest, Miss Kenyon."

"Well, if I may be so bold as to ask, sir, what is the pay and what are the duties of the position?"

Mr. Kelly, thrilled with Bernice's confident and businesslike manner, detailed the pay scale, the duties of the position, and the hours that a stenographer might be required to work. Bernice stated that the job sounded exactly what she was looking for and that she would be happy to accept the position if he was ready to offer it to her. The only formality left before she was hired was to pass a short proficiency exam for shorthand. The test results showed that she had excelled, and Mr. Kelly hired her on the spot.

Bernice started at the courthouse early the next morning. She was given an orientation and tour of the courthouse by Mrs. Olive Brown, secretary to Judge Thrasher. She was allowed to sit next to Mrs. Brown and listen in on the day's proceedings. At the end of the day, Mrs. Brown instructed Bernice in the various types of proceedings she would be attending, and provided the shorthand symbols for the legal language she was required to record. Bernice continued to sit in on court proceedings the next week, watching Mrs. Brown intently as the woman temporarily performed the duties of a court stenographer.

Bernice began recording court proceedings during her second week of employment. Mrs. Brown, sitting at her side to answer questions, was very impressed with Bernice's skills and her excellent work ethic. By the third week, Mrs. Brown felt that Bernice was proficient enough to work on her own. Judge Thrasher was quite pleased to have a stenographer of Bernice's caliber in his courtroom. He was delighted to find that Bernice possessed far more confidence than any other young stenographer he'd encountered. When asked to read back testimony, Bernice read it with confidence. Challenges from seasoned attorneys regarding her accuracy were met in the same manner. Bernice never failed to hold her ground. Judge Thrasher's courtroom took on an air of professionalism that had been sorely lacking. He appreciated that Bernice did not hesitate to speak up when she could not hear or did not understand witness testimony or attorney examination. As a result, they formed an excellent team. Within the space of a few months, Bernice's reputation within the courthouse staff had risen from novice to expert. Bernice was happier than she had ever been. She had found her true calling.

Morna and Dora were elated at the change in Bernice's

behavior at home. She lost her sharp tongue and the tension in the household vanished. Morna was content to provide support and took over the running of the house. She thrived on nurturing Bernice and Dora, who were both comfortable letting Morna take care of them. The years that followed in the Main Street house would prove to be the happiest in their lives.

Meanwhile, their sister, Edith, continued to reside with her parents at the River Street home in Salamanca. She kept herself busy teaching at the elementary school while she waited patiently for Lynn Blessing to propose marriage. However, whenever the subject of marriage arose, Lynn claimed he could not honestly entertain the possibility of marriage until he was set financially. He refused to accept financial support from his father lest he become his puppet.

So, the waiting continued until the spring of 1906, when Edith announced that unless Lynn proposed marriage to her that evening, their lengthy engagement was over. Faced with the prospect of losing her, Lynn relented and asked Scott for Edith's hand in marriage. Olive was ecstatic when Scott gave Lynn his consent to marry his daughter. She and Addie wasted no time launching into plans for the wedding of their children.

Edith flourished in the limelight of the wedding preparations. The highlight for her was the day she was accompanied by her mother, her sisters, and Addie Blessing on a visit to the seamstress in Salamanca to order her wedding gown. They oohed and aahed over photographs in several gown catalogues until Edith came across the "Cinderella Wedding Gown." The dress had a sweetheart bodice lined with princess seams that complemented the A-line pleats of the chapel-length skirt. Beautiful beading and embroidery covered the fabric, adding an elegant touch. All the women approved.

Once the shop owner finished taking Edith's measurements, the group of women headed uptown to the Dudley Hotel for lunch.

Olive's giddiness prompted her to order champagne for everyone, raising the eyebrows of their waiter. They spent several hours languishing over their midday meal, but when it came time to depart, Olive's eyes filled with tears.

"Mother! Whatever is the matter?" Edith asked, voicing everyone's concern.

"Oh, girls! These are tears of joy not sadness. I've waited so long for this moment. I can only hope that we will be repeating this experience three more times with the rest of you girls. I am truly the happiest woman in the world today. You have no idea how much this means to me!"

The girls surrounded their mother with hugs. Their own eyes brimmed with tears.

Two weeks later the same group assembled again at the tailor's shop for Edith's fitting. When she emerged from the dressing room, they gasped. The fairy-tale-like gown fit Edith perfectly, both physically and emotionally. Bernice sighed as she pictured her sister walking down the aisle to meet her dashing young groom at the altar. Shaking her head, she returned to reality and rushed over to Edith to give her a hug.

"No! No! You mustn't crush the gown! It's only basted together! I leave it that way so that I can make any necessary adjustments before the final stitching," called out the seamstress.

Bernice stopped short as her eyes met Edith's. "I love you, Edith," she mouthed silently.

"I love you, too, Bernie," she mouthed back. Edith knew that nothing could come between them. Not marriage, not birth, not life, nor death could sever their bond.

The marriage ceremony between Lynn Blessing and Edith Kenyon took place in June at the quaint Saint Mary's Episcopal Church on Wildwood Street in Salamanca. Everyone who was anyone in Cattaraugus County attended. When Morna played Mendelssohn's Wedding March on the church organ, every head turned to watch Scott and Edith as they began their slow procession down the aisle.

Lynn, who had not yet seen Edith's dress, beamed with pride. Edith indeed looked like Cinderella gliding down the aisle to meet her Prince Charming. Scott relinquished his daughter to Lynn, who stood mesmerized as gentle tears slid down his cheeks. Edith smiled and reached up to brush his tears away. Lynn responded with a gentle touch to her cheek. There wasn't a dry eye in the house, including the hardscrabble entrepreneur, Mr. J.H. Blessing.

At the end of the lengthy ceremony, the priest said to Lynn "You may kiss the bride." Lynn wrapped his new wife in his arms and they locked into a kiss so personal that the audience felt like peeping toms peering into a bedroom window. Then the couple turned and faced the audience.

"Ladies and Gentleman! I announce to you for the first time, Mr. And Mrs. John Lynn Blessing!" the priest said in a booming voice.

The crowd rose from their pews cheering and clapping as they emptied the aisles one pew at a time. Morna, Dora, and Bernice threw handfuls of rice as their sister and her new husband crossed the threshold of the church doorway and through a corridor formed by the guests.

A carriage, decorated with bells and silver and white ribbons, waited at the end of the sidewalk. A tuxedoed driver held the door for Edith and helped her step into the shiny, black enameled coach. Edith tossed her wedding bouquet over the throng and all eyes watched as the flowers sailed over the heads of the hopeful Kenyon sisters into the hands of a very young girl. Olive sighed at the irony of the situation. Bernice saw her mother's expression and felt guilty.

Lynn followed his wife into the carriage and waved to the crowd as the driver took up the horse's reins. The crowd watched as the carriage made its way up Wildwood Street, on its way to the Kenyon house for the wedding reception.

Edith and Lynn's wedding reception was an elaborate affair. Beer, wine, champagne, and other liquid refreshments were abundant. When the five-star dinner was over, J.H. stood on a chair, and tapping his glass, proposed a toast to the Kenyon family, hailing the union of the newlyweds as the formal merging of the two families. Scott stood up and made a similar toast, acknowledging that he welcomed the addition of Lynn Blessing into the Kenyon fold. The toasts signaled that it was time for the newlywed's first dance. A small orchestra was on hand and when Lynn and Edith took to the wooden dance floor that had been laid over the lawn, the band began playing the "Blue Danube Waltz." The watching women grew maudlin. They sniffed into to handkerchiefs and daubed at their eyes. Their husbands took their hands and for a few minutes, long-lost young love was rekindled. When the waltz ended, it was Scott and J.H.'s turn to dance with Edith. Then J.H. beckoned everyone to take to the dance floor and they were happy to oblige.

Eventually, as with most parties, the younger set took over the dance floor. Their elders were content to sit and cheer as the youngsters "broke loose" on the dance floor. The new one-step and other ragtime dances were popular.

Bernice sat at a table with Orla Black and his wife Mary, watching the dancers bob. When Mary got up to dance a standard waltz with her father, Orla said, "Well, Bernie, old pal! When can I expect to be invited to *your* gala wedding event?"

"At the rate I'm going, Orla, that may be never," Bernice replied with a sigh.

"What a shame, Bernie! I can't for the life me figure out why some man hasn't already swept you off your feet. What's with that?" he asked between sips of champagne.

"You may not like the answer, my dear friend. Are sure you want to know?"

"Hmmm. Now I'm intrigued. Let me have it straight up. I

hope I can handle it. Sounds serious!"

"In all honesty, Orla, I haven't found a man who was my equal. The men who have courted me have been handsome, interesting, and intelligent, but they lacked one important quality. They were not powerful. I could have chewed them up and spit them out within six months of our wedding. All of the good, strong men like yourself have already been taken. But I still hold out hope. Maybe my king will arrive soon. Who knows? Until then, I have no choice but to suffer this long and lonely wait," Bernice said with slow deliberation.

Orla gazed at Bernice and slipped his hand over hers. "Do you remember that evening at your thirteenth birthday party when we were in your father's study? Do you happen to remember that brief moment before the gravy dripped off my chin and onto the floor?"

"Yes. Orla, I shall always cherish that moment. I felt as if I had gazed into your soul. It was wonderful, wasn't it?"

"I have always regretted that I did not seize that moment."

Bernice averted her eyes from his and gently slid her hand out from under his palm. "That was a long time ago, Orla. We were mere children. Let's not spoil that moment or our friendship with silly regrets. You have Mary now, and your children, and your thriving law practice. Be grateful, Orla," Bernice said, standing. She leaned over and kissed him gently on the cheek. "Thank you for being my good friend all of these years, Orla Black. It has meant the world to me. I look forward to many more years of your friendship. See you in the courtroom."

Orla's gaze lingered as Bernice walked away.

As dusk approached, the party began to wind down. Lynn and Edith's departure for the train station signaled its end; they were bound for a week's honeymoon at Niagara Falls. Bernice, Morna and Dora followed closely on the Erie train, ready for a good night's sleep at home in Randolph.

Winfield Scott Kenyon

Olive Guernsey Kenyon

Young Bernice Guernsey Kenyon

Morna Guernsey Kenyon

Dora Guernsey Kenyon

Edith Guernsey Kenyon Blessing

Addie Blessing

John Lynn Blessing

Bernice Kenyon Farnsworth at fifty

Bernice Kenyon's 1930 Chevrolet Sport Coupe

McGraw house – back view

Harold Farnsworth

Alfred "Freddy" Lindsay

CHAPTER THIRTEEN

LIFE FOR THE KENYON SISTERS QUICKLY SETTLED back into a pleasant routine. Morna rose early each weekday morning to prepare Bernice's breakfast and lay out her business attire. After Bernice ate and read the morning paper, she readied herself for the hour-long ride to Little Valley. She enjoyed the ride to and from the courthouse as it gave her time alone.

She solved problems and laid out many plans during her daily commute. However, her contentment with her life was seriously marred by an aching desire to fill the loneliness in her heart. She wanted what every other woman around her seemed to possess. She longed for a husband and a house full of children.

At night, in her darkened bedroom when she could no longer bury her emotions under the press of daily physical activity, Bernice's loneliness would seep out. She felt as though she was only half the person she wanted to be. Only a man could make her feel whole, and that man had not appeared. At twenty-seven, Bernice was worried about spending her entire life alone. Sometimes she would recall the words Orla said on the evening of Edith's wedding. She would never admit to him that she, too, wished he had "seized the moment." If she had responded to him that night, she feared that Orla might do something they'd both regret.

A strong and powerful man had replaced the chubby, graceless boy Orla had been as a youth. Bernice had long watched in silent admiration as he argued cases before the court in Little Valley. He was tough and tenacious, yet able to captivate the jury by playing on their emotions. Often, he held jurors spellbound during his closing arguments. And, as his reputation as a successful litigator grew in Cattaraugus County, she gradually saw more and more of him in Judge Thrasher's courtroom.

Meanwhile, Edith and Lynn took up residence in the Kenyon's Salamanca house. They wasted no time producing their first child, John Walter Blessing, in April 1907. His birth was a huge event for the Kenyon and Blessing families.

Morna and Dora were more than happy to take on the role of Auntie. Bernice however, was reluctant. She refused to fulfill her maternal instincts by living vicariously through her sister's offspring. Either way, she preferred to let Morna and Dora fill the traditional role, while she remained aloof from Grandma Olive's 'Little Johnny.'

Addie spent so much time at the Kenyon house with Johnny and Olive that it seemed odd on the rare days that she was not there. Both families had blended so well it became difficult to distinguish one from the other.

J.H. quickly tired of the newness of his grandson and returned to his studio in Salamanca within a few days of Johnny's birth. He grew irritated with Lynn when he discovered that his son preferred to stay home with his new son rather than attend to business downtown. It wasn't too long before he started berating his son for displaying such woman-like behavior. After a few unsavory verbal lashings from his father, Lynn begrudgingly returned to his father's studio. J.H. grew increasingly abusive with Lynn as it became clear his son did not share his fervor for the Protestant work ethic and unbridled capitalism. Lynn's life became an unbearable string of weekdays spent with a man he grew to dislike. The problem between Lynn and his father was due to a disparity of character. Where J.H. was aggressive, Lynn was passive. J.H. cared nothing about the plight of his fellow man, whereas Lynn cared too much about them. Lynn did not know that his father was ashamed of him. J.H. kept quiet about his disdain for his son only because a rupture might erode his powerful public persona.

Lynn immersed himself in a dream world. He drew cartoons in his spare time, fantasizing about a career as a famous artist. But Lynn lacked his father's ambition and drive, and thus did nothing to further that dream. At best, the cartooning became a mechanism for coping with the miserable time he spent in his father's studio. Residence in the Kenyon household suited Lynn well. No one expected much of him and he was unconditionally accepted for who he was. Olive and Scott cared only that Lynn made their daughter, Edith, supremely happy and was already producing grandchildren. They grew to love their son-in-law and his sensitive nature.

Their comfortable lives on River Street changed abruptly one fateful evening in the fall of 1907. Scott had been searching the house for Olive and he found her lying on the dining room floor. Unable to rouse her, he immediately sent for a doctor.

After making a lengthy examination of Olive, who had been somewhat revived and moved to her bedroom, Dr. Charles Willis gathered the family in the parlor downstairs. "I'm afraid I have some very bad news for you," he said. "Mrs. Kenyon is suffering from an incurable disease of the heart. You may know it by its old name – dropsy, or hydrops. Now we call it congestive heart failure. Olive seems to have had this condition for quite some time and it is a testament to her strong will that she's been able to function. I say this because I believe the disease is in an advanced stage. I can make her comfortable for now, but she will deteriorate regardless of any remedy I might offer. I am sorry to be the bearer of this bad news."

Scott sat motionless trying to digest this news. Edith clutched Lynn's hand and leaned on him for support. The doctor waited for someone to say something. Finally, Scott broke the uncomfortable silence. "May I assume, Doctor Willis, that this disease will eventually take my wife's life?"

"Yes, Mr. Kenyon," he responded quietly. "It will most certainly prove to be fatal for her."

"How long do we have before she dies?" Scott asked without emotion.

"At best," the doctor informed him, "one or two years. Maybe three. We will have to perform some tests to determine just how advanced her disease is before I can say more."

Scott made arrangements with the doctor for an appointment in his office the next day. Then he bade the doctor good evening and escorted him to the front door. Scott returned to parlor where and sat with Edith and Lynn. When Edith cried and leaned on Lynn's shoulder, Scott walked over and tried to comfort her, but he too was in a bad way. He excused himself and walked up the stairs to Olive's bedroom. Halfway up he stopped and called out, "Lynn, you'd better give my girls a call in Randolph. They need to know what has happened. I don't think I could do that right now. Can you handle that for me, son?"

"Yes, Scott, I can and I will," Lynn said as strongly as he could, masking his nervousness at having to something so distasteful. Lynn made the awful call. Bernice answered the phone.

"Bernice?"

"Yes, Lynn, this is Bernice," she responded. "What's wrong? You sound concerned."

Lynn stuttered and stammered before mustering the courage to deliver the bad news about Olive. "Your father asked me to call you," he began. "I'm afraid I have some bad news, Bernice. It's about your mother."

Wild thoughts raced through Bernice's mind. "What is it, Lynn? What happened to my mother?" she asked, shouting into the phone.

"Your father found your mother collapsed in the dining room

this evening and sent for the doctor. I'm afraid to say that the news is bad," Lynn said in a very quiet voice. "Doctor Willis has informed us that your mother is suffering from an incurable disease of the heart. I believe he called it congestive heart failure. Your mother's days are numbered, I'm sorry to say."

There was no response for a long time. Finally, Bernice said, "I see, Lynn. Where is my father? Why are you calling me and not him?"

"He is upstairs with your mother, Bernice, and could not bring himself to tell you right now. I think he is suffering from the shock of the news. I also think it would be wise if you and your sisters made for Salamanca first thing tomorrow morning. Your father will need all of the support he can get now. Don't you agree?"

"Lynn, I don't need you to tell me what I need do in this situation," she snapped. "Of course we will be on the first train tomorrow morning. I will have to make arrangements at the courthouse when I get there. Please have my father call me this evening as soon as he up to it."

"I'm sorry, Bernice," Lynn offered. "I'm only trying to fill in for your father. I didn't mean to imply that you wouldn't want to come right away. I hope you believe that."

"Yes, yes, Lynn. I apologize. You must realize that this news is quite sudden. Thank you for calling. I have to go now. I'll have to tell Morna and Dora. And we will need to pack. We'll be staying for an extended period. Have the housekeeper prepare rooms for us, please. Goodbye, Lynn," Bernice said as she hung up the phone.

Bernice headed upstairs to Morna's bedroom. Then she asked Morna to come with her to see Dora. Dora's reaction was typical; she fainted, and that made Morna panic. "Really, now, Dora," Bernice said. "This is not the time for one of your spells. This is about Mama, not you! So snap out of it and let's get packing. We're going to have to stay at Mama and Papa's house for several days. We'll leave on the first train for Salamanca. I'm going to walk up to the livery stable now and make arrangements to be taken over to the depot tomorrow morning."

The trio was in such a hurry to reach their mother that they made arrangements at the Salamanca train station for their luggage to be delivered later in the day. They hired a motorcar taxi to take them to the house on River Street. Had the circumstances been different, they might have marveled at the experience of taking their first trip by motorcar, but the novelty was lost on the young women. Bernice paid the driver and the sisters raced up the walk to the house and burst into the foyer much to Edith's alarm.

"Where's Mama?" Bernice demanded. "Is she lucid? Can we talk to her?"

"Yes, Bernice! Calm down! She's much better this morning. Papa is upstairs with her in her bedroom. She's very excited to see all of you. But, please, make your visit a little subdued. She is quite weak."

Bernice headed up the stairs, forgetting to remove her hat and gloves. She stopped suddenly and faced Edith who was still standing at the foot of the stairs.

"Does Mama know about her condition?" Bernice asked.

"Sort of," Edith replied. "Papa wants the doctor to give her the details. He just can't bring himself to tell her everything, if you know what I mean."

Bernice went back down a few steps and spoke in a hushed tone. "How is Papa doing?"

Edith sighed, "He went on a bender last night, Bernie. It was ugly. He emptied a bottle of scotch and then cried half the night, cursing God for treating Mama so badly. It broke my heart. I'm worried as much about him as I am about Mama." Edith broke into sobs, prompting Bernice to rush down the stairs and join Morna and Dora as they hugged Edith.

"Now, now, Edith. We're all here now. You're not alone in this. We'll weather this storm together. Let's try to stay strong, eh? Mama and Papa need us now, more than ever. It's our turn to care for them now. And we're going to do it as capably as they did for us, right?"

All three of her sisters nodded in agreement and wiped tears from their eyes. In that moment, Bernice took on the position of oldest sister without having to struggle or ask for it. The sisters knew deep down that Bernice was the strongest and most capable of the four of them, regardless of her age.

"Now," Bernice said, "we're going up to see Mama one at a time. I'll go first. We'll keep our visits short and we are not to make a big deal out of her condition. In fact, I think we should avoid mentioning it right now unless she brings it up. Right?"

"Right!" the girls said in unison.

Bernice turned and went back up the stairs. At the top, she turned right and approached her mother's bedroom door. Then she stopped, took a deep breath, exhaled quietly, and knocked gently.

"Papa? Mama?" she called out. "It's me, Bernice. Can I come in?"

She heard her father's voice, but could not make out what he was saying. With much trepidation, she opened the door to a very sad scene. Her father was sitting on a chair next to Olive's bed where she lay covered by a blanket. He held her left hand in both of his. He kept kissing her hand and mumbling something incoherent. Olive was fast asleep, unaware of his presence.

"Papa," Bernice said quietly, "It's me, Bernice. Can I come in?"

Scott turned his head as soon as he heard her voice. Shocked at his appearance, Bernice inhaled sharply. His eyes were blood red, his face haggard, and he was uncharacteristically disheveled. Bernice rushed over to his side and kissed him on the cheek.

"Papa," she said, "let me take over for a while. You look so tired. Why not get a little rest while I sit with Mama?"

Scott shook his head vigorously at the suggestion. "No, Bernie, I'm never to going to leave your mother's side again. She will be fine as long as I am here to protect her. I've always protected her and I'm not going to stop now. If I leave her, she might die. I can't let that happen. I just can't let that happen! What would I be without her, Bernie? She's my life. She's everything. I won't let her leave me. I won't!"

A chill ran through Bernice upon hearing her father's declaration. Seeing him like this, she knew her life and the lives of her sisters were never going to be the same. She drew upon the inner strength nurtured so many years ago by her father, and eventually talked him into leaving the room. She stationed Morna at her mother's side after eliciting a promise that if anything changed in Olive's condition Morna would call him immediately.

Bernice gently steered her father into his bedroom next door and forced him to lie down. His babbling continued. Finally, sheer exhaustion and inebriation took its toll. Mercifully, Scott passed out. Bernice stayed with him for ten minutes to make sure he was indeed fully asleep.

Gazing at her watch, Bernice realized that she had not called the courthouse. She dashed out of the room, downstairs, and picked up the telephone in the parlor. When Mrs. Brown answered the phone, Bernice asked that she fill in for her in Judge Thrasher's courtroom for the rest of the week, if necessary. Bernice headed back upstairs with Dora in tow, for a powwow with Edith and Morna.

The girls talked seriously for the first time in years. Bernice explained that life in the Kenyon family had, as of that moment, changed forever. Since Edith had little Johnny to care for, it was decided that Morna and Dora would move into the River Street house and assume fulltime care of their parents. Bernice reasoned that since she had her job at the courthouse she wouldn't be of much use during the week anyway, so she would remain in Randolph. She would visit every weekend to give the girls a break and to spend time with her parents.

Bernice rang up Dr. Willis to inform him that her mother was not strong enough to take a trip down to his office for further examination. The doctor agreed to see Olive again at their home, and would continue to do so until she was strong enough to come to his office.

Olive woke after lunch and Morna and Dora visited with her. When Bernice joined them, Olive asked if she could have some time alone with Bernice. Once Morna and Dora left, Olive wasted no time getting down to business. "Bernice, you are strongest of my daughters and I need you to tell me the truth about my condition. How bad is it, dear?"

"Thanks for the compliment, if that is what is was, Mama," Bernice said with a small smile. "It's not good news. Are you sure you're ready for this?"

"Yes, dear," Olive answered, "I've been ill for quite some time, as you must already know. I thought that maybe I could will it away, but that was quite foolish of me. I need to know, Bernice. I need to prepare myself and your father for what lies ahead."

"Well," Bernice began tentatively, "I'm not up on all the facts yet, Mama, but Dr. Willis believes you are suffering from a disease called congestive heart failure. It used to be called dropsy. He says that it is incurable and that your heart will continue to slowly fail."

"Yes," Olive said. "I understand. Go on. How much time do I have?"

"Oh, Mama," pleaded Bernice. "Isn't this something you should be discussing with Dr. Willis? He's the expert, not I."

"I want to hear it from someone I love, Bernice, not from a stranger. How long, Bernice?" Olive asked with steel in her voice.

Bernice sighed and looked down at the wooden bedroom

floor. "Two, maybe three years, Mama. But Dr. Willis still needs to run some tests to be sure."

"Does your father know this?" Olive asked.

"Yes, he does."

"And what was his reaction?"

"He drank himself into a stupor last night. I had quite a time getting him to leave your side this morning. He's sleeping it off in his bedroom. I'm worried about him, Mama. I've never seen him this way," Bernice said.

"Your father has always seen himself as my champion and my guardian," Olive explained. "And he has done an exemplary job at both. However, I think he knows that this time he can't come to my rescue. That's going to be hard on him. Can you think of any way to overcome this? You know him better than I do. And the thought of leaving him to suffer endlessly is more than I can bear."

The two women talked for the better part of an hour, discussing the best course of action to take with Scott. In the end, they decided he would need to be drawn into the tasks required to physically care for Olive so that he could feel needed. Perhaps it would diminish his feelings of helplessness. Bernice's task was to convincing her father that assisting his wife was what he wanted to do.

Bernice was waiting in the kitchen for Scott when he finally emerged from his bedroom late that evening. She wasted no time putting her mother's plan into action. "Well, well," Bernice exclaimed as Scott came in to get something to eat. "Look at what the cat dragged in!"

"Oh, shut up," Scott muttered. "I need your jokes like I need a hole in my head."

"Well," Bernice replied, "I see that you haven't lost your sense of humor. However, I'm not sure about your dignity. The jury's out on that one, Papa."

"Okay, Bernie," Scott said sharply. "Where are we headed with this conversation?"

"I think we're headed in the direction of 'Father makes a horse's ass of himself."

"Keep your opinions to yourself! You're not the one who's just been told your spouse of almost 40 years is lying at death's door!"

"You won't get any pity from me, Papa. I thought you were the tough guy around here. What's happened to that?" Bernice asked.

"The tough guy just got his ass whipped. That's what!" Scott shouted back at her.

"Papa! Quiet down," Bernice hissed. "Mama will hear you and I don't want to upset her! Is this your solution to Mama's dilemma? You're going to wallow in self-pity while your wife lies upstairs alone and afraid? You know, ever since we were little girls, Papa, the four of us thought of you as the quintessential white knight in shining armor. Please don't disappoint us now, Papa, not when we that white knight so badly."

The anger drained from Scott's face as he listened to Bernice's plea. He sank heavily in a kitchen chair, buried his face in his hands, and sobbed. "I can't help it, Bernie," Scott said between gasps. "I just can't help it! There's nothing I can do for your mother. Nothing! No matter what I do, she is going to die! How will I ever make it without her? I can't even remember what my life was like before I married your mother. It's as if we have been together forever. And now God is going to take her away from me just like that. I'm not ready to say goodbye to her. I'll never be ready to say goodbye to her."

Bernice rose and walked over to Scott. She cradled him in her arms and spoke to him softly. "No, Papa. You're wrong. There's a lot you can do for her. You can make her last days on earth the best of her life. She needs you now more than ever. You have two or three long years left with one another. Mama is going to be cooped up in her bedroom and you know how miserable that will be for her. She needs someone to take her out of doors into her precious garden. She'll need someone to take her out in a wheelchair in the spring when the lilacs and the jonquils are in bloom. Who will sit with her on the porch in the heat of summer and watch the raindrops bounce off the sidewalk? Who will take her to see the glorious color of the trees that line the river in autumn? Who will sit with her and sip hot chocolate in front of the warm fireplace in the dead cold of winter? Who will do these things if you don't? Mama needs you. You can be there for her now, can't you, Papa?"

Scott stopped crying and looked up at his daughter.

"You should have been a lawyer, Bernie. You could convince an Eskimo to skinny dip in a frozen lake at the North Pole during a blizzard," he said quietly. "Of course I can do those things. I can do much more than that. You're absolutely right. This isn't about me. It's about your mother."

Scott sat up straight in his chair and wiped the tears from his cheeks with both hands. His chair scraped noisily against the wood floor as he stood and squared his shoulders. "I'm going up to see your mother as soon as I get cleaned up. Does she know about her condition and the consequences of it, Bernie?" he asked.

"Yes," Bernice replied, "she does. We had a long talk about it earlier this afternoon. She's good with it, Papa. She's more worried about you than she is for herself."

"That's my Olive!" Scott remarked, "Unselfish to the end. God, I love that woman and I'm going to do the best by her that I can. You mark my words, Bernie. Her last days on this earth will be her best. I'll see to it. Thank you for making me see my selfishness. I might have soaked myself in self-pity for a long time if it wasn't for you. I'd have ruined everything."

"Oh," Bernice said, "I doubt it would have lasted too long,

Papa. I just sped up the process. Go see Mama, would you? She's waiting for you."

Bernice placed her hands on her father's cheeks and kissed him on the forehead. Scott smiled, kissed her back on each cheek, and left the kitchen. Bernice waited until he left the room before she sank back into her chair. Suddenly the weight of the situation bore down upon her and she buckled. She was mentally and physically exhausted.

Slowly, feeling as though she'd aged a decade, Bernice made her way upstairs to her room. She passed her mother's bedroom door and smiled when she heard her parents talking. She entered her room quietly and lay down upon the bed.

As tired as she was, sleep would not come. She realized that she would most likely have to dedicate her life to caring for her father and her two sisters, Morna and Dora. She accepted the fact that she would most likely never marry and, consequently, would never have children. She felt trapped. She felt betrayed by her father because he had not told her this would likely be her fate when he encouraged her to be an independent child. She'd made a poor trade, she decided. However, the deed was done and she would do her best in accepting the responsibility of caring for her family.

True to his word, Dr. Willis made Olive's final years comfortable by the administration of digitalis, a long forgotten drug. It regulated her heart rate and helped rid the body of the excess fluids that built up in her lungs and extremities due to sluggish blood circulation.

Scott became Olive's constant companion and they were rarely apart. Scott grew more accepting of Olive's impending departure and without realizing it, he built a plethora of memories that would sustain him in the lonely years that would follow her death.

Bernice made her pilgrimage to the River Street house every

Saturday morning to see her parents. Her life became limited to workdays in Little Valley and weekends in Salamanca. It left her no time for herself, a fact that went completely unnoticed by her family. And, just as unnoticed, Bernice slipped into quiet depression.

Olive remained with her family for another two and a half years. She was alive for the birth of her second grandson, Rupert Lynn Blessing, in the spring of 1909. However, by the following winter, her health had declined substantially, regardless of the digitalis dosage Dr. Willis administered. Once she became bed-ridden, Scott and her dear friend Addie took turns reading to her every day, as her eyesight had failed by then. Without vision, Olive's daily habit of letter writing ended. Many of her recent letters were for Bernice, even thought she knew her daughter would be there every Saturday. Over the years, she had filled reams of paper chronicling her life and the lives of those around her. Olive loved to be dramatic in her letters, which gave Bernice great pleasure. Occasionally, Bernice took the time to write back to her mother.

Death was an unwelcome but constant visitor in the Kenyon house. Thanksgiving and Christmas of 1909 were somber events for Olive was too weak to be moved downstairs for the festivities. She struggled for each breath and sitting with her, listening to her gasp for air, was painful. The family's deathwatch lasted all through winter but her demise did not come until spring.

On Saturday, April 16, 1910, Olive Guernsey Kenyon took her last breath at ten o'clock in the morning. Scott would swear later that Olive waited for Bernice to arrive before she allowed herself to die. Her immediate family was present, as was Dr. Willis and Addie Blessing. Scott's knees buckled and he fainted when the doctor pronounced her dead. Dora was upstaged for the first time in her life.

Although every newspaper from Jamestown to Olean

announced her death, the report in Randolph's *Register* summed it up best:

> "Mrs. Olive Guernsey Kenyon, wife of Winfield Scott Kenyon, died at their home on River Street, Salamanca, at 10 o'clock Saturday morning. She was a patient sufferer and death came as a welcome relief.
>
> During her long life in the Randolph area, Mrs. Kenyon was held in the highest esteem by the entire community. Although always frail, she gave of her strength unstintingly in the service of family and friends and was ever ready to extend a helping hand to the needy. Many will learn of her death with feelings of regret and the bereaved family will have the sympathy of all."

On the morning of Monday, April 18, after a ten o'clock prayer vigil in the River Street house, Olive's casket was loaded onto the Erie train number 7 and transported to Randolph. Her funeral service was held at the Congregational Church at two o'clock that same afternoon. She was interred immediately following the service at the Randolph Cemetery in one of the five plots Scott had purchased soon after receiving the news of Olive's deteriorating condition. Only Edith would be excluded from eventual interment there. Edith chose instead to be buried next to Lynn and his family in Salamanca's Wildwood Cemetery.

The advent of spring came and went without notice for the Kenyon family. Even the warmth of the lengthening spring days failed to remove the chill in their hearts. Scott withered physically but he also stopped managing his fortune and, for that matter, his life. He stayed up late and slept until afternoon. No one, not even his beloved Bernice, could stoke his interest in world beyond River Street in Salamanca. His only interest was reminiscing about his life with Olive. His conversations were punctuated with remarks about how Olive did this and how Olive did that. Most of his friends grew tired of it and avoided him. Only J.H. stayed true to his good friend. They spent many an evening together, hoisting glasses filled with an inch or two of scotch.

Relieved of her obligation to spend each weekend in Salamanca, Bernice spent less and less time at the house on River Street. She spoke with her father frequently by phone even though he hated the impersonality of the device. Every conversation ended with a plea to his daughter for a visit. When she could no longer invent excuses, Bernice would make the short trek to Salamanca for the weekend.

Scott was not the reason for the infrequency of her visits. Bernice could not bear to see the bliss of Edith's married life. Her depression would peak after each visit and once back at home in Randolph, she'd sit dejectedly in a rocking chair on her porch, staring into space, completely unaware that passersby could observe her sorrow.

Her life was marked only by the comings and goings of people at the courthouse. Judge Thomas Dowd replaced Judge Thrasher in January of 1911. Elmer Kelley, the County Clerk who had hired Bernice, had not lasted past the year he had hired her. His replacement was Charles Miller, who was replaced by Frank Merrill in 1916. Judge Dowd was followed by Judge George Larkin, in 1917. Judge Larkin presided over the County Court, the Surrogate Court, and the Children's Court. Bernice enjoyed being around Judge Larkin and following him into the courtrooms made her dullard life a little brighter.

Meanwhile, Scott worked himself into a frenzy when the United States joined the fighting of World War I, the war to end all wars, in April 1917. His had bitter memories from his service in the Civil War, fifty years earlier. Fighting for your country at home made sense to Scott, but he couldn't comprehend the benefit of fighting for your country abroad. His continual rantings brought on his first heart attack in the late summer of 1918.

Dr. Willis attended to Scott and managed to bring him back to health. He warned the family, however, that Scott must stay calm and stay off spirits if he wanted to live much longer. Scott, being a stubborn man, paid no attention to the doctor's warning and continued his one-man campaign to stop America's intervention in what he called Europe's Civil War. And his good friend, Scotch Whiskey, helped to fuel his campaign night after night. Scott's refusal to change cost him his life. He continued to drink to excess even after World War I was finally over, in November 1918. Morna found her father's lifeless body in his bed on the morning of March 13, 1919. An autopsy by the County Coroner set the cause of death as myocardial infarction, heart attack.

Scott was laid to rest next to his beloved wife, Olive, in the Randolph Cemetery. His funeral, like Olive's was well attended. As a veteran of the Civil War, he was given a hero's burial. When it was over, Bernice went into the deepest depression of her life. She did not want to face life without her father. She had not realized, until his death, what an important role he still played in her life. She returned to her house in Randolph and did not emerge for several weeks.

Judge Larkin paid a visit to Bernice in Randolph in an effort to convince her to return to work. He found her in a shocking state of depression and disarray. He pretended not to notice her deplorable condition and instead focused on his intent to persuade her to return to the Cattaraugus County Courthouse.

"With all due respect, Judge Larkin," Bernice said after Judge Larkin remarked on the improving weather conditions, "you didn't come here to discuss the weather, did you?"

"No," he said. "I came here to ask you to return to your duties at the courthouse, Miss Kenyon. I need you. The County needs you and the Great State of New York needs you. My courtroom has been seriously harmed by your absence."

"I don't know if I want to return, Judge," she responded. "Something happened to me the day my Papa died. Life just sort of stopped, you see. I stopped with it. I can't seem to get going again. Have you ever experienced that, Judge?"

"No," he answered, "I haven't. I wish I could offer you some advice gained from personal experience, but I can't. I have, however lost both of my parents, so I can sympathize with the loss of your father."

"And," she inquired, "how did you deal with that loss?"

"At first I didn't deal well with it at all. It was hard to get up in the morning and even harder to get to bed at night. Eventually the wounds I suffered from the losses of my parents scabbed over and I was able to move on. I forced myself to do it at first and then later it became natural."

"I see," she said flatly. "I can't seem to heal at all, Judge. The wound is wide open. I don't even want it to close."

"Miss Kenyon," he said, "may I be frank with you?"

"Yes."

"It has been a sincere pleasure working with a woman of your caliber in my courtroom. I have never had the pleasure of working with anyone who operates at your level of excellence. It truly sickens me to see you wallowing in this cesspool of emotion and wasting that excellence. Come back, Miss Kenyon. It will be your salvation. I promise you that."

Bernice sat and stared at Judge Larkin for a moment and then did something that took him by surprise. She threw back her head and laughed.

"You know what," she finally said, "I appreciate your candor. My father was the only man alive who dared to speak to me in such a brash manner. He was always brutally honest with me. You've made me realize what I will miss most about him. He never held anything back and he was always honest with me. That's more than I can say for most of the people I meet. How will

I ever replace that?"

"You won't, Miss Kenyon," Judge Larkin said. "There will never be another Scott Kenyon. He's gone, but you're not. It is that simple. He would want you to go on living your life. You know that, don't you?"

After a moment of reflection Bernice said, "Yes, Judge, I suppose you're right. He would. I guess I'll have to figure a way to pull myself up by my bootstraps, so to speak. I'll be back to work next Monday. I promise. I'll do my best to get over this. Papa would want that and I should, too. Enough is enough."

"Excellent," Judge Larkin exclaimed, slapping a hand on his thigh. "I assure you that it will prove to be the best medicine. See you Monday, Miss Kenyon!"

He rose and Bernice escorted him to the door. When he departed, she leaned back against it. She looked up at the ceiling as she spoke to her unseen father, "I can do this, Papa. I have to do this. If I don't I will surely die. I see that I'm not so ready to die after all. Help me, from the grave, Papa, will you? I need you to watch over me. I've always needed you to watch over me. I feel so alone, Papa. So alone."

Bernice returned to the courthouse on Monday, as promised. She was embarrassed by all the attention from her co-workers. Once she resumed her duties with Judge Larkin, she knew his advice was astute. She quickly immersed herself in work and eventually the pain of the loss of her father diminished.

Edith rang up Bernice at home one day and hit her with a bombshell. Lynn had discovered that Scott Kenyon was just about destitute by the time he died. Apparently, he had ignored his finances for years and allowed his wealth to waste away. The sisters had avoided Surrogate Court proceedings only because Bernice had shrewdly convinced her father to sign everything over to the girls after his first heart attack. They decided to sell the River Street house in Salamanca and move Edith's family to a less expensive property on Broad Street. Edith, Lynn, their two boys and their daughter, Olive, born in November 1911, moved into the new house, along with Morna and Dora. The sisters shared equally in the ownership of the new house and the proceeds from the sale of their parent's home. Bernice took her share in cash and began investing in real estate.

By early 1920, Bernice decided that she needed some extracurricular activity and applied for membership in the Randolph Chapter of the Daughters of the American Revolution. As proof of her eligibility, a copy of Allan Bent's book, "The Bent Family in America," accompanied her membership application. Bent's volume was published in 1900 at the height of America's interest in genealogy. The history chronicled the arrival of the Bent family in the Colonies in 1636 on the HMS Confidence and the eventual enlistment of David Bent, who fought in the Battle of Lexington during the Revolutionary War. Bernice was related to David Bent through her mother's family. The president of the Randolph Chapter was duly impressed and personally forwarded Bernice's application onto headquarters in Washington, D.C. They wasted no time in approving her membership. Her acceptance into the D.A.R. was a source of great pride for Bernice, for official membership established her as a true American blue blood. Bernice loved the meetings and their monthly fundraisers. And it helped to fill the loneliness of her private life.

Bernice also began to take interest in the Children's Home again. She campaigned for donations to the Home and helped to raise a record amount for the underprivileged children. She continued with this effort for the rest of her life. The town looked up to her as a pillar of their community and she basked in the attention and status it brought her.

J.H. Blessing suffered a stroke in the autumn of 1920 and sadly, Addie Blessing died suddenly in her sleep that winter. Lynn took over his father's photography studio in Salamanca when J.H.

failed to regain the use of his right side. J.H. sold his farmhouse and bought a small clapboard house on Clinton Street, not far from downtown Salamanca.

Three more routine years passed and Bernice hardly noticed. Her sister's family was blessed by the arrival of one more child; Robert William Blessing was born in April 1923, when Edith was forty-six years old. The sisters felt that the hand of providence had finally blessed them once again.

Their sleepy, rural county was awakened briefly when Judge Larkin announced his intention to relinquish his role as Cattaraugus County Court and Children's Court Judge in late 1923. Most felt he was far too young to give up his judgeship, but Larkin had other plans. He intended to secure a seat on the New York State Supreme Court. The hotly contested election of County Court Judge in November proved to be a fateful one for Bernice; her good friend, Orla Black, won it.

Orla had risen into prominence in Cattaraugus County and his fame as a litigator had spread throughout western New York. The Cattaraugus County district attorney groaned whenever he had to do battle with Orla in the courtroom because Orla's success rate was phenomenal. His knowledge of the law was surpassed only by his ability as an orator. The district attorney was ecstatic when he learned that his nemesis was finally gone from the defense counsel table in the Cattaraugus County courtroom.

Orla's first point of business on January 2, 1924, as Cattaraugus County Court and Children's Court Judge, was to appoint Bernice Kenyon as his secretary and court stenographer. This gave Bernice her first opportunity to conduct business in chambers as well as in the courtroom. Thus began the most successful partnership between a judge and his secretary in the history of Cattaraugus County.

CHAPTER FOURTEEN

ORLA EDISON BLACK WAS BORN ON AUGUST 24, 1880 in Knox, Pennsylvania. He was raised by William and Catherine Black, who instilled in him the importance of the Protestant Ethic: hard work is the proponent of a person's calling, and worldly success is a sign of personal salvation. His parents challenged Orla to work hard, be honest, play fair, and, above all, win at everything he chose to do. They also warned him of the consequences if he did not adhere to these tenets. It was only natural that Orla chose to study law at Syracuse University after graduating with honors from high school.

Orla excelled in college and quickly assumed the role of leader. He joined clubs and organizations whenever it enhanced his standing, and eventually he became their director or president. In his senior year at college, Orla entered and won the prestigious Chancellor's Day Oratorical Contest. Everyone at Syracuse knew Orla was meant for big things.

Orla graduated from Syracuse University in 1904 with a Bachelor of Laws. He passed the State of New York bar exam on his first attempt. Title Guarantee and Trust Company in New York City snapped him up immediately and hired him for their legal department. However, Orla was bored and quit a few months later. Erie Railroad hired him for their claims division in New Jersey, but that job lacked the challenges he craved. He quit after only two months in their employ.

In early 1906, Orla Black partnered with his college pal, Henry Nevin, and opened a law office in Salamanca, New York. This time he got it right. Within months, he began to rack up victories in seemingly hopeless cases in Cattaraugus County Court. It wasn't too long before clients came knocking and their success was assured.

Orla remained partners with Henry Nevin until 1915, when he decided to strike out on his own. He began taking on more criminal cases and his success continued. Unlike many of his colleagues, Orla would not defend a client if he were not convinced of the man's innocence. He wanted no part of what he called "sleazy lawyering," and would not help guilty men walk free. Many jurors assumed that Orla's clients were innocent just because they had Orla standing with them at the defense table.

It was a natural progression that Orla became a judge; he was the right man at the right time in Cattaraugus County. The Eighteenth Amendment to the United States Constitution was passed in January 1919. The National Prohibition Act was designed to reduce drunkenness in the country and therefore reduce crime, but it had exactly the opposite effect. The Eighteenth Amendment increased alcohol consumption per capita and Cattaraugus County found itself rife with crime.

Cattaraugus County lies very close to the Canadian border and it soon became a corridor for illegal shipments of Canadian booze. By the time Orla ran for election in 1923, the citizens of Cattaraugus County were howling for blood. Their meager law enforcement agencies were ill equipped to handle the lawlessness spreading like a disease throughout their towns and villages. The local citizenry wanted a judge who would throw the book at perpetrators who did get caught and then lock them up for good. They knew Orla Black could get it done. They were not disappointed. When it came to justice, Orla delivered.

It wasn't long after his election that Orla's reputation as a tough, merciless judge spread throughout the county. He became known as 'Old Hard Ass.' Every thug and thief knew he would serve the maximum penalty if he was caught, tried, and convicted in Old Hard Ass's courtroom.

Bernice played an important role in that courtroom. She scheduled the daily docket, recorded all courtroom proceedings, oversaw the mountain of paperwork, and handled Orla's correspondence.

As an officer of the court, Bernice was in direct contact with every important person in state and federal law enforcement, the New York Court System, and the New York Department of Corrections. They all had to pass through her to get to Orla. She felt fulfilled for the first time in her life. Her dreams of being an important cog in the wheels of justice had finally come to fruition. It was an added bonus that she had a modicum of control over an important and powerful man.

Wherever Bernice went, she was recognized immediately. People fawned over her. It was, Good day, Miss Kenyon! Yes, Miss Kenyon! Right away, Miss Kenyon! Whatever you say, Miss Kenyon! As time wore on, she usurped some of Orla's power simply because she was aligned so closely to him.

At monthly D.A.R. meetings in Randolph, the members no longer whispered their little quips of pity for poor, unmarried Bernice Kenyon. Instead, they greeted her as soon as she walked in and huddled around her as if she were a celebrity. For the first time in their lives, these women regretted their decisions to go along with the status quo and marry rather than take the risk of carving out their own destinies.

Bernice served as a role model and the women started removing their blinders, taking a good look at their own lives. They realized that Bernice never had to ask anyone for permission to do anything. Conversely, the women's husbands treated them much like children and controlled every aspect of their wives' lives. In fact, if their husbands had disapproved of their membership in the D.A.R, they would never have been allowed to join in the first place. In a small way, Bernice became a champion to these women and they in turn saw to it that their daughters would have more opportunities.

Because of their close friendship, Orla took Bernice into his confidence on all legal matters. In his chambers, it was not uncommon to hear them discussing the merits of the case being heard before him. Orla trusted his friend's input and was always willing to hear her point of view and allow her to attempt to sway his judgment, even though she was rarely successful.

Bernice had sat in on many famous trials during her tenure as a court stenographer in the Cattaraugus County Court. For example, she recorded every word of the nationally famous murder trial of Augustin Sanchez.

Sanchez was a migrant worker who murdered a co-worker, Jose Lizirraga, in Olean, New York. Lizirraga was killed in November 1919 for the wages he'd saved while employed at the Lackawanna Steel Company near Buffalo. The men were traveling together, returning to their homes in Mexico. Lizirraga had lost his job, the result of a strike at the steel plant that had begun two months earlier.

Sanchez was a Mexican national when he committed the murder and the Mexican government petitioned unsuccessfully for his death sentenced to be commuted to imprisonment for life. His impending execution was thrust into the public limelight when a famous attorney/investigator, Grace Humiston, threw considerable doubt on Sanchez's guilt. Her involvement was to no avail. Sanchez was electrocuted at Sing Sing Prison on January 17, 1921.

Bernice corresponded extensively with the warden at Sing Sing after the conclusion of the Sanchez trial. Warden Lewis E. Lawes was a vocal opponent of the death penalty and Bernice became one of Lawes' staunchest supporters in his campaign to abolish the death penalty, and for penal reform in general. This was the only subject on which she and Orla disagreed. Orla did not believe that criminals could be reformed and he supported the death penalty as a strong deterrent to crime. He would laugh when Bernice launched into an impassioned argument about the death penalty and penal reform. He would come to regret his insensitivity years later.

Bernice and Orla's personal and professional relationship progressed smoothly for five years following his election as County judge. That ended in September 1929 with the filing of charges against Herman Warner and Harry Race. Neither Orla nor Bernice could have known that the seemingly routine case would propel her towards a date with destiny.

On August 31, 1929, Harry Race summoned a cab in Gowanda, New York. Herman Warner responded to the call in his Oakland All-American Six sedan. He picked up Harry at the boarding house in which Harry had been residing for several months. Both men, unbeknownst to each another, were convicted felons. Harry gave Herman the address of his destination and the two started out down Jamestown Street. Within moments, they were stopped by two Gowanda police officers in front of the Hollywood movie theater. The officers recognized both men and knew they were both felons. The officers rousted them out of the cab and gave it a thorough search. One of them discovered a gun tucked into a pocket in the driver's side door.

"Well, well, boys!" Officer Albert Goss said upon discovery of the weapon. "What do we have here? Looks like a gun to me! And, if I'm not mistaken, you two are felons, aren't ya? And felons can't possess firearms, right?"

Officer Henry Friese chimed in and said, "I guess we got a couple of chicken-thieves today, Goss. Turn around you two. You're under arrest for burglary, larceny, and possession of a firearm by a felon. Ted Elliott saw you leaving his chicken coop last night with one of his pullets in hand, Herman. Was Harry your lookout last night?"

"No," Herman exclaimed. "I never met this guy in my life! And that's my gun. You guys know us cabbies have to carry protection from the criminal-types. This guy don't know nothin' about nothin'. He's just a regular fare I picked up a minute ago."

"You've nothing on me, officers," Harry grinned. "Looks like you're going to have to let me go, eh?"

"Oh! A real wisecracker," said Officer Friese. "Seems to me we found this gun on Harry, didn't we Goss?"

"Well, by god, I think your right, Friese," Goss said sarcastically, "We did find this gun on Harry, didn't we? Cuff him. You're both going down to the stationhouse on Main to be booked. Turn around like Goss said!"

Harry's face turned red and he started shouting obscenities as the officers slammed him onto the hood of the cab and handcuffed him.

"Keep it up, asshole and we'll add resisting arrest to the charges. Now get moving! Into the squad car, you two. Now!" Friese growled.

The commotion on the street brought out curious onlookers from Grace's Luncheonette. While Friese placed Herman and Harry in the back seat of the squad car, Goss began questioning men from the luncheonette. It didn't take long to produce a few witnesses were willing to swear they saw Harry brandish a gun at the Saturday Night Dance at the Gowanda Grange last weekend. And since none of them could read or write, Goss and Friese were happy to write their statements up for them and have them affix their X's at the bottom. Satisfied that it was all a done deal, the two officers transported the pair to the station on Main Street where they were formally booked on charges. The County Sheriff's Office dispatched a car later that evening and transported Harry and Herman to the county jail in Little Valley, where they awaited their arraignment on the following Monday.

After being searched and fingerprinted, Harry and Herman

were transferred to adjoining cells in the basement of the jail. Once they were alone, Harry began questioning Herman about the chicken theft. It turned out Herman had indeed stolen the chicken from the Elliott farm chicken coop. He apologized to Harry for involving him in the whole ordeal. By the time they were ready to turn in for the night, the pair had hatched a plan that would clear Harry of all the charges Goss and Friese filed against him. Herman promised to swear out an affidavit stating that Harry had no part in the burglary and that the gun was his, not Harry's.

When their court-appointed attorney appeared at their cells on Monday morning, Herman kept his word and swore out the affidavit as promised. The attorney, however, was less than reassuring that it would be sufficient to convince Judge Black to drop the charges against Harry. He explained that the word of a convicted felon would mean nothing to the judge. In addition, he informed them, there was the matter of the statements made by the men in Gowanda regarding the alleged brandishing of the gun by Harry. Things did not look good for him.

Harry could not believe his bad luck. This was not the first time he had been framed by law enforcement officers. In 1918, he had been charged with a violation of the Mann Act. The Act made the transportation of a female across state lines for the purposes of prostitution or immoral conduct a felony offense.

Harry had been living with a Canadian girl in his hometown, Montpelier, Vermont. When word of his living situation became common knowledge, a group of Christian women appeared at the police station and demanded that something be done about "the man who was living in sin with his whore." At first, Harry was arrested and charged with Breach of Peace, a simple misdemeanor. He was fined ten dollars and court costs. The judge advised him to move the girl out of his house before there was any further trouble. Harry did not heed his advice and the next time the police came knocking at his door, Harry was charged with the more serious crime of being in violation of the Mann Act because the girl was a Canadian citizen. The district attorney argued that she had been brought across the border for immoral purposes. Since Harry was not yet twenty-one years old, he was remanded to the State Boys Reformatory. With his conviction, Harry Race became a felon.

Harry served a year and a half of an indeterminate sentence and was released on parole. Within six months, he skipped out on his parole, moved around the eastern seaboard and eventually ended up in Gowanda, where his uncle Franklin Farnsworth lived.

Harry knew that once Judge Black found out about his felony conviction, he would be considered a sexual deviant. To make matters worse, his name wasn't really Harry Race. His real name was Harold Clifford Farnsworth and he knew that it was only a matter time before his fingerprints gave him away.

Bernice walked into the courthouse promptly at eight o'clock the morning of September 2, 1929. She had spent the previous weekend at the Chautauqua Institute situated thirty miles west of Randolph. The institute had an international reputation as a center for the arts, education, and religion. She had rented a room at the institute's prestigious Athenaeum Hotel and spent the weekend in the company of professors, clergymen, and scholars.

Bernice always felt recharged after a weekend spent lounging on the porch of the Athenaeum Hotel, which had a spectacular view of Chautauqua Lake. The conversations there were stimulating and enlightening. Furthermore, she generally found a sympathetic ear with a liberal person willing to talk with her about penal reform and inmate rights.

That Monday morning, Bernice reviewed the day's caseload. It hadn't been a busy weekend. There was only one arraignment and when she read Harry's name, a thrill ran through her. "Harry Race," she said aloud. "What an exciting name. I wonder if he lives up to it."

Orla strode into the courthouse at nine o'clock and headed for his chambers. Bernice had the paperwork for the day's docket laid out on his desk so he could familiarize himself with each case. This was important, as Orla was the judge for all three courtrooms in the courthouse. He presided over every case in the County, Surrogate, and Children's courts.

Since the County Court cases were always held first, Orla opened the folder of paperwork for Herman Warner and Harry Race's arraignment. Bernice came into his chambers just as he had finished reading the material.

"Good morning, Bernice," he said as he gave her a quick glance. "How was your weekend at the Institute?"

"Stimulating as always, Orla. I do wish that you and Mary would come up and join me one weekend before the weather turns foul. I think you might find it enlightening. An eclectic group of individuals gathers at that hotel."

"Hmmm," Orla replied distractedly. "Mary doesn't go much for the intellectual group, I'm afraid. And although she would enjoy the religious discussions, I would be bored out of my mind. So, thanks, but no thanks. Looks like we have a cut-and-dried case here with two losers this morning."

"Now really, Orla! Did you leave your objectivity home this morning?"

"No, but the affidavits sworn out on this Race fellow are pretty damning. The officers state that the gun in question was in his possession. Didn't we have Warner in here last year for public drunkenness?" Orla asked.

"No," Bernice said. "You convicted him of third degree burglary several years ago in the Children's Court. He was a minor and spent time in the State Boy's Reformatory."

"Hmmph," Orla responded. "Looks like I didn't give him a long enough sentence. He's back at it again, isn't he?"

"For Pete's sake, Orla!" Bernice exclaimed. "When are you

going to realize that stiff sentences don't reform the common criminal? They need to be counseled and educated during their incarceration so they don't become repeat offenders."

"Don't get started on me with that penal reform crap this morning, Bernice!" he shot back. "I've had a weekend filled with sick teenagers and a very tired and cranky wife. Let's get this show on the road, shall we?"

"Fine!" she said indignantly. "I'll get the bailiff to transfer the prisoners over from the jailhouse. He'll let you know when they arrive in the courtroom."

Bernice strode out of the judge's chambers and barked an order at Bill Cheney, the court bailiff. "Bring Race and Wagner in from the jail, Bill. Judge Black's calendar is full in Surrogate and Children's Court today. We need to get moving!"

"Okay, okay, Miss Kenyon," Bill said as he jumped to his feet. "You don't have to be so cross!"

Bernice shot him one of her famous icy glares as he scurried out of the courtroom. She sat at her stenographer's table and checked to see that her paperwork was in order. Bill still hadn't returned with the prisoners, so she took a moment to reflect on her most recent real estate transaction. She had sold her last rental house in Randolph the week before, to the renter who occupied the house for several years.

Bernice had dabbled in real estate since the death of her father in 1919. She bought and sold many properties over the years, as well as a few rental units. Earlier in the year, she had felt the urge to sell off all of her properties, and so she did just that. She had no way of knowing the Great Depression would cause major economic havoc in just a few weeks.

Bernice kept one piece of property in Salamanca, on Broad Street, and gave it to Morna and Dora to allow Edith and Lynn more privacy and a break from being responsible for two adult relatives. Then she acquired a log cabin from the Reeves family, near Coldspring, for herself. The Reeves had recently moved to Los Angeles for the favorable weather. The only other property Bernice still owned was the Randolph house on Main Street. She knew it had to go, but couldn't bring herself to sell it just yet. That house had been a symbol of her freedom years ago and she was emotionally attached.

Eventually, Bernice rose from her chair in the courtroom and walked over to a window. Although she was looking at the landscape, her mind was elsewhere. She was barely aware when Harry Race and Herman Warner entered the courtroom in the company of their court-appointed attorney, Warren Caswell. Close behind them was the district attorney, A. Edward Krieger. The DA was more commonly known by the rank he had held during World War I; everyone called him Colonel Krieger.

As she turned her attention to the prisoners, she stopped abruptly. Harry Race did embody the excitement of his name! He was five foot nine inches, well proportioned, quite masculine, and extremely good-looking. Her heart skipped a beat and she felt as though she had seen him before. The man was unaware of her presence, however, as he was engaged in an intense discussion with his attorney.

Bernice quickly returned to her seat at the stenographer's table and readied herself to record the details of the morning's proceeding. She removed the oilcloth cover from her well-used stenographic machine and typed in details concerning the hearing that was about to take place. Then, she waited for Bill to summon Orla into the courtroom. She cast another gaze at Harry. Again, the odd feeling of familiarity washed over her. As she scrutinized the handsome blonde, curly-locked man, he raised his head and their eyes met. What happened next changed their lives forever.

In an instant, her perception of reality was transformed. She sat transfixed, losing herself in the depths of his blue eyes. She felt as if she were descending a broad tunnel of light, then a moment of reunion and recognition. Somewhere off in the distance, she distinctly heard the shrill cry of an eagle and ancient images popped into her mind. The morphing images were interrupted by two balls of golden light that rose slowly in an arc, heading towards each other. When the balls merged, they created a brilliant flash of light and Bernice found herself back in the courtroom, still staring into Harry's ice-blue eyes. She drew in a sharp gasp of air, realizing she had forgotten to breathe.

Warren Caswell, the court-appointed attorney, was startled by Bernice's behavior. "Miss Kenyon," he said with concern, "are you all right?"

For a moment, Bernice didn't answer. She was unable to unlock her gaze until Harry finally broke the spell by blinking several times. Then he gave her a small, sheepish smile.

"Oh," she replied. "Why, yes, yes, Mr. Caswell. I don't know quite what came over me. I apologize if I've startled you."

The booming voice of the bailiff saved Bernice from further embarrassment when he announced the arrival of Judge Black in the courtroom.

"All rise," he commanded. "The Supreme Court of the County of Cattaraugus for the State of New York is now in session, the honorable Judge Black presiding."

Orla, stocky and powerful in his traditional black judge's robe, strode out from his chamber, stepped up to bench and sat down. "Please be seated, Miss Kenyon, Mr. Krieger. The accused may approach the bench with counsel at this time," he said to the three men standing by the defense table.

When Harry Race, Herman Warner, and District Attorney Colonel Krieger stood before him, Orla began by reading the charges against Herman Warner. When he was done, he asked Herman for his plea.

"Guilty on both counts your honor," Herman said in a low, weak voice.

"Do you realize, Mr. Warner, that by pleading guilty to these charges you are waiving all rights to trial by a jury of your peers?"

"Yes, your Honor, I do," Herman replied.

"Counsel," Orla asked Warren Caswell, "have you informed your client as to the possible ramifications of his guilty plea?"

"Yes, your Honor, I have," Mr. Caswell replied, "My client is fully aware of the penalties for both counts."

"Fine. Then let it be recorded that Herman Warner has entered a plea of guilty to the charges of third degree burglary and larceny. I remand you to the custody of the Sheriff of Cattaraugus County where you shall remain in custody until such time as you will appear again in this courtroom for sentencing," Orla announced. "May I have a date for his sentencing, Miss Kenyon?"

"Yes, your Honor. We have the date of September the nineteenth of this year, at ten o'clock in the morning," she said.

"Very good," said Orla. "And now for Mr. Harry Race. Mr. Race, you are accused of third degree burglary, larceny and possession of a firearm by a convicted felon. How do you plead, Mr. Race," he asked.

"Your Honor," interrupted Mr. Caswell, "I would like to move that all charges brought against my client be dropped at this time for insufficient evidence."

"What does the State have to say to this motion, Mr. Krieger," Orla asked as he pivoted his head in the Colonel's direction.

"With all due respect your honor," Colonel Krieger began, "I believe that the State has provided ample proof that Mr. Race should indeed stand trial for these serious charges. His association with Mr. Warner bears considerable weight that he may indeed be an accomplice to the crimes of third degree burglary and larceny. Both defendants are known convicted felons and it is likely that they worked in concert to perpetrate this crime. Furthermore, your Honor, I would like to point out the sworn affidavits by three eyewitnesses who saw the accused brandish the weapon in question at a dance last Saturday night. And, I might also add, we have the sworn affidavits by officers Goss and Friese in which they clearly state that the gun was found in Mr. Race's possession at the time of his arrest."

"Yes, I see the affidavits in regards to the felony weapon possession charge, however, Mr. Krieger, I do not see any statements in regards to Mr. Race's involvement in the burglary and larceny charges. Is there any evidence that ties Mr. Race to those charges other than his association with Mr. Warner?"

"Not at this time, your Honor," Colonel Krieger said reluctantly.

"Then let it be recorded that I find that the charge of third degree burglary and larceny are unfounded at this time. They will be dropped. As for the charge of possession of a firearm by a felon, Mr. Caswell, is there any reason why this charges against your client should not stand?" Orla asked.

"Yes, your Honor. I would like to draw your attention to the sworn affidavit made today by Herman Warner who states that the weapon in question was in his possession at the time of his arrest and not in Mr. Race's possession."

"Mr. Caswell, please. Do you really think the court would be willing to take the word of a convicted felon over the word of two fine, upstanding law officers and three outstanding citizens? I think not. Let it be recorded that the charge of possession of a firearm by a convicted felon will stand," Orla decreed. "How do you plead to this charge, Mr. Race?"

"Your Honor," Harry shouted, "I've been framed I tell you! Those two officers trumped up these charges after they found the gun in Herman's car door pocket. They're framing me because they knew that the burglary charges wouldn't stand!"

Orla pounded his gavel vehemently as he shouted, "Order, Mr. Race! Order, please, or I'll have you removed from this courtroom. May I remind you that this is not a trial but an arraignment? You'll have your chance in court if you so desire. How do you plead to the charge of gun possession by a convicted felon? Guilty or not guilty, please, Mr. Race."

Harry hung his head and murmured his reply in a voice so low that neither Orla nor Bernice could hear it.

"Your Honor, if you please, I could not hear the defendant's reply," Bernice said.

"Speak up now, Mr. Race. The court needs to hear your plea," Orla instructed Harry.

Harry raised his head, squared his shoulders, narrowed his eyelids, and fixed a steely gaze on Orla. In a loud growl, he said, "Not guilty, your honor! NOT GUILTY!"

Bernice had to fight the urge to stand up and cheer at Harry's fine show of bravado. It was unusual to see a defendant stand up to the great and powerful Orla Black. Instead, Bernice continued to clatter away at the steno machine's keys.

"I might remind you, Mr. Race, that you are standing before a duly elected judge who commands the respect due his position," Orla said in admonishment. "I accept your not guilty plea. May I have a date for trial, Miss Kenyon?"

"Yes, your honor. I believe that we will have sufficient time for trial beginning on October the first of this year," Bernice said after consulting the court calendar once again.

"Very well. Does that date suit the State, Mr. Krieger?" he asked.

"Yes, your Honor. That suits the State just fine," Colonel Krieger replied.

"Very good. I remand you, Harry Race, to the custody of the Sheriff of Cattaraugus County where you shall remain in custody until such time as you will appear for trial on the charge as stated. And, since the accused is a convicted felon with no ties in this community, there will be no bail. This court stands adjourned,"

Orla stated as he banged the gavel down, rose up from his chair, and headed immediately for the door leading to his chambers.

As soon as Orla exited the courtroom, Bernice went straight to the table where Harry was conferring with Warren Caswell.

"Excuse me for interrupting, Mr. Race. I'd like to introduce myself, if you don't mind," Bernice said as she stuck her hand out. "My name is Bernice Kenyon and I'd like to speak with you privately, later, if that is all right with you?"

"I don't mind. I think I might enjoy that, Miss Kenyon," he said, taking her outstretched hand gently in his.

The touch of Harry's skin sent a thrill up Bernice's spine and caused a pinkish blush to spread across her cheeks.

"That would be wonderful, Mr. Race," she said as she bowed her head demurely to avoid eye contact. "I'll make arrangements to see you at the jail after I get off work today."

Bernice wheeled around and sped off to Orla's chambers with Harry's paperwork in hand. Once inside, she closed the door and started in on Orla immediately. "Orla Black!" she began, "Have you no sense at all? Can't you see that this Race fellow has been framed by the officers in Gowanda?"

"What the devil has come over you now, Bernice? I saw no such thing! The evidence was pretty clear if you ask me."

"Pretty clear? Pretty clear, you say?" she asked, raising her voice. "Why a school boy could see through the phony affidavits the officers collected from that bunch of farm boys in Gowanda. They couldn't even read and write, for God's sake! Look at them again, Orla! They all read exactly the same, word for word. And to make matters worse they're signed with X's!"

"Don't shake those damn papers in my face, Bernice!" Orla warned. "You may be my good friend, but don't push your luck. Your behavior is out of line. There are five, count them, five sworn affidavits that place that gun in Race's possession. What is it to you anyway? Do you know this guy?"

"No, I do not know Mr. Race," she said, "I never laid eyes on him before today. I just hate it when I see bad cops railroad innocent men just because they have a prior record. And this one smells badly of it!"

"So, what's it to you anyway?" Orla asked, "The guy's obviously a big-time criminal. Just look at his clothes. For Chrisssakes, he dresses better than I do and I make a pretty decent wage. Where do you think he got the money for his expensive outfit? It wasn't from working at the corner drugstore, Bernice. He's a crook and he deserves what he gets. Even if he was innocent on this charge, I call it delayed justice. I guarantee you this guy has gotten away with a lot of other crimes. Now lay off me, would you? If he's so innocent then a jury will acquit him!"

"In Cattaraugus County? I sincerely doubt that, Orla. He doesn't stand an ice cube's chance in hell and you know it! What is he looking at for the felony gun possession? Seven years?"

"Yes," Orla said. "The maximum penalty is seven years. What of it?"

"Well," she said, "that's a long time, isn't it, Orla? And what's Herman Warner going to get for his crimes?"

"I figure he's going to go up for five years. Why?"

"Well," she said, "don't you find it compelling that Warner is willing to add a substantial amount of prison time to an already lengthy prison sentence in admitting that the gun was his and not Race's? Now why would he do that, Orla, if the gun was Race's and not his?"

Orla's face darkened as he realized that he had walked into a well-laid trap. He stood up from his chair, placed both hands palm down on his desk, and leaned towards Bernice. "Let me make myself perfectly clear here," Orla said slowly and deliberately as the veins of his neck bulged. "I don't give a tinker's damn about Warner or Race or any other goddamn criminal that walks into my courtroom, Bernice. When you choose to go against the law, you pay the price. These guys always try to protect their bosses by taking the rap for them. I think this Race character is pretty high up in the criminal world and he's going down for felony gun possession. The evidence proves it and, you're right, no jury in the world is going to see it otherwise. End of story. The charges stand and we are not going to discuss the merits of this case again. Do you understand me, Bernice?"

Bernice stood stock still as she saw Orla in a totally different light. Judge Orla Black didn't really care about justice or truth or fairness or anything else. Orla's world was black or white; there was no gray in between. In that moment, Orla had strengthened Bernice's resolve to personally ensure Harry Race would receive justice, if it were the last thing she ever did.

"Yes," she said icily, as she checked her watch, "I think I understand you completely, Judge Black. We are due in Surrogate Court in twenty minutes. I'll have everything ready and waiting for you when you arrive."

Bernice spun around, opened the chamber door, and walked out. Their lifelong friendship had just been shattered and the passion she'd had for the job she loved was gone. She would never regain that passion again.

Bernice, you are living in a fantasy world, she told herself as she walked from one courtroom to another. *You've been party to one miscarriage of justice after another. It's time for a change, Bernice Guernsey Kenyon! A very big change.*

It was difficult for Bernice to get through the rest of the day. At first, she fumed about her conversation with Orla after Harry's arraignment, but slowly her resentment and disillusionment prodded her into formulating a plan to gain Harry's release. By the end of the day, she decided that Warren Caswell was not the right attorney for Harry. She placed a call to criminal attorney Dean Graswell's office, pretending to be a concerned relative, and retained him for Harry's defense. Then she marched over to the jailhouse next door to see her good friend, Undersheriff Leone Pickup. Leone was less than pleased when she announced she wanted a private interview with Harry in the jail's Attorney Consultation Room.

"Have you lost your mind, Bernice," he asked. "I'm not going to let you sit in that room alone with a convicted felon!"

"Oh, yes you are, Leone. Furthermore, you are going to stand watch and make sure we're not disturbed. By anyone!"

"What makes you think that you can strong-arm me into doing something that is not only illegal, but dangerous?"

"Leone, my good friend, may I remind you that I have been watching over your wife's real estate dealings for the past three years? And that I have been very discreet in doing so? How do think your life at home will be if I tell her I've been influencing *her* on your behalf and that you've known about her real estate holdings all this time. Hmmm?"

"That's extortion!" Leone exclaimed. "You wouldn't do that to me, would you?"

"Deny me access to Harry Race, Leone, and you'll find out just what I might do," Bernice shot back.

Leone leaned back in his wood swivel chair and stared at Bernice for moment, pondering what might happen if Bernice carried out her threat.

"Humph!" he snorted in reply. "What in the world is so important about seeing this Race character that would lead you to stoop this low?"

"That is none of your business, Leone! Just move him up to the Consultation Room. I need only fifteen minutes. You can stand outside the door. Trust me, nothing will happen."

"All right, all right, I'll do it" Leone agreed with reluctance. "But you'll have to wait until supper time is over and the jail settles down for the night. Come back at six-thirty. Don't ask for another minute more. You won't get it no matter what threats you conjure up. Understand?"

"Thank you, Leone," Bernice said as she leaned over and kissed the undersheriff on the forehead. "Sorry about the threat, but this is important to me. See you at six-thirty." She started to leave, but then turned around. "One more thing, Leone," she said, "no one is know anything about my meeting with Harry Race, all right?"

"Are you kidding me, Bernice?" Leone asked incredulously. "Sheriff Carlson would have my head if he found out about this! I promise you, my lips are sealed."

"Very good then, Leone, I'll see you at six-thirty."

Bernice left the gothic-style brick courthouse via the main entrance and walked down the Court Street. She headed over to the Palace Hotel where she ate supper and waited for her appointed meeting time with Harry. The thought of meeting Harry in person caused her stomach to flutter.

Six-thirty found her waiting anxiously at the door to the Attorney Consultation Room. Her heart pounded as she heard the sound of Leone's and Harry's footsteps coming down the corridor. For a split second she panicked, thinking Harry might not want anything to do with her. Then she panicked thinking about being alone with him. What if he really is the hardened criminal Orla felt he was?

Then, there was Harry, wearing handcuffs, directly in front of her. He smiled just slightly and she almost swooned. Steadying herself by leading against the wall, she drew on all her masculine training to buck herself up.

Bernice smiled, extended her hand towards Harry and he grasped it with both of his cuffed hands. The most pleasurable feeling swept through her small frame. Once again, a feeling of familiarity washed over her. "Thank you for meeting with me, Mr. Race. There is much I wish to discuss with you," Bernice said as Leone opened the door to the sparse consultation room.

"Thank you, ma'am. I sure appreciate the opportunity to get out of that damp cell," Harry replied.

All three entered the consultation room and Leone told Harry to sit down. "Now listen here, you," Leone said as Harry and Bernice sat down facing one another across a wood table. "I'm gonna be just outside that door the whole time you two are in here. If I hear one thing I don't like I'm comin' in here with my .38 and I'm not asking any questions. You get what I mean?" said Leone in a low growl, slapping the pistol on his hip for emphasis.

"Yes, Sheriff. I understand completely, sir. You won't have any trouble from me,'" Harry assured him.

Leone walked to the door and gave Harry one last stern look before he closed it behind him. Bernice let out a quiet laugh. "Don't worry about him, Mr. Race," she said. "He's a real teddy bear. Leone's just trying to protect me. We've been friends a long time."

"Well, that's good to know, ma'am," Harry replied, "Have we met before? I just can't shake the feeling that I've met you somewhere."

"How odd that you say that, Mr. Race. I can't help but feel the same way, but, no, I don't believe we met before today. Can we please dispense with the formalities? Please call me Bernice. May I call you Harry?" she asked.

"Yes, of course, ma'am… I mean Bernice. Can I ask why we're here today?"

"Certainly, you may," Bernice said. "You see, I've been working in the courthouse for many years. In the past, I've turned a blind eye to the many small injustices that I have borne witness to here in the courtroom. I have tried to justify them to myself, but in your case, I guess it was the straw that broke the camel's back. You're innocent of the felony gun possession charge, aren't you Harry?"

"Absolutely," Harry replied hastily. "Those cops in

Gowanda trumped up the charge because I mouthed off to them. I wish I could learn to keep my big mouth shut. It seems to always get me in trouble."

"I believe you, Harry. I sensed a goodness in you when I first laid eyes on you in the courtroom this morning. I want to help you. Think of it as a sort of penance for my past transgressions. I've hired a competent defense attorney for you. Your court-appointed attorney, Warren Caswell is good attorney, but he's no match against Colonel Krieger. I hate to admit it, but Judge Black has it out for you. He can be a formidable foe. By the way, I trust that this conversation between you and me will be held in the strictest confidence?"

"Yes, yes, of course, of course!" Harry said. "I can't believe you are willing to help a total stranger like this. I must be dreaming. No one has ever helped me in my life."

"Somehow, Harry, I can't help but believe we are far from total strangers. Don't you feel it, too?" Bernice asked, gazing straight into his clear blue eyes.

"Yes, I do. I really do," Harry replied as he moved his shackled hands across the table and slipped them gently over her small, delicate fist. For a precious few moments, they simply looked at one another, enjoying the intimacy.

Unexpected as it was, Bernice knew this was the man she had been waiting for all her life, which further galvanized her resolve to see him set free. They spent the few remaining minutes of her visit planning a strategy to gain his freedom. By the time Leone opened the door saying time's up, their plan was set. Bernice watched wistfully as Leone escorted Harry back down the corridor. The long ride home to Coldspring was harder than ever.

CHAPTER FIFTEEN

THE WAIT FOR HARRY'S OCTOBER TRIAL DATE dragged on forever. Bernice and Harry continued their clandestine meetings in the consultation room, much to Leone's chagrin. At first, their conversations were limited to plotting strategy for Harry's trial. It wasn't long, however, before the meetings took on a more personal tone.

Harry confided in Bernice as soon as he was sure he could trust her. He revealed his true name, Harold Farnsworth, and was candid about his brief criminal record. In turn, Bernice shared personal information about herself. Harry spoke about his childhood and his dreams, and the more he talked, the more Bernice became spellbound by the man. Harry's early life had been marked by the tragic death of his mother, Ann, when he was eleven years old.

The Farnsworths owned a small farm on the outskirts of Montpelier, Vermont. Harry's early life was normal and happy and he enjoyed helping his father Alva, work the farm, starting when he was just six years old. Alva slowly allowed his son to shoulder as much farm responsibility as the boy could handle. Harry thrived in the idyllic country atmosphere. That all changed when Harry turned eleven.

Harry awoke as usual at 3:30 one morning, expecting to find his mother in the kitchen preparing breakfast for him, his younger sister, Patty, and their father. However, as he descended the stairs he knew instantly that something was terribly wrong. There was no odor of frying bacon and the house was eerily dark and quiet. Upon entering the kitchen, he spied a handwritten note propped up in the center of the kitchen table. He struggled to read the note. Harry's schooling had taken a back burner when the demands of the farm needed to be met. The note was written in his father's small, tight handwriting:

> Harry – Your mother has taken ill and I have taken her to see Doc Smith in town. Be a good boy and tend to the animals without me. Patty can help you. We will be back as soon as we can. – Dad.

It took Harry and Patty a couple of extra hours to feed the animals and clean out the barn without the help of their father. Having accomplished everything that needed tending, there was little they could do except wait for their parents to return. It was a long wait. Alva did not return until late that evening.

The children were shocked at the sight of their father when he walked through the front door. His eyes were bloodshot and his clothing was rumpled and disheveled. He smelled terribly of liquor and could barely stand. When they asked him where their mother was, he roared something unintelligible and went up the stairs by pulling himself up, one step at a time, hanging onto the stair rail. Twice he slipped and fell to the bottom, only to start up the stairs again. When Harry tried to help him up, Alva swatted the boy with the back of his hand, knocking him to the ground. Patty wailed and called for her mother, as they had never seen such violence. Harry begged his father for information about his mother, but Alva ignored him. Both children spent a fitful night listening to their father's ranting. Finally, at around one o'clock in the morning, Alva fell silent.

Patty and Harry rose at the usual time and tended to the farm animals by themselves for the second day in the row. Finally, around noon, Alva came downstairs. He smelled horrible and looked even worse. When the children asked again where their mother was, Alva began sobbing into his farm-roughened hands.

"Oh, God, how do I say this you? How... how... how?" he moaned.

A frightened Harry and Patty began crying, too. Harry crossed the room, put his arms around his father's torso, and tried his best to console the man. Patty sat down on the divan and continued to cry.

"Dad," said Harry, "please calm down. It's ok. Patty and I are here. Calm down, Dad. Where's Mama? Where is she? We need to know. We're very scared, Dad. We need to know where Mama is."

Harry got up and went over to Patty, to help ease her sobs. Then he took a deep breath and expelled it in a big whoosh. "Kids," he began, "I don't know how to tell you this, but here goes. Your mama is gone."

Patty stared open-mouthed and Harry felt as if he'd been whacked in the forehead. He stumbled backwards and fell onto the living room end table, then landed on the floor. Gone? Harry tried to understand the word. What does he mean, "gone"? Had his mother abandoned them? Why would his mother ever do such a thing?

"I couldn't wake your mother up yesterday morning," Alva continued. "So I quick got her downstairs and into the buggy. I took her over to Doc Smith's house as fast as I could. There was nothing he could do for her. The Doc told me she died before we even got there. He says he thinks she had a stroke while she was sleeping. I'm sorry, kids. I did everything I could. Everything!"

The children rushed to their father and encircled him with their arms. That brief moment proved to be the last time the three would ever emotionally connect.

Alva tried his best to carry on with the farm, but it was physically impossible without the help of his wife. The added responsibility of two children proved overwhelming. Soon, every task on the farm became too much for him to handle. Sensing his impending financial doom, Alva dropped into a deep depression. He rose from bed late and many days he accomplished nothing in the way of farm work.

When the local banker came to foreclose on the property, he found twelve-year-old Harry in charge of the farm. Patty was in the kitchen cleaning up after breakfast. Alva was in bed and refused to come down. The banker was forced to return with the sheriff in order to properly serve and enforce the Order to Vacate on Alva. Harry and Patty were given ten minutes to pack their personal belongings and place them just off the front porch of their home. Alva refused to gather his belongings and the task was left to the sheriff, who hastily stuffed all of Alva's clothing into a feed sack. The sheriff handed the sack to Alva, just as a locksmith arrived and began replacing the locks on the front and back doors of the house. Alva sat and watched the whole procedure as if he were a dispassionate onlooker rather than a captive participant.

If it were not for Alva's brother, Frank Farnsworth, who knows what would have become of them that day. Upon hearing that Alva's family had been displaced, Frank hitched up his wood cart and drove down to their farm. Once there, he coaxed Alva onto the cart and hoisted up the kids and their belongings. They stayed on Frank's farm until Alva finally secured work in a factory in Montpelier. There, they settled in a coldwater flat in a very seedy section of downtown.

Harry and Patty had to make their way themselves. Patty eventually grabbed the first young man she could find and married at the age of fourteen. Harry took to the streets of Montpelier and spent the next few years mostly in trouble. Alva never recovered from his depression and became an alcoholic. He never noticed when his fifteen-year-old son stopped coming home at night.

Bernice watched Harry physically transform as he finished his story. His erect shoulders and back were now curved, and his head slumped forward, creating the impression of a sad, lost little boy. Her eyes brimmed with tears as she ran her fingers through Harry's curly locks. "Now, now, Harry. It's all okay now. Everything is going to be fine. You'll see, Harry. Just fine."

October 1, which had loomed way off in the distance, crashed down upon them. The court proceeding went quickly. Harry's attorney, Dean Graswell, argued successfully for the inclusion of Harry's Motor Vehicle Permit, issued to him by the Canadian Immigration Officer at the border the day of the Gowanda Dance. Colonel Krieger countered that the certificate might be a forgery and Orla agreed to a continuance while they waited for an official document from Canada to be presented to the court. A new court date was set for early November.

The November date arrived but no copy of the Canadian Motor Vehicle Permit was available yet. Orla once again granted a continuance of four weeks, with the collective thinking that this would be more than sufficient time for the Canadian officials to comply with the court's request.

Late December found the court still without documentation from Canada. Orla granted what he deemed the final continuance. He made sure Dean Graswell and Harry understood that if the document was not in hand by the next court date, the trial would have to proceed without it. Bernice and Harry waited nervously for the paperwork to arrive. However, it didn't show up by his trial date.

When court convened for Harry's trial on Monday, January 27, 1930, Bernice sat at her stenographer's table typing fast and praying for a miracle. Attorney Graswell tried in vain to reason with Orla regarding the missing document. Orla was steadfast and ordered the trial commence immediately. Before Colonel Krieger could utter a word for the State of New York, Graswell announced that his client was eager to have the trial proceed.

Harry opted to forego a trial by jury and, upon establishing that, Graswell asked Orla for the mercy of the court. Orla showed none. The trial took less than hour. Orla made his ruling immediately after both sides finished their closing arguments.

Judge Orla Black ruled that Harry Race was guilty of the charge that lay before the court. In lieu of the considerable time allowed by the court for the continuance of the trial, he pronounced sentence immediately. Harry received the maximum penalty of seven years detention and was remanded to the Auburn State Penitentiary.

Neither Harry nor Bernice was surprised at the outcome, it was part of their strategy. Bernice knew that the document would arrive eventually; the Canadians were notoriously slow in cooperating with United States authorities. Bernice planned to have Attorney Dean Graswell file for a new trial for Harry when the official Motor Vehicle Permit arrived. With Harry's acquittal based on irrefutable evidence, he would be released from prison within days of the ruling. Confident with their plan, Bernice bade Harry farewell on the morning of January 29 as he boarded Leone's squad car bound for the Auburn Penitentiary.

Harold and Bernice communicated by mail several times each week. Their letters were full of hope and they wrote about what they would do once Harry was released. Harry dreamed of a chicken farm and wrote often about it. Bernice replied that she was keen on the idea of a business they could manage together. She dreamed of the day that she could walk into Orla's chambers and announce her resignation.

Unbelievably, the Canadian Motor Vehicle Permit did not arrive at the Cattaraugus County Courthouse until March 14. Attorney Dean Graswell filed a motion for a new trial on March 18, based on the discovery of new evidence. He also contacted the warden at the Elmira State Prison in order to arrange for Herman Warner to swear out a new affidavit regarding his possession of the gun in question. Bernice was very pleased with the turn of events even though the process was taking so long.

The wheels of justice, however, came to a complete halt. Herman Warner's affidavit did not materialize in March, April, or May of 1930. The wait was agonizing for Bernice. In her mind, Harry's release had already taken place.

In early May, Bernice decided to visit Harry in Auburn. She marched over to the Wilhelm-Randolph Garage on Jamestown Street and talked to Walter Wilhelm about purchasing a new car. He suggested that she might like a seven-passenger Chevrolet sedan, something suitable for a woman "of her age." Bernice bristled at the inference and insisted she was looking for something sporty, not old and stodgy. She glanced through the Chevrolet brochures and found just what she wanted: a 1930 Chevrolet Sport Coupe with a rear rumble seat. Walter just about swallowed his uppers when she made the announcement.

"Miss Kenyon, with all due respect, that is not the right car for you. You would be so much more comfortable in the sedan!"

"Mr. Wilhelm," she began sternly, "I am perfectly capable 'at my age' of knowing what is best for me. Thank you for your suggestion, but my mind is set on a Sport Coupe. Please make an inquiry as to its availability and let me know its cost when delivered here to Randolph. I want one as soon as possible. I will be paying cash upon delivery. And I will need driving lessons from you or someone on your staff."

Begrudgingly, Walter Wilhelm procured a Sport Coupe for Bernice through a dealer in Buffalo after she approved the price of $565. The dealer said he was waiting for a fresh batch of cars to roll off the assembly line the following Friday and would arrange for the vehicle to be shipped by rail to the Randolph depot directly from the factory. He estimated its arrival would be Wednesday of the following week.

At eight-thirty on the morning of Friday, May 9, 1930, a pea-green Chevrolet Sport Coupe, Engine Serial Number 1809585, rolled off the Buffalo plant assembly line. It was delivered immediately to the plant's rail yard for loading. The dock manager recorded and then stamped the car's serial number 12AD47873 onto a long thin strip of paper. He pasted the strip on the windshield of the car and a destination slip that read:

Miss Bernice Kenyon
c/o Wilhelm-Randolph Garage
Walter Wilhelm, Prop.
18 Jamestown Street
Randolph, NY
Terms: COD

The car arrived on schedule and Bernice was thrilled. She arranged to begin driving lessons and proved to be a natural. She procured her driver's license in Little Valley ten days after receiving delivery of her car.

The staff at the County building was abuzz after Bernice was seen pulling the new Sport Coupe into the horse lot across the street from the courthouse. Their tongues wagged for days.

"Didn't anybody inform Miss Kenyon that there is a depression going on here?" asked some.

"How unladylike!" scoffed the older women, elevating their snippy little noses in the air.

As usual, Bernice could not have cared less about their narrow opinions. She strolled into the Courthouse like a conquering soldier. She made sure to wish everyone a good morning.

Orla was waiting for her in the courtroom. "Causing trouble again, Bernice?"

"Why, Orla, whatever do you mean?"

"Well, let's see. For starters, two people have barged in to inform me of your new car. You have the entire building buzzing like a nest of very nosy bees. Need I go further?" Orla asked with a sly grin on his face.

Bernice brushed him off. "I have nothing to do with the antics of those gossipmongers. Besides, I'm not always the one who creates fodder for the gossip machine. I'm just their current victim."

"When did you get the car, Bernice?" Orla asked. "And whatever possessed you to purchase a car, anyway?"

"It arrived the week before last. I ordered it after deciding to travel more. I want to get off the beaten path like my father and I used to do when we went on vacation years ago. In fact, that reminds me. I'd like a day off so I can try out my new machine!"

Orla approved Bernice's request for a day off the following Friday, and Bernice arranged to have a temporary stenographer take her place. She was excited about the prospect of seeing Harry again. It had been four months since his trial.

Bernice thought about the status of his trial as she made the five-hour trip to Auburn on a beautiful morning in late May. She arrived at a boarding house on Fitch Street at three in the afternoon and checked into a room. She ate a light dinner at a restaurant on State Street, then returned to her room and remained there until the next morning.

She rose early, ate breakfast with the proprietress of the boarding house, and made the short trip over to the prison in her car. She parked across the street and then entered the formidable State Street gate. The prison gate consisted of a row of heavy glass doors flanked by two tall, crenellated stone towers attached to stone walls that encircled the entire prison compound. Bernice pushed open one of the glass doors and, in doing so, began the lengthy inmate visitor process.

When the admissions process was complete, Bernice was ushered to the visiting area, a long hallway-like room pounding with a cacophony of voices. The setup reminded her of an exaggerated row of bank teller windows. Each window had an occupant seated on both sides of a wire-reinforced glass with a mouthpiece in the center the two people used for communication. They had to speak loudly for their words to penetrate the mesh over each mouthpiece.

Bernice made her way to window 16 and sat down. She tried to block out the ambient sound. Harry showed up after a couple of minutes but the visit didn't go well. Bernice simply could not adjust to the noise level around her. She found herself asking Harry to repeat himself over and over. As the minutes wore on, she became frustrated and then angry. She had no choice but to cut the visit short. Harry smiled and told her he understood. She said she would write to him immediately upon returning home to make sure he understood everything she had tried to discuss with him. They pressed their hands together on the glass and said goodbye. Bernice raced out of the prison, fighting back tears.

The drive home to Randolph was long and lonely. Bernice cried, screamed, and schemed the entire trip. She could not understand why life had dealt her such a harsh fate. Her separation from Harry was the focus of her life during his incarceration. Everything in Bernice's life revolved around the day Harry would be released from prison.

She reported for work as usual the following Monday morning but was as vague as possible when pressed for details concerning her motor trip. Every morning she raced into the courthouse to see if Herman Warner's affidavit had arrived in the mail. It was hard to believe how slow the wheels of justice moved for some, and how fast it moved for others. The waiting made Bernice a nervous wreck.

Herman Warner's affidavit arrived on June 6 and was entered into evidence on June 10. Orla took the matter of a new trial for Harry into submission, but stalled his decision, using the burgeoning county docket as an excuse for the delay. Bernice was tortured by Orla's reluctance to reach a decision. She had to sit dispassionately through each of Dean Graswell's appearances on behalf of Harry. Her dislike for Orla increased with each delay.

Finally, on January 9, 1931, Orla allowed both the defense and the prosecution the opportunity to argue for and against a new trial for Harry Race, also known as Harold Clifford Farnsworth. Dean Graswell presented to the court the Canadian Motor Vehicle Permit and Herman Warner's sworn statement as "irrefutable evidence that Mr. Farnsworth has been the victim of a gross miscarriage of justice."

Colonel Krieger countered that the Canadian permit did not specify what time of day Mr. Farnsworth entered Canada and more importantly, it did not address his return to the United States, therefore, in his estimation, it was entirely possible that Farnsworth could have made it back to Gowanda on the day in question. When Colonel Krieger finished his impassioned argument against the granting of a new trial, Judge Orla Black ruled on the motion. It read in part:

> "…on this date to show cause why such new trial should not be granted; now, after reading and filing the affidavits above-mentioned, and having heard the district attorney in opposition to said motion, and having no further affidavits having been filed herein, and the matter having been adjourned to this date, it is ORDERED that the defendant's motion for a new trial upon the grounds of newly discovered evidence, be hereby, in all things, denied."

The word "denied" rang again and again in Bernice's head. Failure to procure Harry a new trial had been inconceivable and she found herself unprepared for this sudden defeat. She had underestimated just how blind Orla's justice could be. Keeping her cool, she recorded the rest of the proceeding and moved on to the next case before the court adjourned. When court recessed for lunch, Bernice exited the courthouse as if nothing were amiss. Once she was far enough away, she unleashed her pent up emotions. Tears flowed with the realization that she would likely have to wait five years for Harry's release from prison. She had to see Harry again before they could proceed any further.

Bernice walked hurriedly back to courthouse and then into Orla's chambers in the Surrogate Courtroom. From there she called the Warden's Office at the Auburn State Penitentiary and inquired into Harry's status. She was informed that Harry was currently listed as "Waiting for Transfer." Bernice informed the warden's secretary that Harold Farnsworth's bid for a retrial had been denied. The secretary responded that Mr. Farnsworth would then be transferred to Great Meadow Prison in Comstock, New York later that week. The assignment would be permanent.

Bernice thanked the woman for the update and pulled down the New York State map from the wall behind her. Saratoga Springs was only forty miles from the prison. She quickly formed a plan and left the Surrogate Courtroom.

Bernice strode back into the County Courtroom and made for Orla's chambers. He was finishing his lunch as she walked in. With false bravado she said, "Orla! Can I interrupt? I have a request to make of you."

"Well," he replied, "you seem awfully chipper after seeing your star criminal lose his only hope for freedom!"

"Granted, Orla," she lied expertly. "I was disappointed with your decision to deny a retrial, but, you're the judge here, not me! I guess Mr. Farnsworth will just have to tough it out and prove me right by becoming a model prisoner. You know he could get out early for good behavior, don't you?"

"Drat," said Orla. "I go through the trouble of locking these bad characters up and what do the bleeding hearts in the correctional department do? Why, they let them out early for good behavior! Good behavior. What a laugh!"

Bernice fumed but kept her voice calm. "Now, now, Orla. Someone has to have some mercy is this world. It makes up for your lack of it."

"Yes, yes, I know, Bernice," Orla replied, "Big bad Orla Black takes advantage of the poor defenseless criminals again.

Boo-hoo, boo-hoo! Now, what is it you want of me?"

"Well, I'd like some time off. I haven't had a real vacation since I don't know when. I thought it might be fun to drive up to Saratoga and spend time soaking in the mineral springs. I hear they've built a new pool complex and I'd like to see it. What do you say about me taking the week after next off?"

"On one condition, Bernice," Orla said. "You must provide a suitable replacement this time. Remember the Fainting Flora I got stuck with the last time you were out? It got so bad that I had to remind the Colonel repeatedly to keep the crime scene photos out of her view. Good help is getting harder to find."

On the following Monday Bernice managed to find a suitable replacement and made sure the following week's docket would be covered. The rest of the week stretched out far into the distance. She daydreamed constantly of meeting Harry at Great Meadow Prison. The mere thought of him elicited a sigh. She felt like a schoolgirl with a new crush. It was both wonderful and tragic. On one hand, Bernice was grateful to have found love, but on the other hand, that love was going to go unrequited for several years.

Bernice left Randolph for Saratoga Springs at eight o'clock in the morning on Saturday, January 17. The weather was crisp and clear. The trip was uneventful, and she arrived in Saratoga at 4:30 in the afternoon. She settled into her hotel room, ate dinner, and by 8:30 had retired for the evening.

Visiting hours for the general prison population at Great Meadow was 9 a.m. to 2:30 p.m. every Saturday and Sunday. Visits were limited to one hour and strictly supervised by correctional officers. Other than a hug in greeting, no physical contact was allowed, nor could there be any exchange of goods.

Bernice left her hotel at half-passed seven on Sunday morning and drove to the prison in Comstock. She arrived there at eight-fifteen in the morning. It took one hour to be searched and processed, as which point she was escorted across the barren dirt yard leading to the visitor's building. Once logged in, she waited another forty-five minutes for Harry to be brought in. At 10:05 a.m., a barrel-chested guard bellowed, "Farnsworth! Visitor for Farnsworth, over here!"

"Yes, right here, sir!" Bernice called out.

"Follow me, ma'am. Your first visit here?" he asked, motioning her through a doorway that led to a large room filled with unmatched chairs.

"Yes, officer," she replied, "This is my first visit."

"Okay, listen up carefully," the officer said, "because you get this speech only once. No physical contact with the inmate during your first visit. No contact of any sort with any inmate other than the one you came to see. You leave the room before the hour is up for any reason, your visit is over. No yelling, no loud talk, no arguing, or the visit is over. Get kicked out twice and your visiting privileges will be permanently revoked. Passing anything, and I mean anything, to an inmate will result in your immediate arrest. When I say the visit is over, don't ask for another minute or two. You won't get it. Any questions, ma'am?"

"No. No questions, sir," she replied.

Bernice was guided to a chair and told to wait. The guard left, then reappeared with Harry in tow. Bernice's heart sunk when she saw him. Harry was dressed in worn, gray, prison-issue clothing topped with a matching gray skullcap. His arms and legs were shackled and he clanked and scraped as he shuffled across the room. She could read the prisoner number on the patch sewn onto his shirt.

"Don't forget that I'm watching you, Farnsworth. I don't put up with no monkey business in my visiting room. You understand?" the guard growled.

"Yes. I understand. Thank you. You'll have no trouble from me," Harry assured him.

Bernice squirmed in her seat, resisting the urge to throw her arms around Harry and hold him tight. She averted her eyes for a moment, taking a few breaths to stop her tears. When the guard stepped away from them, Harry spoke quietly. "Bernie, please stop crying. You'll embarrass me. Be a good girl now and look brave for me, would you? I know that these chains shock you, but they are only temporary. When I have a permanent cell and job assignment, I can visit without them. Now look up at me for god's sake, would you?"

Bernice lifted her head and stared into Harry's eyes. Suddenly, everything was all right. The institutional green walls disappeared. Her tears receded and she smiled sweetly. The stress in her shoulders vanished. She relaxed and felt surprisingly happy. She was with the man she loved and nothing else mattered. For the rest of the visit it was if they were the only two people in the room.

Their visits at the Cattaraugus County Jail had trained them to get to the heart of matters very quickly and so they lost no time with nonsense pleasantries. Bernice assured Harry that Orla's ruling ended all possibility of a retrial. All they could do was wait. Bernice gave him the only advice she could offer. "Harry, you are stuck here for at least two to three more years. Prisoners who display good behavior are paroled early. It's our only hope. You have to walk the straight and narrow. I know that must be hard to hear, given your circumstances, but that's all that is left to us now. Can you do it, Harry?"

"Sixteen months ago I could not have said yes. However, since you've come into my life, I can honestly say that, yes, I can, and I will! You are the first person since my mother died who had any faith in me. You have no idea what that means to me. I won't let you down, Bernie. I will walk out of here as early as they will allow. I will be a model prisoner. Guaranteed."

They spoke about money transfers to Harry's prison account and accurate mailing addresses, and then used the rest of their time speaking softly to each other. A casual observer might have assumed they were old friends rather than new lovers.

Eventually, the guard came over and terminated their visit. Bernice stood immediately and said goodbye to Harry. She reminded him that she would return the following Saturday, before returning to Randolph. Without the slightest regret, she walked out of the visitor's building, back across the dirt yard, through the door to the Visitor's Reception Building and then out to the parking lot. She smiled when she saw her new sport coupe. The car gave her unprecedented freedom.

Bernice spent the rest of the week luxuriating in the mineral baths at the posh Gideon Putnam Hotel in Sarasota Springs. She walked through the quaint town every day, and dined in their wonderful restaurants. When the following Saturday arrived, she checked out of the Gideon Putnam and drove up to Comstock.

The second visit went as well, actually better, than the first. Harry was ushered in without chains, signaling his transfer into the general prison population. Miraculously, he had been assigned to work in the warden's office as a file clerk. His cellmate, an older man in for a life sentence, was an "okay guy." Everything seemed to be working out. When the visit was over, Bernice left the prison physically rested and spiritually recharged. She headed home to Randolph and was looking forward to one last day of rest before returning to work on Monday.

Back at the prison, Harry was returned to his cell when Bernice left the visiting area. He immediately wrote a letter to Bernice again expressing his thanks for having her in his life. Then he started laying out his vision to create a farm business for them, so their plans would be in place when he was released.

As time passed, Bernice and Harry settled into a routine of letter writing, where they freely shared the most personal details of their lives and hopes. Rather than wither as the months made their slow way through the years, their love for each other intensified.

Chapter Sixteen

Bernice and Harry's lives, although inextricably linked by their frequent correspondence, were otherwise gray and solitary. Bernice's infrequent visits to Great Meadow Prison were the only thing that brought vivid color into their bleak existences. Separately, they moved through the machinations of their lives in robotic fashion.

It proved easy for Bernice to keep her visits to Great Meadow Prison a secret. The court in Cattaraugus County had little interaction with the Comstock prison because most convicted criminals were incarcerated closer to home. This policy had been instituted long before Orla Black's tenure to ensure visits to inmates from close relatives did not become a hardship.

Bernice had a hard time coping with Harry's absence and her frequent bouts of depression continued. Morna and Dora worried about their sister's psychological well-being and were mystified as to the cause of her sadness. They made frequent overtures to cheer her up but finally Bernice grew very irritated with their efforts and announced she had decided to move away from Randolph.

In August 1932, Bernice moved into the log cabin that she had purchased three years earlier from the Reeves family. Because she had bought the property just before the onset of the Great Depression, she hadn't been able to rent it out. However, she found the cabin so charming that she kept it, unoccupied, rather than sell it. The property was located in Steamburg, a rural area in the town of Coldspring.

Morna was horrified at the remote location and the condition of the log cabin when she went there with Bernice to clean its interior. The cabin was the only house visible on Price's Corners Road, a mile from Highway 17. Nature had taken over the exterior, making the cabin appear neglected, abandoned, and dilapidated. Wild honeysuckle had completely obscured all four sides of the building. Clematis vines covered the roof and chimney in a riot of white, red, and pink flowers that hung in curled stringers from the roof's edges. They were able to walk to the front of the cabin along a narrow, cleared path that had been cut by workers Bernice had hired earlier in the week.

Inside they discovered mouse droppings littering the floors of every room. The odor of mouse urine and mold permeated everything. It took the entire weekend for Bernice and Morna to scrub the rooms, walls, floor, and meager furnishings. Morna was incensed that her sister would even consider living in such Spartan and unsanitary conditions. Once the wild, tangled foliage was cleared from the cabin, Bernice moved in.

After unpacking her clothing and putting her personal articles in place, she sat down to write a letter to Harry.

My Dearest Harry,

I am happy to say that I have finally moved into my little cabin retreat. It is so wonderful to view the natural setting from each of its old, distorted glass windows. It is so quaint and cozy here that I am sure it will be hard for me to leave each morning for work. The tranquility it offers should be a blessing for me, I'm sure. I only wish that you were here to share it with me.

Morna and Dora are certain I have completely lost my mind in deciding to take up residence here. They are also sure I will be attacked by some monstrous animal they have conjured in their minds. I often wonder how I could be related to them, as we are so very different from one another. It is big relief for me to get away from their constant chattering and meddlesome ways.

Honestly, though, I reluctantly admit that I do fear a black bear may roam into the yard one day. They have been seen in the area recently, I'm told. Because of that news, I have decided to buy a pistol and carry it with me in my purse. Orla has agreed to issue me a permit to carry a concealed weapon so that I may do just that. (One of the few benefits of working with him!) And, as I have told you in some of our past conversations, I am very proficient in the use of handguns, so you needn't worry about me using the pistol safely.

What size pistol do you recommend I purchase? I sold my pistol to a gun collector several years ago and now I sincerely regret having done so. Make a recommendation in your next letter and I will drive into Jamestown to a gun shop and purchase one.

I will be up to visit you again soon. It has been too long since we have seen one another and I find that our separation is becoming unbearable again. I long for your presence in a way that I have never experienced in my lifetime. I know that you must feel the same as I do. It is our little cross to bear, I'm afraid to say. I am wracked with emotion as I wonder when we will be able to be together outside of those confining prison walls. Enough of that though, as I find I am repeating myself in many of my letters to you. I do it because it comforts me to be able to express my emotions to you. I have no one else to confide in here.

Be safe, Harry, and continue to be a good inmate. I am very, very proud of you!

Yours truly,

Bernice

Harry responded as soon as he finished reading Bernice's letter. He suggested she buy a .32 caliber pistol. Even though it was considered a weak caliber, he felt that it would be easy for her to conceal and loud enough to scare off any wild animals she might encounter near the cabin. Bernice drove to a gun shop in

Jamestown a few days later purchased a .32 caliber H&R pistol with white grips. It fit perfectly in her small clutch purses. She rarely left the cabin without it.

Orla, true to his word, granted her a concealed gun permit. He used her position with the court to justify its issuance. No one questioned the granting of the permit because the County Court was overrun with criminal cases involving dangerous characters. Threats to wreak revenge were heard often enough following the convictions and sentencing.

Back at Great Meadow Prison, Harry's situation was going well, considering he was incarcerated. Warden Joseph Brophy had been impressed by Harry's work ethic from day one and often kept Harry after hours to work on special projects. Because Harry was hardly ever around the other inmates, he didn't run afoul with them, and in fact, was treated as a non-entity by the general prison population. All this helped him realize his goal for an early release.

In late February 1933, Harry's cellmate got sick and was permanently transferred to the prison hospital ward after a diagnosis of lung cancer. The two men had gotten along well and Harry was sorry to see him go.

Late in the day on March 5, a guard appeared at Harry's cell door with his new cellmate. The man was short, muscular, baby-faced, and young. Silently, they sized each other up. The man extended his hand after the guard slammed the cell door and left.

"Alfred Lindsay's my name," he said shaking Harry's hand. "My friends call me Freddy. I'm from Lowell, Massachusetts."

"Harold Farnsworth," Harry replied. "My friends call me Harry. What brings you to Great Meadow?"

"Well, that's a long story," Freddy said with a sardonic grin. "Warden Lawes just kicked me out of Sing Sing."

"After what I've heard about Sing Sing, that might be a good thing," said Harry.

"Nah, that's not true. The warden has turned the place around pretty much. Since he took over, things got much better there. He brought in the Mutual Welfare League program and that gave us a lot of privileges we didn't have before. But, that's what got me in trouble with him in the end."

"Oh?" said Harry. "How's that?"

"That's kinda a long story," Freddy said with a sigh, "Would it be okay if I told you about it tomorrow? I haven't slept since last night when we left Sing Sing. It was a pretty rough trip out here. Roads aren't too good in some places. I really need some sleep."

"Sure, kid. We've got all the time in the world for that, don't we?" Harry said with a smile.

"Harry, you seem like an okay guy. I'm glad I got you for a cellmate. I was a little worried about that." Freddy walked over to the bunk bed that took up a good portion of the ten-foot by seven-foot cell.

"Yeah, kid," Harry said. "Me, too. I was a little worried about that myself. Go ahead and get some sleep. I work late most days in the warden's office. We can talk tomorrow night when I get back."

Freddy unfolded the thin, bare mattress that lay on the lower bed and plopped down without bothering with the bedding. Within a minute, he was sound asleep. True to his word, Freddy recounted the events that led up to his forced transfer from Sing Sing late the next night when Harry returned from the warden's office.

Lewis Lawes became warden at Sing Sing in 1920. The five wardens who had immediately preceded him had each lasted less than eleven months. Sing Sing was notorious for its overcrowded and oppressive conditions. However, Warden Lawes moved quickly and decisively to eradicate these conditions and improve the morale of the general prison population. His first act was to re-institute the liberal Mutual Welfare League originally introduced at Sing Sing by Charles Mott Osborne in December 1914. He also convinced New York Governor Al Smith to allow him start publishing the prison's newspaper, the *Sing Sing Bulletin*, again. Prior to the paper's recent demise, it had distributed copies throughout the entire New York Prison system, and at its peak, the *Bulletin* had a circulation of five thousand copies.

Lawes also organized and promoted prison baseball and football teams, and a prison band. Freddy Lindsay, a horn and tuba player, signed up for the band as soon as he was eligible. Freddy had entered Sing Sing in 1927 to serve a nine-year prison sentence.

Things went extremely well for Lawes and his inmates until one day in February 1933. Trouble began after he authorized the addition of a black inmate to the prison band. Eight members of the band were so furious that they staged a protest strike on February 28. Lawes thought the inmates would soon come to their senses and see that their refusal to participate in band practice was futile. He fully expected them to return to the band for the weekly march-up on March 4. He was wrong. Not one of the striking band members took part.

Immediately following the march-up, Lawes called all strikers into his office. Freddy Lindsay was among them. The strike concerned Lawes on many levels, for his control over the inmates had been severely compromised by their protest.

"Sit down, boys," Lawes said, waving towards the two rows of chairs in front of his large, imposing desk. "We need to have a serious talk about your strike. As you know, I am probably the most lenient warden the New York Prison System has ever seen. I have instituted many radical policies and activities over my thirteen-year tenure as warden of this prison. I have done so that you men could have opportunities to turn your lives around and steer you away from future criminal activities. However, I am extremely concerned regards your decision to strike in response to the addition of a Negro to the prison band. I may have been too lenient with you and the other men incarcerated behind our prison walls." Lawes paused to let that sink in, and then continued. "I am concerned because you feel as though you have a right to strike. That is the action of free men, not the action of men who are incarcerated. Imprisoned men have no rights whatsoever. I have made a large mistake here in allowing you to feel as though you have a right to act in such a free manner." Lawes paused again.

"Therefore, I have decided to disband the prison band for six months. I have done this so that time will dissipate the effects of your strike. And, because you have negatively influenced the general population of this prison by acting like free men, I have ordered that each of you be transferred from Sing Sing to other prisons throughout the New York prison system, effective immediately. I have ordered this so that I may effectively break up your little 'Prison Union.' And, I am sorry to inform you, that each of you will be penalized with the loss of sixty days of your good behavior time for your infractions."

One of the men started to respond, but was immediately cut off by Warden Lawes before he could complete his first sentence. "Silence!" Lawes said in a voice of absolute authority. "As I said earlier, you have no rights. Therefore, I will not allow any of you to speak in your own defense. Guard, get these men out of my office and process them downstairs for immediate release to the prisons I have designated."

The men sat shocked. None had anticipated the warden's swift and brutal response. They naively believed the warden had called them into his office to negotiate their return to the band.

The guard broke their stunned silence. "Hey!" he shouted, "You heard the warden. Get up and get out of here now! Form a single line and get marching. Let's go! Now!"

The group of dejected men marched out of the warden's office and headed down to the prison basement. They were surprised to find their sparse personal belongings already waiting for them in neat piles on a wood table. Within the hour, they were piled into waiting cars bound for unknown destinations. Word of Lawes brutal and swift response reverberated throughout the prison and Lawes regained his position of authority and respect. The entire incident, from the start of Lawes' speech, to prisoner removal had taken less than three hours.

Harry sat quietly for a minute following the end of Freddy's story. "Geez Louise!" Harry exclaimed, after letting out a loud whistle. "That's one hell of a story, Freddy. I'm surprised I didn't pick up on it in the warden's office today. I'll have to keep my ears and my eyes open to see how Warden Brophy feels about you. Can I give you some advice, kid?"

"Yeah," said Freddy. "I sure could use some. I'm worried that the warden and the guards will get after me for what I done."

"Listen," Harry advised, "Brophy's not too bad a guy. He's tough, but he's not as crooked as some other wardens. If I know him, and I do, he'll be waiting to see how you behave before he decides what to do with you. If you keep your nose clean, he'll eventually forget about you. As far as the guards are concerned, they'll treat you pretty rough for a while all right, but they'll ease up if you do good. Keep your mouth shut about your trouble at Sing Sing. Tell no one, and I mean no one, about it. It'll pass."

"Thanks, Harry." said Freddy, "I think my stretch of bad luck ended when they put me in here with you. Maybe I can do somethin' for you sometime, huh?"

"Ah, think nothing of it, Freddy. Let's get some shuteye. It's late and five o'clock is gonna come quick."

From that day forward, Freddy looked up to Harry as if he was an older brother and their bond grew stronger over time. It was so strong, in fact, that rumors throughout their cellblock claimed the two had become lovers. Homosexuality in prison is the norm, so no one was surprised at their pairing. Necessity in prison is indeed the mother of invention.

Chapter Seventeen

THE MORNING OF JANUARY 2, 1934 BEGAN in its usual manner at Great Meadow Prison with the opening of the cell doors in each cellblock. The cell doors, controlled remotely from guard stations located on each tier, were unbolted with a loud snap promptly at five o'clock. Like a row of falling dominoes, the unsnapping of each lock began at one end of the tier and cascaded rhythmically until it reached the furthermost cells on each side of the long gallery. Harry and Freddy were awakened by the familiar noise. They threw back their bedding, sat upright, spun their bodies so their feet hit the floor, and leapt up. Two guards were standing at the door to Freddy and Harry's cell. Freddy instantly recognized them as officers Frank O'Hearn and Ed Blasdell and knew their visit could mean only one thing; Freddy's mother had been ill for several months.

"Prisoner A. Lindsay, number 12073," said Officer O'Hearn, "the warden regrets to inform you that your mother, Mrs. Anna Hopkins, has passed away. In accordance with regulations as set forth by the New York State Prison System, you have been granted two days leave so that you may attend her funeral. Officer Blasdell and I will escort you immediately to New York City."

Freddy, stood motionless a moment. His head rang as if he'd just received a severe blow to the head. Then his legs buckled and he collapsed on the concrete cell floor, sobbing loudly. The sound of his sobbing set off a chain reaction along the cellblock. It took very little to ignite a riot in the tense, agitated inmate population. Their loud voices grew to a deafening din within seconds. Officers O'Hearn and Blasdell advanced quickly towards Freddy who had curled himself into a fetal position on the floor. Harry got to him first.

"Freddy!" Harry yelled, lifting up his cellmate and cradling him in his arms. "Freddy! Stop for god's sake! They'll throw you in the hole and you'll miss your mother's funeral! Please, Freddy, get a hold of yourself!"

"I shoulda been there for her, Harry!" he said haltingly through sobs. "I shoulda been there! It's all my fault."

"You will be there for her, Freddy. They've come to take you to her funeral." Harry's voice was calm and soothing. "Now pull yourself together, kid. Pull yourself together!"

Harry pulled Freddy to a standing position as two other block guards began shoving the other inmates back into their cells. Freddy continued to rave about his worthlessness and Harry knew he'd better stop him before O'Hearn and Blasdell stepped in to forcefully subdue him.

Finally, Freddy looked up at Harry and almost trancelike, Freddy stopped crying and regained his composure. "I'm sorry, boss," Freddy said to Officer O'Hearn, now standing in front of him with a set of handcuffs dangling. "I couldn't help myself."

"Are you gonna be okay for the trip into the city, Lindsay?" asked O'Hearn, "We don't want any trouble from you."

"Yeah, I'm okay," said Freddy, his breath hitching a few times. "I wasn't ready for the news, that's all. Just wasn't ready, you know what I mean?"

"Okay, then, let's get going," O'Hearn said as he clipped his handcuffs back onto his utility belt. "It's a long ride to the city."

O'Hearn led Freddy out of cell. Officer Blasdell turned and gave Harry a look that could be interpreted only as "thank you." When the cell door slammed shut, Harry returned the unusual gesture with a wan smile indicating 'you're welcome.' He sat down on Freddy's bunk and began to cry as memories of his own mother's death flooded back. He regained his composure by the time the block guards opened the cell doors again half of an hour later.

Freddy returned to Great Meadow at half-passed seven on the evening of January 6. When Harry got back to the cell at eight-fifteen, he was greeted by a sullen and brooding Freddy.

"Hey, kid," said Harry, "how did everything go?"

Freddy pretended he hadn't heard Harry speak. He sat motionless on his bed with his hands on his knees and his head hung down almost as far. Harry decided to leave Freddy alone, rather than risk agitating him and creating a scene.

Freddy was never the same after that. He sat and moped about letting his mother down and was often uncommunicative. Harry quickly learned that when Freddy got into one these moods, it was best to leave him be until it passed. His attempts to get Freddy to talk about his feelings were fruitless. Only once did Freddy speak about what was bothering him. "My life is a big pile of crap. That's all it ever was and so what's the use anyway?"

While Harry remained at the same job in the warden's office during his stay at Great Meadow, Freddy was transferred to many areas of the prison. None of the guards liked him and they got rid of him as soon as a vacancy opened up elsewhere.

Officer Paul Kearn, assigned to the prison garage, said it best during a conversation with another officer. "That Lindsay character gives me the heebie-jeebies. He just sits and stares at the floor. Makes me wonder just what the hell is going on in that guy's head! I couldn't wait to get him out of the motor pool! I sent him over to the mess hall to replace an inmate who got released. They can have him! I hope he doesn't ever come back here."

The mess hall proved to be Freddy's last job assignment. He and Harry went up before the prison parole board on July 2, 1934. They were both granted parole and received the same release date, August 13, 1934.

When Bernice received the news that Harry would soon be

released, she re-read his letter over and over just to make sure she understood correctly. She wasted no time putting into action the plan she and Harry had worked on over the years. As soon as she got off of work that day, she drove up to Ira Bennett's farm located just south of her cabin on Price's Corners Road.

Ira had another property for sale on McGraw Road in Coldspring, located a mile west of her cabin. After a quick tour of the farm, she negotiated a deal with Mr. Bennett to buy the property once Harry arrived home from Great Meadow Prison. Under the terms of the deal, Bernice traded her cabin plus $1,500 cash. The price was a bit steep for the 114-acre parcel with an old farmhouse and large barn. However, Bernice was confident that with a little fixing up, the place would be perfect for her and Harry to get started on their business.

The next three weeks crawled by for both as Bernice waited for Harry's release. Bernice arranged for time off from work well in advance of his release date, and began making inquiries into the purchase of farm animals and equipment. She was savvy enough to leave the actual selection of these items up to Harry. With the exception of raising several batches of chicks for sale with her neighbor, Nora Moynihan, Bernice knew very little about the art of farming. That was one area her father had neglected in his daughter's education.

Bernice arrived at the Gideon Putnam Hotel in Sarasota Springs on the evening of August 12 and rented a room. Her anticipation of meeting Harry as a free man kept her sleepless most of the night. When she arose at six o'clock the next morning, she took extreme care in making sure she looked her best. She changed her clothes several times until she finally settled on an outfit she'd worn many times on her secret sojourns to Buffalo over the last few years.

No one was aware that Bernice, driven by depression and loneliness, often travelled to downtown Buffalo on weekends for clandestine visits to speakeasies and then legal bars when prohibition ended. There, she engaged in conversation and flirted with many men to satisfy her hunger for Harry's company. She often wore a stylish hat and a seductive dress during her visits. Her outfit was often accessorized with a wispy feather boa that she would drape around her neck. The feather boa's fringe framed her delicate face and helped make her look years younger than her actual age. A photo of Bernice taken by her brother-in-law, Lynn Blessing, captured this look during a sitting at his studio in Salamanca. Bernice loved the photo so much that it was prominently displayed on her fireplace mantle.

When Bernice was satisfied with her outfit, she took the elevator down to the hotel lobby. Men and women turned to watch as she walked by, and she enjoyed the stares, taking them as confirmation that she had selected the right outfit for Harry's first glimpse of her at the prison gate.

Her stomach was aflutter from the moment she started her Sport Coupe until she heard the familiar grinding sound her tires made in the gravel-lined prison parking lot. Bernice's mind raced as she wondered how Harry would react to her as a free man. She parked her car and quickly joined the small throng of people waiting excitedly for their loved ones to walk out of the prison. Bernice chose to stand aside from the group, preferring to avoid fraternizing with them.

The group was rewarded for their patience at exactly nine o'clock. The heavy glass doors swung open revealing the first two men to exit the prison. Bernice held her breath and hoped Harry would come out next. Right on cue, Harry, and a short, muscular young man, swung the glass doors open again. Bernice rushed towards him. Harry was shaking the young man's hand as Bernice approached. He broke into a big grin as soon as he saw her and ran to meet her on the sidewalk. They embraced and hung on to each other as if someone would change his mind and order him back into prison.

When they broke from their long embrace, Bernice felt a silly urge creep up on her. Feeling like a very young girl welcoming a brave soldier home from war, she stepped back, raised her hand to her forehead in a salute and said, "Welcome home from battle, Private Farnsworth. Job well done!"

Harry threw his head back and let out a loud laugh. "Thank you, ma'am! I just want to know where the celebration party is being held!"

"Follow me young man and I'll escort you to that party!" Bernice replied.

They laughed and hugged all the way back to the car. There was a moment of awkwardness when Harry discovered Bernice would be doing the driving. Bernice waved off his disappointment and promised he could do most of the driving once he got his driver's license back. She started the engine on the Sport Coupe with a flick of the key. Harry was amazed at how easy it was to start the car. His incarceration had caused him to miss the advent of the self-starting motor. In the coming weeks he learned there were a lot more things he'd he had missed during his years in prison.

The happy couple chatted excitedly all the way to Glens Falls where they stopped at a diner for a late breakfast. Harry savored each bite. Bernice literally glowed through the entire meal. When they finished eating, they set out again on their journey back to Cattaraugus County.

Eventually their conversation turned to the business aspects of the farm. They were so engrossed that they didn't notice the hours passing until Bernice pulled up in front of the darkened silhouette of her log cabin.

"I can't believe we are home already," said Bernice. "Well, let's get out and see what you think of the place. Don't forget the suitcases, Harry!"

Bernice walked up the path to the front door to the cabin and fumbled for her door key. Harry was right behind her with Bernice's bag and his meager belongings.

"Uh, Bernice?" said Harry sheepishly while she continued to search for the door key.

"Yes, Harry, what is it?"

"Umm, Bernice, I was kind of wondering where I'm supposed to sleep tonight."

"Oh!" exclaimed Bernice, her face reddening. "Don't worry about that, Harry. I have a spare bedroom all ready for you."

"Okay. Well, thanks, Bernie," he said awkwardly.

Ira Bennett was out of town until the following week, so there was little for Harry to do once he stowed his possessions. Within a few days, though, Harry and Bernice settled into a comfortable routine. She rose at six o'clock and left for work at eight. She returned from work at half-passed five each evening.

Bernice was thrilled to discover that Harry was a decent cook. She was not domestic in any sense of the word. Harry teased her about it constantly even though he really couldn't have cared less about her lack of housekeeping skills. He was glad to do anything he could for Bernice. She was his salvation and he was gracious in his appreciation. Harry was prepared to do anything for Bernice, and vice versa.

During their first days together, they discovered they were quite compatible. As a result, their love for one another entered a new phase. Bernice got the clear impression that Harry might actually find her physically attractive, in spite of their age difference. She noticed the way he looked at her when he thought she wasn't paying attention.

As it always happens, inevitable change occurs where and when it's least expected. That change occurred for Bernice and Harry on the evening of August 22, 1934 as they took part in the Randolph Daughters of the American Revolution's annual Traveling Supper.

A travelling supper is an event where each course of a meal is served in a separate residence. The diners go from house to house where they consume one course. Bernice, dying for an opportunity to show Harry off, bought tickets for the event, which was a benefit for the Randolph Children's Home.

The first course, an appetizer, was served in the Meyers home on Main Street at five-thirty in the evening. The conversation was stimulating and the diners had to be reminded not to dawdle lest they spoil the rest of their meal.

The second course was soup at a house on Church Street, salad on New Street, and the main course at a house on the corner of Center and Washington streets. They finished the main course at seven-thirty and headed out for dessert, at Bernice's stone house on Main. Morna, Dora and Edith, were hosting the finale.

Harry and Bernice were at the tail end of the procession of cars heading down Washington Street towards Main. They followed Rufus Mathers and Mildred Millhausen, riding in an older Model T Ford. Harry and Bernice chuckled as they eavesdropped on the non-stop chattering that drifted back towards them from the Model T. Rufus and Mildred could have been the models for the popular comic strip characters, "Mutt and Jeff." In fact, that's what everyone in town called them. But they couldn't have been more opposite in appearance. Rufus stood six feet three inches to Mildred's five-foot one. Where Rufus was thin as a rail, Mildred was obese. Rufus rarely spoke and Mildred never shut up. It was widely rumored around town that she even talked in her sleep.

As they followed Rufus's Model T, they suddenly heard a loud snap followed by an even louder grinding noise coming from the car ahead. Harry, who had received his driver's license, stomped on the brake, bringing the Sport Coupe to a sudden halt. He noticed that the Model T was leaning heavily towards the right front tire.

Rufus got out of the car, crossed around the front, and stood scratching his thinning scalp. The wheel of his car was broken. Meanwhile, Mildred squeezed out of the passenger seat and stood next to Rufus. "What are we going to now Rufus? We're going to miss my favorite course. Now, you know that dessert is my favorite course, don't you, Rufus. Well, of course you do. Rufus?"

Rufus wasn't listening to a word coming out of Mildred's mouth. Harry called out and asked Rufus if he needed help, but Rufus shrugged him off.

"Mildred," Rufus said, "get into the back seat."

"Get into the back seat? How's that going to fix a broken wheel, Rufus? Now that's not going to get us any closer to dessert, I'm sure! We need to hitch a ride with Bernice and her new beau if we going to get over to Main Street in time. That's what we need to do!"

"Just get into the back seat, Mildred," Rufus drawled.

"Well. I never, Rufus!" exclaimed Mildred, crossing her arms over her ample breasts, demonstrating her defiance. "I do believe that you have lost your mind, Rufus. Get into the back seat? That's nuts! I won't do it, I tell you! I won't do it! Let's get into Bernice's car. They've got a rumble seat, Rufus!"

"Just get into the back seat," Rufus said again as he gently pushed her towards the rear door. In mid-protest, Mildred gave up and climbed into the back seat.

"Now scoot over to the other side," he instructed.

"Scoot over? What's that going to do? We're wasting valuable time here Rufus. This reminds me of time my father ...."

"Just scoot over, Mildred," Rufus said in his flat, monotone giving her a slight shove in the right direction.

Mildred scooted over, although it took a couple of spurts. She stopped when she reached the other side of the cab. Slowly, the car began to creak as the right front-end rose in response to Mildred's counter-balancing weight. Within a few seconds, the car was sitting completely upright. Rufus picked up the broken wood-spoked wheel and placed it in the front seat of the car. Then he walked around the car and got in. He shifted the car into first gear and headed out once again for Main Street. Mildred, who was now taking complete credit for saving dessert, chattered away.

Bernice and Harold burst out laughing and kept laughing until they could hardly breathe. When they regained their composure, Harry shifted the Sport Coupe into first and followed Rufus towards dessert.

Morna, an outstanding cook, served Featherweight Cake, poached pears and coffee. It was the perfect ending to an evening filled with culinary delights and stimulating conversation. Harry was the hit of the evening when he told the story of how Rufus "came to dessert on three wheels and Mildred." The audience laughed and applauded and Rufus and Mildred grinned broadly, as they enjoyed being the center of attention.

The guests stayed a respectable forty minutes then filtered out two-by-two. After the last couple had left, the Kenyon girls started to tidy up the dining room and kitchen. Harry and Lynn went out to the front porch for a smoke while the women fluttered about the dining room and kitchen. Edith wasted no time taking advantage of the absence of the men. She was blunt when she started her conversation with Bernice in the kitchen.

"Bernice, I was waiting for a moment to speak with you privately amongst us girls. Dear, whatever are you doing with this Farnsworth man? Don't you know what the gossipers are saying about you? They're calling you a loose woman, in case you didn't know! For the love of God, Bernice, you have an unmarried man living with you in the same house!"

"Edith, for your information," Bernice replied hotly, "I am in love with this man. So, that's what I am 'doing' with him. Furthermore, I have absolutely no carnal knowledge of Harry Farnsworth. You of all people should know me better than that!"

"Oh, Bernice!" said Edith waving her hand in dismissal, "Give the man some money and send him on his way. That's all he really wants from you. Can't you see that?"

Bernice's face turned purple with rage in response to Edith's comment. "Oh!" she said loudly, "I get it! Who in their right mind would want poor old Bernice Kenyon, right? She's so undesirable that her boyfriend wants her only for her money? Is that it? Well, Edith, my dear sister, I'm going to show you who wants Bernice Guernsey Kenyon! Good evening to all of you. Harry and his loose woman are leaving!"

Her sisters never had a chance to utter another word. Bernice shot out of the kitchen banging the door loudly against the wall. She continued through the dining room and then into the foyer. There she met Lynn and Harry.

"We're leaving now, Harry," she said with a growl. "Good evening, Lynn."

Harry shot Lynn a questioning look that was returned with a shoulder shrug. Harry complied with Bernice and followed her out the front door. When they were both seated in the car, Harry said, "What happened back there, Bernie?"

"Nothing that concerns you, Harry," said Bernice. "Edith and I had a small disagreement. I'm sure it will blow over by tomorrow. Forget about it."

"Okay. Let's go home. Ira's due back tomorrow, isn't he?"

"Yes. We'll sign the papers tomorrow or the next day. That brings me to a topic that I think we have ignored long enough, Harry. Do you want to marry me? I need to know right now, Harry. Yes or no. Which is it?"

Harry gulped. "Wow!" he said. "You don't pull any punches, do you Bernie? I like that about you. Marriage is the topic I've been too shy to bring up. But since you have the courage, the answer is yes, Bernice Kenyon, I want you to marry you. Will you marry me?"

"Oh, Harry!" Bernice exclaimed. "That's all I have dreamed of lately. Yes. A thousand times, yes. I would love to marry you!"

Bernice grabbed Harry by both cheeks and planted a long kiss on his lips. She wrapped her arm around him and laid her head on his shoulder as he drove back to their cabin. They were so elated with the prospect of marriage that they floated home.

Bernice wasted no time in getting Harry to the altar. Harry called in sick for her from a neighbor's farm the very next morning. When he returned Bernice was dressed and ready to leave for the courthouse in Smethport, Pennsylvania. She knew they could apply for a marriage license and be married immediately at the local courthouse.

First, they drove into downtown Randolph and paid a visit to Harold Williams who owned a jewelry store on Main Street. They purchased matching gold bands and left for Smethport from his store.

It was a simple matter to apply for a license once they arrived at the McKean County Courthouse in Smethport. They filled out the marriage license application and handed it to the clerk. To make things appear more normal, Bernice shaved off ten years from her age and Harry added five to his. The clerk processed their completed marriage license application immediately. Fifteen minutes later, they were taking their wedding vows in front of Charles Heath, McKean County Justice of the Peace. It took less than a half an hour for Bernice Guernsey Kenyon to become Mrs. Harold Clifford Farnsworth.

Bernice and Harry celebrated their union over lunch at a nearby restaurant. They knew the meal would be the last of their extravagances for a while. Almost all of Bernice's savings was needed to go into the purchase of livestock and equipment. She agreed to keep her position at the courthouse until the farm was turning a profit. They planned to sell milk right away to the dairy in Steamburg.

After lunch, they headed back to Steamburg and Ira Bennett's farm. Ira was indeed back from Missouri and ready to close his real estate transaction with Bernice and Harry. They drove out to the McGraw farm, followed closely by Ira who preferred to ride in a horse-drawn buggy. They toured the house and barn and surveyed the land. When Harry announced that he was satisfied with the farm, they signed the land contract. Ira congratulated them and left.

Bernice and Harry walked the short distance to the enormous grassy field that lay behind their new house. They stopped and gazed out at the landscape.

"Harry!" exclaimed Bernice, "Can you believe all this land is ours? Can you believe this is real? It seems like it was just a pipe dream."

Harry, who had his back to Bernice, said nothing in reply. Bernice walked around to see if something was wrong. His face was wet with tears.

"Oh, Harry!" said Bernice, "Whatever is the matter?"

"Nothing's the matter," Harry said quietly. "These aren't tears of sadness, Bernie. They're tears of joy. I have dreamed of regaining my farm since I was twelve years old. And now, here it is! You have made me the happiest man on earth. I hope you realize that. I will never forget this day for the rest of my life!"

They stood arm in arm, laughing and looking their farmland from right to left and up and down. As the late summer sun shone warmly on them and cast its golden glow, they strolled back to the car. High overhead they heard the sudden cry of an eagle. The sound sent shivers down Bernice's neck and made the hairs on her arms stand up.

"What's the matter?" asked Harry.

"I just got the chills when I heard that eagle cry. It's such a lonely sound, isn't it, Harry?" Bernice was looking up, hoping to spot the bird.

"Yeah, well, I guess so." Harry replied, "Say, we should get going, huh? We've got a lot of work ahead of us. I'd like to move in tomorrow, what do you say?"

"Yes, Harry. I would like to move in right away. The sooner we get started the sooner I can quit my job at the courthouse."

They drove the short distance back to Bernice's cabin. Harry made a quick dinner as Bernice started to pack. When darkness had settled, Harry announced it was time for bed. Bernice froze in her tracks. This was the moment she had been looking forward to, and dreading.

Harry, realizing that Bernice was nervous, played with her and stroked her cheek gently. He assured her that everything would be fine. Eventually they wound up in the bedroom.

Harry disrobed Bernice, and then disrobed himself. Harry led her to the bed and caressed her tenderly until she relaxed. Their lovemaking was spontaneous and fresh. Bernice forgot her insecurities. She let herself go and soaked up the carnal pleasure that had been denied her for so long. When their lovemaking peaked and subsided, Harry lay with his head on her bare breast. They were quiet for a long time, wishing that the moment might last forever.

Bernice broke the silence. "Harry. You know how I just tell things the way that I see them, right?"

"Yeah, I kind of like that about you, Bernie. You know that," said Harry sleepily.

"Well, I've been thinking about our relationship," she began, "and I haven't been sure what role you fill in my life. On one hand you feel like the husband I never had and, I hope you understand what I'm about to say, sometimes you feel like the son I never had, too. What do think about that, Harry?"

Harry snuggled into Bernice's breast. "Doesn't bother me any, Bernie. I have a confession to make to you. Sometimes you feel like my lover and sometimes you feel like the mother I lost so young. Does it really make any difference how we fulfill each other? It just works, Bernie. Let's leave it alone. What do you say?"

"Yes," agreed Bernice, running her fingers through Harry's curly hair. "You're right, Harry. Who cares as long as it works for us? I love you, Harry."

The morning sun found them in the same position.

They moved Bernice's sparse belongings into the farmhouse and quickly discovered the plumbing had deteriorated so thoroughly that it was useless throughout the house. When they visited Ira Bennett to discuss this problem, he did the honorable thing. He sent his hired hand, William Whitmore, to make the necessary repairs. William was what folks in the area called "slow." His thought processes took a little longer than for other people. However, William's work ethic was excellent and the quality of his work was excellent.

The plumbing repairs proved to be extensive. Bernice agreed to have William move into the house for three weeks while he completed the repairs. It was a great relief when the work was completed and Harry was finally able to pump up the water bladder for the first time. He beamed with satisfaction when Bernice squealed with delight at the sight of water streaming from the kitchen faucet.

"This marriage thing ain't too bad after all!" Harry exclaimed while walking proudly back to the house.

As September slid into October, their farm began to take shape. They stocked the barn with used tools and equipment. They purchased livestock auctions throughout Cattaraugus and Chautauqua counties. They bought and stockpiled enough feed to carry them through the harvest of their own hay, oats, and corn the following year.

Harry taught Bernice how to care for the livestock and was amazed she was willing to milk the cows alongside him. In five short weeks of marriage, they had become a formidable team.

It wasn't long before the workload became too large for the pair of them to handle. Bernice could help with the milking and nothing more. She tried to pick up the load of cleaning and caring for the farm animals in the barn, but she wasn't strong enough to do the manual labor.

The end of November found a far different Bernice and Harry. As the weather got colder, the daily regimen of work was beginning to crush Harry. Bernice was finding it difficult to keep up with her fulltime job, plus help Harry on the farm. They discussed hiring help, but couldn't see how they could possibly afford it. On the first day of December, Harry presented Bernice with a solution.

Harry said he had a good friend by the name of Freddy Lindsay who might be interested in coming out and working for them cheaply. Harry proposed offering Freddy room, board, and ten dollars a month in cash to come and work for them. Bernice thought that the proposal sounded good and agreed that Harry should write to Freddy in New Rochelle and offer him the job. Harry neglected to tell Bernice that Freddy was his former cellmate in Great Meadow Prison. He justified the omission by telling himself that Bernice would pre-judge Freddy if she knew the truth.

Harry sat down and wrote a letter to Freddy. He placed it into the mailbox at the post office in Steamburg after he dropped off the milk the next morning. All he could do was to wait for Freddy's reply. Harry suspected that Freddy might be having a hard time gaining employment because of his prison record.

Freddy wrote back immediately. He eagerly accepted the offer. He told Harry he had been unable to find a job because he'd been convicted of stealing from his last employer. He also said he would leave the next day and hitchhike to Coldspring.

Freddy did leave the very next day, December 6, after a

tearful goodbye to his sister, Helen Short. Helen had weathered many stormy sessions with her husband over Freddy's presence in the house. Her husband did not want a convicted felon in his home and he complained constantly about being forced live with "her convict brother."

Helen gave Freddy a five-dollar bill and a big hug at the back door to her small home. She wished him good luck and watched him walk away. She loved her brother dearly, but she was glad to see him go. Her marriage could not have survived with Freddy living there with them.

Freddy turned and waved goodbye to her one last time. Helen waved back enthusiastically in hopes that it would disguise the sadness she felt for her older brother. When he disappeared from view, she let out a large sigh, brushed the tears from her eyes and walked slowly back into her house.

Freddy, ever impulsive, should have checked the weather report before leaving on a four-hundred-mile hitchhiking adventure. He was plagued by bad weather from the start of the journey to its bitter end. He repeatedly found himself stranded in small New York towns along Route 17. By the time he got to Coldspring twelve days later, on December 18, he was literally half-dead from starvation and exhaustion.

A farmer from Cherry Creek in Chautauqua County pulled up to Bernice's farmhouse in an old jalopy. He had to go up to the house and knock on the door, asking Harry to help him carry Freddy from the car. Freddy was flush with fever and dehydrated. Harry got Freddy on his feet and then draped the boy over one shoulder. His friend smelled atrocious and was black with dirt. When Bernice caught sight of Freddy, she was far from pleased.

With great difficulty, Harry eventually got Freddy up the stairs and into bed in the spare room. Bernice stood in the hallway, watching as Harry cleaned Freddy up a bit. She marveled at how familiar Harry was with Freddy. It was at that moment she realized the truth. Harry and Freddy had been locked up together in Great Meadow.

Harry removed Freddy's shirt and revealed something very few people knew about him. He was sleeved with tattoos from his neck all the way down to his ankles and wrists. Even his hands bore evidence of tattooing. Bernice's hand flew to her mouth as she gasped in shock. She grabbed the door by its handle and closed it quickly. Harry, lost for the moment in caring for his friend, barely noticed her presence and her sudden departure.

When Harry finally left Freddy's room Bernice was waiting for him.

"Harry Farnsworth!" she yelled, "How could you bring that man into our house! He's a convict, isn't he?"

"Now, Bernice!" said Harry, "I was going to tell you after you met him. I just wanted you to judge him for himself, that's all. I sure didn't expect him to show up in this condition. Give him a chance, Bernice. He's not as bad as he seems! Trust me, I know him."

"No!" Bernice said with authority, "I want that man out of our house. I don't like him one single bit."

"All right, all right," agreed Harry, "But I can't toss him out right now. He's pretty sick. You can see that for yourself. Let me nurse him back to health, okay?"

Bernice hesitated and said, "All right, Harry. But when he's better, he goes, agreed?"

"Right, he goes," Harry said reassuringly.

By the time Freddy was well enough to get out of bed, Harry had convinced Bernice that Freddy was their only hope for the financial success of their farm. With great reluctance, Bernice agreed to allow Freddy to stay long enough to get the farm in order and start raising chickens for sale.

Freddy and Bernice and did not get along well but they did their best to tolerate each other. They also privately complained to Harry on a daily basis. Harry played both sides of the fence as he walked the precariously thin line that separated him from Bernice and Freddy.

The tension in the house increased slowly but steadily. One day, when Bernice refused to allow Harry and Freddy go to town together in the car, Freddy did a slow burn. While Harry was gone, he slouched against the fence with a straw hanging out of his mouth, staring at Bernice with contempt while she tended to the animals in the yard between the house and the barn. This unnerved Bernice completely. Badly frightened, she rushed into the house and locked the door behind her. When Harry finally returned, she became completely undone as she told Harry what Freddy had done.

"That man is dangerous, Harry. Get him off our property, now!" she demanded between sobs.

Harry said she was imagining things and calmed her down. Outside, a mean little smile spread across Freddy's face, as he listened to every word they said.

"I'll fix that snobby, D.A.R. bitch yet!" he muttered and slipped quietly into the house through the seldom-used front door. He headed straight up to his bedroom in order to avoid a confrontation with Bernice.

Bernice resigned her position at the courthouse in late December. Orla was furious when he learned that Bernice had been carrying on a correspondence with Harry for years and actually married the man. He was angry that she had been playing him like a fiddle for years. After that, the once true friends could barely tolerate each other but they had to interact occasionally over business matters.

Bernice's constant presence in the house ramped up the discord between her and Freddy. Harry found himself spending more and more time playing referee to their constant bickering. He was worried that he would lose Freddy's help if the fighting did not stop.

Things came to a head on one cold night in early January of 1935. Freddy arrived home late after a night of drinking with a group of musicians in Randolph. He found the doors locked, which prompted him to stand back and hurl insults at Bernice from the porch. Freddy was trying his best to provoke her into yet another one of their frequent verbal battles. Instead, Harry stormed out of the door and threw a punch at Freddy. Freddy avoided the blow and unleashed his rage on Harry.

As drunk as he was, Freddy pummeled Harry with blow after blow to his head and body. He retreated when Bernice arrived with a broom and beat him back down and off the front porch. He ran away and hid in the barn for the rest of the night.

Bernice tended to Harry's wounds and demanded that he call the Sheriff and have Freddy arrested for assault and battery. Harry would hear none of it. He had started the fight, not Freddy. And he would not be party to having anyone arrested. He argued with Bernice until he convinced her that they really needed Freddy to make their dreams for the chicken farm to come true.

"Give me two more months and an early spring and we won't need Freddy anymore. I promise, Bernie!" he said.

Reluctantly she gave in again, knowing that it was a mistake to keep Freddy around.

Freddy and Harry patched things up the next morning. Freddy blamed his actions on the booze and promised not to drink anymore. He made Harry promise that he would talk to Bernice about giving him orders. He said he hated taking orders from a woman. "Isn't natural," he grumbled.

However, Bernice was far too independent and controlling to give up ordering around her farmhand. She and Harry argued frequently about this over the next two months. Harry had his hands full trying to keep the peace.

As their relationship continued to deteriorate, Bernice began calling Freddy 'young man,' which only further enraged him.

Whenever he said something to Bernice that she didn't like, she chastised him by saying "You can't talk to me that way, young man! I'm a member of the Daughters of the Revolution!"

Unknowingly, Bernice was striking a very dangerous chord in Freddy. His family, although upper crust at one time, had fallen into disgrace because Freddy's father worked briefly as a circus performer. As a child, Freddy had to put up with a constant barrage of insults and taunts from the kids at his school. Everyone in Lowell, Massachusetts, his hometown, deliberately crossed the street whenever any members of his family walked towards them. Freddy's first brush with the law occurred after he assaulted the son of the town's mayor. Freddy's father, Alfred Sr., was able to get his son off by paying a large sum of money to the mayor. Soon afterwards, the family moved to Providence, Rhode Island, ending Freddy's persecution by his peers. The damage had been done, however. Freddy was convinced everyone he met sensed his unworthiness. He fared little better in Providence, where his life of crime began after the death of his father in 1923.

Bernice was unwittingly stoking the old, smoldering anger that had lain dormant in Freddy for many years. His anger, coupled with his self-hate for not being a good son to his mother, had been building. And, like hot, molten lava pressing against the thin crust of a dome, Freddy's simmer of raw hate was waiting for an opportunity to surge and unleash its fury.

Freddy was extremely unhappy living on the farm and having to interact with Bernice every day. He went to Harry, threatening to quit and go back to New Rochelle. Harry convinced him to stay just a little longer, promising to make Freddy a partner in their chicken farm. Harry never divulged this promise to Bernice. He hoped that with some luck, he could manage to get rid of Freddy when he was no longer needed.

Harry longed to be successful. He paid cash for everything they bought for their farm. The auctioneers and the auction cashiers didn't treat him like an ex-con. Instead, because they, too, were desperate for cash sales, they treated Harry Farnsworth like a man of wealth and influence. He vowed that no one was going to stop him from achieving that status on a permanent basis. He considered Freddy a necessary sacrifice in his quest of that goal.

On Monday, March 4, 1935, Freddy and Bernice got into another huge argument. Freddy had made the mistake of fetching Harry from the barn without Bernice's orders to do so. "This is my farm, young man, and I'll say what's to be done around here and when it's to be done!" Bernice's tongue was relentless as it scathed Freddy's ego with personal insults.

Finally, Harry returned from the barn and Freddy screamed out his rage. He demanded that Harry choose between him and Bernice. Harry had no choice but to order Freddy off the farm. Freddy threw his meager belongings together and kept up a constant barrage of cursing. He called Harry a welcher for not keeping his promise about the partnership. Fortunately, Bernice was out of earshot and did not hear that remark. Harry literally shoved Freddy past Bernice and pushed him out the front door.

"Go! Freddy. Before we're all sorry that you stayed."

Freddy turned and walked away. He went up McGraw Road to Price's Corners. He turned right at Price's Corners and stopped in at the Moynihan Farm looking for Bernice's friend, Nora Moynihan. Nora Moynihan was known to be an easy touch for a handout. She knew Freddy from her frequent visits to the Farnsworth's farm and invited him in for a bite to eat. Freddy told her that the Farnsworth's had turned him out without a penny.

"They owe me one month's salary, those rotten welchers!" he exclaimed.

Nora became concerned about Freddy's outbursts and threats directed at the Farnsworths, and managed to get rid of him right away.

Freddy left the Moynihan farm, turned left at Highway 17,

and walked up to Houlihan's Garage located in Steamburg. He went in and took a seat on a stool near the pot-bellied woodstove. He sat there with his head in his hands and brooded for several hours without speaking to anyone coming or going from the garage.

At three o'clock, Bernice and Harold pulled up to the front of the garage. They were looking for Freddy. They knew Freddy was likely to be there after they stopped in to see Nora Moynihan on their way to Steamburg.

Harry emerged from car, leaving Bernice behind to wait for him. He entered the garage and coaxed Freddy to come outside and talk with him. Harry buttered him up good. He assured Freddy that he was a valuable asset to their farm, which they had realized shortly after he left. Harry went into Jaquay's store across the street and came out with five pouches of Duke's rolling tobacco for Freddy.

"Come back to the house and let's talk, Freddy," he pleaded, handing over the tobacco.

"I don't take orders from any woman, Harry. Your woman doesn't show me any respect when she does that."

"Never mind the woman!" said Harry while pointing to his own chest. "I'm in charge here!"

Harry convinced Freddy to come back to the farm and he offered him a ride in the Sport Coupe. Freddy declined. He needed to think about things and said he'd walk back to the farm. The Farnsworths drove off, figuring Freddy would return later that evening.

Instead, Freddy returned to the Moynihan farm in the hopes of spending the night there. He had decided not to return to the Farnsworth farm to work. He planned to return to the Farnsworths in the morning, demand his back pay, and catch the next bus bound for New York City.

Freddy fixed some broken boards on Nora's barn and

repaired a few small farm tools in exchange for a vegetable supper. After he ate, Nora declined to put him up for the night and Freddy headed down the road at dusk. He hid along the darkened road and returned to Nora's house when she left, walking in the opposite direction. He took a set of keys from a hook by Nora's front door. The keys were to a vacant house Nora's brother had abandoned a few years back. He piled blankets, sheets and a lantern into a small wheelbarrow. He wheeled the load to the vacant house up the road and set up there for the night.

Freddy's resolve to leave for New York City was further cemented that evening. He planned out exactly what he was going to say to the Farnsworths in the morning. Satisfied with his decision, Freddy relaxed and enjoyed the comfort of the old homestead. He found some books, read for a while, then drifted off to sleep around two o'clock in the morning.

CHAPTER EIGHTEEN

THE SUN ROSE SLOWLY ON THE icy blue horizon. The date was March 5, 1935. By eight o'clock, bright yellow rays of sunlight shot through the dirty living room window of the abandoned clapboard farmhouse on Price's Corners Road. The rays crept across the pine floorboards as if they were in search of the blanket-wrapped figure lying motionless in the far corner of the room.

Freddy jolted awake as the bright sunrays reached his face. He rubbed the sleep from his eyes and wondered what time it might be. Seeing that the sun was sitting on the eastern horizon, he figured it was still morning. Reluctantly he peeled off the blankets that swaddled him and stood up in the freezing cold room. As he stretched his limbs, his mind began to tick off what he must do this morning before he began his journey back to New York City. A visit to Harold and Bernice was at the top of that list.

He immediately exited the house through the front door. Once outside, Freddy turned left and headed through a field that lay behind the house. He struck out on a diagonal path he knew would eventually lead him right up to the Farnsworth's back door. He arrived at there at 9:20 in the morning.

Freddy walked up to the back door and knocked loudly. He waited a few moments. Harry opened the door.

"Freddy!" Harold exclaimed, "I'd given up on you coming back. Come on in!"

Freddy stared at Harold for a few moments as confusion ran its course in his head. He hadn't considered the possibility that Harold and Bernice might think he was returning to work for them after showing up a day later. He entered the house, frantically trying to formulate an alternative plan of action. Thankfully, Bernice was not in the room when he entered the kitchen. She was out in the barn finishing her morning chores.

Harry chattered away for a few minutes about putting their plans for the chicken farm into action. "Say! I almost forgot! We got that new kerosene-fired egg incubator this morning," Harry said waving his hand in the direction to the basement door. "Come on down to the cellar and let's fire it up! I'm curious to see it work."

Freddy's eyebrows furrowed and his lips frowned as he reluctantly followed Harold down the cellar stairs. He didn't like this unexpected turn of events at all. As they approached the incubator lying on top of the basement bench, he resolved to take control of the situation.

"Uh, Harry, there's something I want to tell you," he began.

"Yeah, I know, kid." Harry said, cutting Freddy off, "You're sorry about yesterday, right? Well, it was pretty stupid of you to walk off like that, you know."

Freddy took offense at being called stupid and he advanced on Harry with clenched fists. "Hey!" shouted Harry as he backed away. "Take it easy, kid!"

"Don't call me 'kid.' And don't you ever call me stupid ever again!" Freddy screamed as he landed a blow to Harry's stomach. The punch was delivered with such force that it caused Harry to double over. He stumbled backwards as Freddy advanced menacingly upon him again. Harry looked down to his right and spotted a double-bitted ax lying on the ground next to him. Freddy had left it there several days ago after splitting a pile of logs that now lay a few feet behind Harry.

Harry reached down and picked up the ax with his right hand. He swung the ax handle down into his waiting left hand and firmly grasped the handle with both hands. He planted his feet and took on a battle-ready stance. Freddy exploded with rage at seeing Harry's threatening response.

Freddy's eyes squinted down to thin slits. The veins in his face and neck began bulged. His face flushed a deep red. "Oh, you want to kill me, do you?" Freddy screamed as spit flew from his mouth. "I'll show you who's going to kill who, you bastard!"

Freddy lunged forward and grabbed the ax with both of his hands. With a quick twisting motion, he violently wrenched it from Harry's grip. He raised the ax up as if he meant to strike Harry. Harry's forearms flew instinctively across his face as he cowered backwards, towards the woodpile.

Freddy was unaware that Bernice had come to the top of the stairs. "You put down that ax this instant, young man, or I'll blow your head off," yelled Bernice. She had her .32 caliber pistol aimed directly at his head.

Bernice raced down the stairs and began to cross the basement's dirt floor as he wheeled around in response to her threat. For a split second, the sight of the drawn pistol caused him to pause. But with the adrenaline rush peaking in his body, Freddy swung the ax with cat-like quickness and accuracy. Before Bernice knew it, the flat of the ax head struck her squarely on the left side of her face. The blow initially produced a soft, fleshy thud that was immediately followed by a sharp cracking sound. Bernice fell both backwards and sideways like a marionette cut loose from its strings.

By then, Freddy was a full-blown raving maniac. All the rage that had been bottled up in him over the course of his lifetime spilled out like caustic acid. He looked down at Bernice's still figure then screamed, "You're no better than me!" He raised the ax and swung it down onto Bernice's neck.

The blow partially severed her neck and the ax became embedded in the moist soil beneath her. Blood gushed from the gaping wound in spurts onto the dirt floor. Freddy wrested the ax from the earth and then he raised it up above his head once more.

"You're no god-damned better than me, you D.A.R. bitch!" he roared, and once again brought the ax down on Bernice's severed neck.

The ax struck almost the exact same spot as it had before. While Freddy once again wrested the ax head from the earth beneath Bernice, Harry finally sprung into action. He had been frozen in shock as he watched, helpless. Realizing that Freddy would make him his next victim, Harry darted around Freddy who still had his back to him. Harry intended to go up the stairs and get out of the basement.

When Harry's sudden movement caught Freddy's attention, Freddy dropped the ax handle and reached for Bernice's pistol. Animal-like, Freddy bounded towards the stairs in hot pursuit of Harry who had already reached the top. Freddy entered the kitchen and spied Harry just as he disappeared through the dining room door. Freddy raced to catch up with him.

When Harry entered the foyer separating the dining room from the living room, Freddy leapt onto Harry's back, still holding the pistol in his right hand. He hung piggyback-style onto Harry by locking his left arm around Harry's neck. Freddy leaned back, stuck the muzzle of the pistol under the base of Harry's skull, and pulled the trigger. The gun's loud report made Freddy's ears ring.

Harry stumbled and staggered but did not fall to the ground. Freddy transferred the pistol from his right hand to his left and placed the muzzle on the left side of Harry's skull. Once again, he pulled the trigger. Immediately after the gun's loud report, Harry felt to the ground on his back, pinning Freddy to the floor beneath him.

Freddy wriggled out from under Harry's body and stood over him, straddling his chest.

"This is for being such a good friend, you son of a bitch!" Freddy said with a growl as he fired another shot point-blank above Harry's right eyebrow.

Freddy stood there, motionless, for a few seconds before he stepped back from Harry's body. The adrenaline in his bloodstream had been completely expended and its absence left him exhausted and out of breath. He stooped to one knee and inhaled deeply until his breathing returned to normal. When he looked over at Harry the shock of what he had just done washed over him. He dropped the gun to the ground and cried.

"Now you've done it, Freddy. Now you've really done it," he lamented through his sobs. "You got Ol' Sparky waiting for you up the river. He knows you're coming. You killed a woman and you killed a man!"

Freddy cried a short while longer and then exclaimed, "Oh my God! What have I done?" He sat down, waiting for his heart to stop pounding.

His thoughts quickly turned from remorse to fear as he realized he must get out of the farmhouse quick. He stood and walked over to where Harry's body lay. He winced looking at the blood draining away from Harry's head wounds onto the scuffed wooden floorboards. Then he went through Harry's pockets searching for cash. There was none.

Remembering that Bernice kept money in a small metal cashbox, he dashed upstairs to the master bedroom and ransacked the room searching for it. When he found the box, he pried it open with his pocketknife. The box was empty.

Reluctantly, he headed to the basement and descended the stairs once again. When he caught sight of Bernice lying in a spreading pool of black blood-soaked dirt, he swooned. He kept himself from falling by grabbing onto the stair handrail with both hands. He sat down heavily on a step and fought off waves of nausea.

Once the sick feeling subsided, Freddy continued down the rest of the stairs and walked up to Bernice's body. Shame swept over him and his face burned hot. Like a child, he straightened Bernice's clothing and pulled her skirt down so that it covered all of her legs. He wanted her to be presentable when they found her body.

Freddy plucked her purse from her fingers and retrieved seven dollars. He replaced the purse and went back upstairs. He went through the same clothes-straightening ritual with Harry who lay blocking the front door. When Harry's clothing was neat, Freddy placed Harry's left arm over his abdomen. Then he picked up the gun and shoved it into his own waistband.

Satisfied that he had left his victims with some dignity, Freddy exited the house through the kitchen's back door. He ran over to the Sport Coupe parked in the yard. He hopped in and gave the keys hanging in the ignition a twist. Within a second, the engine roared to life. Freddy slipped the car into first gear and made a U-turn. He headed out to McGraw Road and turned left towards Price's Corners Road. He stopped long enough to toss out two milk cans. The noise of them knocking against each other as the car rocked to and fro on the rutted dirt road annoyed him.

When Freddy reached Price's Corners Road, he turned left and then stopped at the abandoned farmhouse where he had spent the previous night. He collected a small bundle of clothing, and headed towards Highway 17. At the junction of Price's Corners Road, Blood Road, and Highway 17, he turned right onto the highway heading towards Olean.

Without knowing it, Freddy was driving squarely into the face of destiny. He would soon become the object of the largest manhunt in New York State history.

~ To be continued: *Coldspring: The Trial* ~

ABOUT THE AUTHORS

CHERI MANCUSO is a native of Salamanca, New York. She has worked in the field of metaphysics for twenty-seven years, primarily as a psychic medium, a healer, and teacher of metaphysics. Cheri has astounded police and other government-run agencies with her help in the investigation of missing persons, murders, and serial killers. She is particularly eager to help with cases of missing children. Additionally, CEO's and executives of Fortune 15 and 500 companies seek her out for her uncanny accuracy in the world of business. A list of her celebrity clientele reads like a list in *Who's Who.* Cheri has been the subject of many television and radio interviews. She has also appeared in print in national magazines such as *W Magazine* and *LA Confidential.* For more information on Cheri Mancuso, visit **www.mediumcheri.com**.

JOHN SCARANO is the first-generation-American son of Italian immigrants and a native of South Plainfield, New Jersey. He served his country during the Vietnam conflict as an enlisted man with the United States Marine Corps. He has studied metaphysics, tarot, mystical symbolism, and numerology for over forty years and currently teaches private classes on these subjects with his partner, Cheri Mancuso. He is clairsentient, clairaudient and is a Reiki Master. *Coldspring* is the result of John and Cheri's creative and psychic talent. It is their first collaborative publication in which the metaphysical arts were used in character development.

Book Endorsements

"Full of fascinating facts—it's a spiritual whodunit! A true karmic saga. I couldn't put this book down from the very first page to the last. Looking forward to the next one!!"

—Tamara Taylor, *Actress*

"*Coldspring* is a deeply profound story that chronicles an undeniable connection between three people through time and beyond. What a page-turner! Bravo!"

—Cindy Collins, *CEO Collins & Associates Public Relations*

"No matter what you believe in spiritually, this book will suck you in from chapter one. It is a fascinating, karmic ride through time!"

—Eva La Rue, *Actress*

"I've finished the edit—and I have to say I am sorry the book ended. Bernice, her sisters, Harry, Freddy, the Blessings, are in my head, rattling around in there. I'm ready to read on. You've done an excellent job assimilating all your research into a very compelling literary story."

—Carla Perry, *Dancing Moon Press*

"*Coldspring* is an easy, pleasurable read. It gets right down to the point and holds you spellbound right up to its climactic finish. I can't wait for more!"

—Cindy Ambuehl, *Actress*

"This unique story truly proves that real life is always more intriguing than fiction. And *Coldspring* turns everything we believe about karma on its head! Very thought provoking."

—Lisa Matsukawa, *Independent Producer, LocalGirl Presents*